It's Another Ace Book from CGP

This book is for 14-16 year olds.

First we wrote loads of great questions
matching our brilliant KS4 Maths Revision Guide.

Then we had a real good stab at making it funny
— so you'll actually <u>want to use it</u>.

Simple as that.

CGP are just the best

The central aim of Coordination Group Publications is to produce
top quality books that are carefully written, immaculately
presented and marvellously funny — whilst always making sure they
exactly cover the National Curriculum for each subject.

And then we supply them to as many people as we possibly can,
as <u>cheaply</u> as we possibly can.

Buy our books — they're ace

Published by Coordination Group Publications Ltd
Illustrated by Lex Ward and Ashley Tyson

Coordinated by June Hall BSc PhD and Mark Haslam BSc

Contributors
Gill Allen
JE Dodds
Mark Haslam
Claire Thompson
Dave Williams

With thanks to Colin Wells for the proof-reading.

ISBN 1-84146-029-X

Groovy website: www.cgpbooks.co.uk

Printed by Elanders Hindson, Newcastle upon Tyne.
Clipart sources: CorelDRAW and VECTOR.
0100

Contents

1.1 Questions on Prime Numbers

Basically, prime numbers don't divide by anything — and actually that's the best way to think of them. Have a go at the questions and you'll see what I mean.

> 1) **Prime Numbers** are all the numbers that **don't** come up in times tables.
>
> 2) The only way to get any **Prime Number** is 1 × **ITSELF.**
>
> 3) For example, the only numbers that multiply to give 5 are 1×5.

Q1 Using any or all of the figures 1, 2, 3, 7 write down:

a) the smallest prime number

b) a prime number greater than 20

c) a prime number between 10 and 20

d) two prime numbers whose sum is 20

e) a number that is not prime.

Don't forget that number one is not a prime — simple as that.

1	②	③	4	⑤	6	7	8	9	10
11	12	13	14	15	16	17	18	19	20
21	22	23	24	25	26	27	28	29	30
31	32	33	34	35	36	37	38	39	40
41	42	43	44	45	46	47	48	49	50
51	52	53	54	55	56	57	58	59	60
61	62	63	64	65	66	67	68	69	70
71	72	73	74	75	76	77	78	79	80
81	82	83	84	85	86	87	88	89	90
91	92	93	94	95	96	97	98	99	100

Q2 Write down the first ten prime numbers.

Q3 Find all the prime numbers between 40 and 50.

Q4 In the <u>ten by ten square</u> opposite, ring all the prime numbers. (The first three have been done for you.)

Q5 Among the prime numbers between 10 and 100, find three which are still prime when their digits are reversed.

This stuff keeps coming up in the Exam — so make sure you can check if a number's prime or not. This is actually dead easy — have a look at the simple method on P.4 of The Revision Guide.

Q6 What is the largest prime less than 500?

Q7 Give a reason for 27 not being a prime number.

Q8 How many prime numbers are even?

Q9 A school ran three evening classes: <u>judo, karate and kendo</u>. The judo class had 29 pupils, the karate class had 27 and the kendo class 23. For which classes did the teacher have difficulty dividing the pupils into equal groups?

Q10 Find three sets of three prime numbers which add up to the following numbers:

10   29   41

1.2 Questions on Multiples and Factors

This is real basic stuff — you just have to know your times tables. The only tricky bit is remembering which is a multiple and which is a factor — so learn the definitions and you won't go far wrong.

The **MULTIPLES** of a number are simply its **TIMES TABLE**	The **FACTORS** of a number are all the numbers that **DIVIDE INTO IT**.
eg The lowest three multiples of 3 are: <u>3</u> because 3 = 3 x 1 <u>6</u> because 6 = 3 x 2 <u>9</u> because 9 = 3 x 3	eg <u>12</u> can be made by: <u>1×12</u> or <u>2×6</u> or <u>3×4</u> so the <u>factors of 12</u> are <u>1, 2, 3, 4, 6, 12</u>.

Q1 From the numbers 1, 3, 4, 5, 6, 9, 10, 17, 23, 26, 27, 36 and 42, write down:

a) all the <u>prime numbers</u>

b) all the <u>multiples</u> of 6

c) all the factors of 48.

Q2 List <u>all</u> the factors of the following numbers: 63, 80, 120, 220

Q3 Express each of the following as the sum of <u>two prime numbers</u>: 10, 20, 30

Q4 Sally is tiling a wall. The wall is 520 cm long and 300 cm high.

a) Without wastage, what is the <u>largest</u> size square tile she can use?

b) Tiles come in packs of 20. What is the <u>minimum</u> number of packs that Sally needs to buy?

c) If Sally buys the minimum number of packs, how many tiles will <u>not</u> be used?

Q5 List all the factors for each of the following numbers

a) 1   c) 15   e) 12   g) 23

b) 3   d) 20   f) 33   h) 49

Q6 Write down the <u>ten lowest multiples</u> for each of the following numbers

a) 18   c) 4   e) 10   g) 15

b) 3   d) 7   f) 11   h) 20

Q7 Which of the following: 1, 2, 3, 4, 7, 8, 9, 12, 15, 23, 24, 36

a) are multiples of 3?

b) are prime numbers?

Basically, prime factors are just factors which are prime numbers — nice and easy, this bit.

Q8 Express the following as a <u>product of prime factors</u>:

a) 7   c) 47   e) 648   g) 405

b) 9   d) 105   f) 210   h) 25920

Q9 a) Write 1575 as a product of its <u>prime factors</u>.

b) If $315 = 3^x \times 5^y \times 7^z$, find x, y and z.

Q10 The prime factorisation of a certain number is $2^3 \times 7 \times 13$.

a) What is the number?

b) What is the prime factorisation of 1/2 of this number?

c) What is the prime factorisation of 1/4 of this number?

d) What is the prime factorisation of 1/8 of this number?

The thing to remember is to always multiply out your answer — if you don't get back to the number you started with you've definitely missed a factor, so try again.

1.2 Questions on Multiples and Factors

Q11 From the numbers 1, 3, 6, 9 and 12, write down:
- **a)** a multiple of 4
- **b)** a prime number
- **c)** two <u>square</u> numbers
- **d)** three factors of 27.

Q12 Which of these numbers are not prime? Show a factor for evidence.
221, 35, 784, 20, 97

Q13 Gary can pay his bill either in all £2 coins or all £5 notes. What is the smallest amount that the bill can be?

Q14 George bought 3 identical lengths of ribbon. He cut the first into an exact number of 2 cm lengths, the second into an exact number of 12 cm lengths and the third into an exact number of 15 cm lengths.
What is the <u>smallest length</u> that the ribbons could have been?

Q15 From the numbers
4, 9, 11, 20, 21, 26, 35, 44, 56, 65, 74, 83
find:
- **a)** <u>any square</u> numbers
- **b)** <u>all</u> the primes
- **c)** <u>all</u> the multiples of 4.

Q16 a) List the numbers between 5 and 35 inclusive which are <u>factors of 64</u>.
- **b)** List the numbers between 5 and 35 which are <u>multiples of 8</u>.
- **c)** Write down the numbers from parts **a)** and **b)** which are <u>both</u> multiples of 8 and factors of 64.

Q17 A packing carton measures 36 cm by 42 cm by 48 cm. The carton is filled with <u>cube</u> shaped boxes of chocolates.
- **a)** How big can the boxes of chocolates be?
- **b)** How many boxes of chocolates will fit in the carton?

Q18 List the first five odd numbers.
- **a)** If added together, what is their total?
- **b)** Write down the prime factorisation of the answer to part **a)**.

Q19 In the set of numbers from 10 to 40 write down:
- **a)** Any square numbers
- **b)** All the prime numbers
- **c)** A factor of 52
- **d)** A number divisible by 17.

Hmmm, some of these don't tell you but they're still looking for factors and multiples. You really need to recognise them so practise them as often as it takes — not just once.

1.3 Questions on Calculator Buttons

Calculators can work wonders, and it's a good idea to find out what those wonders are. You'll save yourself loads of time in the Exam — and that means you can spend more time on the really hard stuff. Hmmm...

The SQUARE, SQUARE ROOT and CUBE ROOT buttons are x^2 $\sqrt{}$ $\sqrt[3]{}$

1) The x^2 button squares the number in the display, ie IT MULTIPLIES IT BY ITSELF.

2) $\sqrt{}$ is the REVERSE PROCESS of x^2 — it gives the SQUARE ROOT.

3) $\sqrt[3]{}$ gives the CUBE ROOT of the number in the display. This is a 2nd function button, it's usually found above the +/- button.

Q1 Using the x^2 button on your calculator, work out:

a) 1^2 d) 15^2 g) $(-4)^2$

b) 12^2 e) $(-3)^2$ h) 1000^2

c) 2^2 f) 20^2 i) 0^2

(for parts **e**) and **g**) use your +/- button.)

OK, you probably know some of the answers already, but at least it checks your calculator actually works.

Q2 Using the $\sqrt{}$ button on your calculator work out:

a) $\sqrt{25}$ d) $\sqrt{5}$ g) $\sqrt{2500}$

b) $\sqrt{0}$ e) $\sqrt{20}$ h) $\sqrt{900}$

c) $\sqrt{169}$ f) $\sqrt{36}$ i) $\sqrt{2}$

Q3 Use the $\sqrt[3]{}$ button on your calculator to work out:

a) $\sqrt[3]{1}$ c) $\sqrt[3]{0}$ e) $\sqrt[3]{8}$ g) $\sqrt[3]{27}$

b) $\sqrt[3]{64}$ d) $\sqrt[3]{1000000}$ f) $\sqrt[3]{-27}$ h) $\sqrt[3]{3}$

Q4 For his birthday Lars Larson was given a new calculator. He pressed the button 2 and then he pressed x^2 12 times. Much to Lars' alarm, a funny symbol appeared in the display. What was the funny symbol and what did it mean?

The MEMORY BUTTONS are Min (Memory In) and MR (Memory Recall)

(On some calculators the memory buttons are called STO (store) and RCL (recall))

Q5 By calculating the bottom line first (the denominator) then using your calculator's memory buttons, work out

a) $\dfrac{19}{1+\sin(45°)}$ c) $\dfrac{20}{\cos(45°)+9}$ e) $\dfrac{16}{12+\tan(45°)}$

b) $\dfrac{\tan(12°)}{16+18^2}$ d) $\dfrac{71}{6+\sqrt[3]{9}}$ f) $\dfrac{10}{17\times\tan(6°)}$

Yeah, you could write the answer down at each step, but don't. Let your calculator do the work — that's what it's there for.

1.3 Questions on Calculator Buttons

OK, so some of these buttons look pretty confusing, but it's really important that you get to grips with exactly what they do:

**Calculators work things out in a certain order:
Brackets, Other, Division, Multiplication, Addition, Subtraction.**

eg $\dfrac{12+13}{46-17}$. Pressing [12] [+] [13] [÷] [46] [−] [17] [=] will give you completely the wrong answer. The calculator will think you mean 12 + 13/46 − 17, because the calculator will do the division before the addition and subtraction. Use the brackets buttons to over-ride BODMAS:

[[--] [12] [+] [13] [--]] [÷] [[--] [46] [−] [17] [--]] [=]

Q6 Using [[-- and --]] in an appropriate manner, calculate:

a) $\dfrac{(23+9)}{(4\times4)}$

b) $\dfrac{6}{(1\times3)(7-5)}$

c) $\dfrac{(8+(6\div2))}{(8\times2)}$

d) $\dfrac{1\times2}{3\times4}$

e) $\dfrac{6}{(6+2)(4-2)}$

f) $\dfrac{4(4+2)}{6(1\times4)}$

Brackets always come in pairs — one bracket on its own is about as much use as one shoe. It's as simple as that.

Q7 Using the [x^y] button on your calculator, find:

a) 1^0

b) 3^{10}

c) 2^{20}

d) π^3

e) 4^{10}

f) $(\tan45°)^{10}$

g) 8^5

h) $(\sin30°)^2$

For entering numbers into your calculator in standard form you need the [EXP] or [EE] button. It actually means $x\ 10^n$ so be careful not to type in the $x\ 10$ part.

Eg to enter 3.4×10^5 you would only need to type [3] [.] [4] [EXP] [5] [=]

and <u>not</u> [3] [.] [4] [×] [10] [x^y] [5] [=]

Q8 Enter the following numbers into your calculator and write down what you get:

a) 4×10^3

b) 1×10^4

c) 6.2×10^5

Q9 Work out (leaving your answers in standard form):

a) $\dfrac{2\times10^2}{5\times10^1}$

b) $\dfrac{4.2\times10^4}{2.1\times10^5}$

c) $\dfrac{1.92\times10^3}{9.6\times10^2}$

d) $\dfrac{2.3\times10^5}{4.6\times10^6}$

e) $\dfrac{7.0\times10^3}{3.5\times10^5}$

f) $\dfrac{4.44\times10^4}{1.11\times10^2}$

Make sure you know where your standard form button is. Take it from me, you'll definitely need it in the Exam.

SECTION ONE — NUMBER

1.4   *Questions on LCM and HCF*

These two fancy names always put people off — but really they're dead easy. Just learn these simple facts:

1)	**The Lowest Common Multiple (LCM) is the <u>SMALLEST</u> number that will <u>DIVIDE BY ALL</u> the numbers in question.**

eg   3, 6, 9, 12, 15 are all multiples of 3
       5, 10, 15, 20, 25 are all multiples of 5
       The lowest number that is in both lists is 15, so 15 is the LCM of 3 and 5.

2)	**The Highest Common Factor (HCF) is the <u>BIGGEST</u> number that will <u>DIVIDE INTO ALL</u> the numbers in question.**

eg   1, 2, 4, 8 are all factors of 8
       1, 2, 3, 4, 6, 12 are all factors of 12
       The highest number that is in both lists is 4, so 4 is the HCF of 8 and 12.

Q1   a) List the <u>first ten</u> multiples of 6, starting at 6.
      b) List the first ten multiples of 5, <u>starting at 5</u>.
      c) What is the <u>LCM</u> of 5 and 6?

I tell you what, it's a lot easier to find the LCM or HCF once you've listed the factors or multiples. If you miss out this step it'll all go horribly wrong, believe me.

Q2   a) List all the factors of 30.
      b) List all the factors of 48.
      c) What is the <u>HCF</u> of 30 and 48?

Q3   For each set of numbers find the HCF.

a) 3, 5	**c)** 10, 15	**e)** 14, 21	**g)** 52, 72
b) 6, 8	**d)** 27, 48	**f)** 16, 32	**h)** 11, 33, 121

Q4   For each set of numbers, find the LCM.

a) 3, 5	**c)** 10, 15	**e)** 14, 21	**g)** 6, 15
b) 6, 8	**d)** 15, 18	**f)** 16, 32	**h)** 11, 33, 44

Q5   Lars, Rita and Alan regularly go swimming. Lars goes every 2 days, Rita goes every 3 days and Alan goes every 5 days. They <u>all</u> went swimming together on Friday 1st June.

      a) On what <u>date</u> will Lars and Rita next go swimming together?
      b) On what <u>date</u> will Rita and Alan next go swimming together?
      c) On what <u>day of the week</u> will all 3 next go swimming together?
      d) Which of the 3 (if any) will go swimming on 15th June?

Q6   For each set of numbers find the HCF

a) 40, 60	**d)** 15, 45	**g)** 32, 64
b) 10, 40, 60	**e)** 15, 30, 45	**h)** 32, 48, 64
c) 10, 24, 40, 60	**f)** 15, 20, 30, 45	**i)** 16, 32, 48, 64

Q7   For each set of numbers find the LCM

a) 40, 60	**d)** 15, 45	**g)** 32, 64
b) 10, 40, 60	**e)** 15, 30, 45	**h)** 32, 48, 64
c) 10, 24, 40, 60	**f)** 15, 20, 30, 45	**i)** 16, 32, 48, 64

1.5 Questions on Fractions without a Calculator

I know doing fractions by hand is pretty scary stuff — so you'd better learn those 4 Manual Methods.

1) *Multiplying*	Multiply top and bottom separately: $\frac{2}{5} \times \frac{3}{7} = \frac{2 \times 3}{5 \times 7} = \frac{6}{35}$
2) *Dividing*	Turn the <u>2nd fraction UPSIDE DOWN</u> and then <u>multiply</u>: $\frac{2}{5} \div \frac{3}{7} = \frac{2}{5} \times \frac{7}{3} = \frac{2 \times 7}{5 \times 3} = \frac{14}{15}$
3) *Adding, Subtracting*	Add or subtract <u>TOP LINES ONLY</u>, but only once the bottom numbers are the same: $\frac{3}{5} + \frac{1}{5} = \frac{3+1}{5}$, $\frac{3}{5} - \frac{1}{5} = \frac{2}{5}$
4) *Cancelling Down*	<u>Divide top and bottom by the same number</u> 'till they won't go any further: $\frac{24}{32} = \frac{24 \div 8}{32 \div 8} = \frac{3}{4}$

Q1 Giving your answer as a fraction in its <u>lowest terms</u>, what fraction of each shape is shaded?

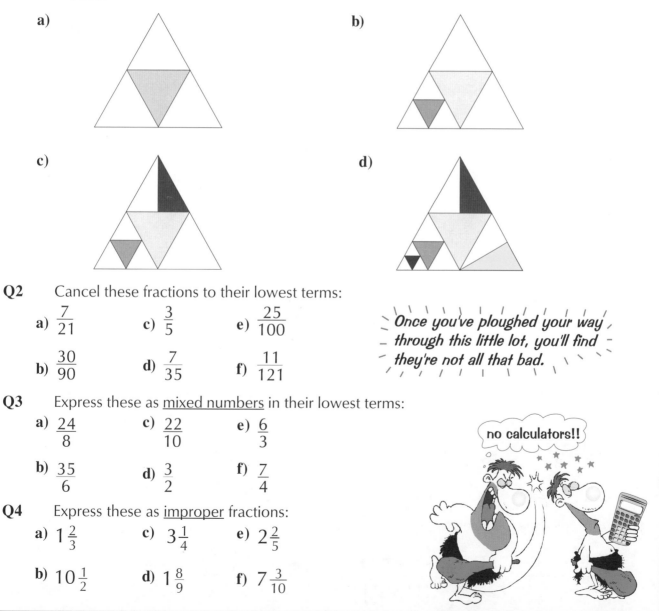

a)

b)

c)

d)

Q2 Cancel these fractions to their lowest terms:

a) $\frac{7}{21}$ c) $\frac{3}{5}$ e) $\frac{25}{100}$

b) $\frac{30}{90}$ d) $\frac{7}{35}$ f) $\frac{11}{121}$

Once you've ploughed your way through this little lot, you'll find they're not all that bad.

Q3 Express these as <u>mixed numbers</u> in their lowest terms:

a) $\frac{24}{8}$ c) $\frac{22}{10}$ e) $\frac{6}{3}$

b) $\frac{35}{6}$ d) $\frac{3}{2}$ f) $\frac{7}{4}$

no calculators!!

Q4 Express these as <u>improper</u> fractions:

a) $1\frac{2}{3}$ c) $3\frac{1}{4}$ e) $2\frac{2}{5}$

b) $10\frac{1}{2}$ d) $1\frac{8}{9}$ f) $7\frac{3}{10}$

SECTION ONE — NUMBER

1.5 Questions on Fractions without a Calculator

Yeah, I agree — this is pretty tedious stuff but it looks like we're stuck with it. And you can make life a whole lot easier if you make the bottom numbers all the same for Q's 5 and 6.

Q5 Arrange the following in <u>ascending</u> order:

$$\frac{3}{6} \quad \frac{6}{3} \quad 3\frac{1}{6} \quad 6\frac{1}{3} \quad \frac{36}{3} \quad \frac{63}{6}$$

Q6 Write the following in <u>descending</u> order:

$$\frac{2}{5} \quad 2\frac{1}{5} \quad 2\frac{1}{3} \quad \frac{3}{4} \quad \frac{15}{10} \quad 1\frac{1}{2}$$

Q7 By giving each pair a <u>common denominator</u>, fill in <, > or = as appropriate:

a) $\frac{4}{5}$ and $\frac{3}{4}$ c) $\frac{3}{6}$ and $\frac{1}{3}$ e) $\frac{1}{12}$ and $\frac{3}{24}$

b) $\frac{3}{7}$ and $\frac{2}{9}$ d) $\frac{4}{10}$ and $\frac{8}{20}$ f) $\frac{14}{7}$ and $\frac{9}{4}$

Don't forget to make the bottom numbers the same when adding (or subtracting) fractions as well. It's all a bit of a breeze, really.

Q8 Add the two fractions, giving your answer as a fraction in its lowest terms:

a) $\frac{7}{8} + \frac{3}{8}$ c) $1\frac{2}{5} + 2\frac{2}{3}$ e) $1\frac{3}{10} + \frac{2}{5}$

b) $\frac{1}{12} + \frac{3}{4}$ d) $\frac{1}{6} + 4\frac{1}{3}$ f) $\frac{1}{2} + \frac{1}{4}$

Q9 Evaluate, giving your answer as a fraction in its <u>lowest terms</u>:

a) $3\frac{1}{2} - \frac{2}{3}$ c) $1\frac{3}{4} - 1\frac{1}{5}$ e) $8 - \frac{1}{8}$

b) $10 - \frac{2}{5}$ d) $4\frac{2}{3} - \frac{7}{9}$ f) $5\frac{1}{5} - \frac{2}{5}$

Q10 Carry out the following multiplications, expressing the answers as fractions in their lowest terms:

a) $\frac{4}{3} \times \frac{3}{4}$ c) $\frac{2}{5} \times \frac{3}{4}$ e) $10\frac{2}{7} \times \frac{7}{9}$

b) $2\frac{1}{6} \times 3\frac{1}{3}$ d) $2\frac{1}{2} \times \frac{3}{5}$ f) $\frac{1}{12} \times \frac{3}{4}$

Q11 Carry out the following divisions, and express each answer in its lowest terms:

a) $\frac{1}{4} \div \frac{3}{8}$ c) $\frac{1}{9} \div \frac{2}{3}$ e) $3\frac{7}{11} \div 1\frac{4}{11}$

b) $1\frac{1}{2} \div \frac{5}{12}$ d) $10\frac{4}{5} \div \frac{9}{10}$ f) $6 \div \frac{4}{5}$

Q12 Simplify the following:

a) $\dfrac{\left(\frac{1}{7} \times \frac{7}{8}\right)}{\frac{1}{8}}$ b) $\dfrac{\left(3\frac{1}{12} \div \frac{1}{6}\right)}{\left(1\frac{1}{5} \times \frac{5}{12}\right)}$ c) $\dfrac{\left(2\frac{2}{3}\right)}{\left(4\frac{1}{2} \times \frac{4}{3}\right)}$

1.5 Questions on Fractions without a Calculator

The cunning bit with these long wordy questions is picking out the important bits and then translating them into numbers. It's not that easy at first, but you'll get better — I guess you've just gotta learn to ignore the waffly stuff.

Q13 In the fast food café, over all the shifts there are eighteen girls and twelve boys waiting at tables. In the kitchen there are six boys and nine girls. What fraction of the <u>kitchen staff</u> are girls, and what fraction of the <u>employees</u> are boys?

Q14

In a survey, people were asked if they liked a new cola drink. One in five thought it was great, four out of fifteen felt there was no difference in taste, three in ten disliked it and <u>the rest</u> offered no opinion.

What fraction of people offered no opinion?

Forget all about cola drinks and red trousers — just write it all as a sum, then do the calculation. Nowt to it

Q15 Neil wore red trousers on a total of 12 days in November.

a) On what fraction of the total number of days in November did Neil wear <u>red trousers</u>?

b) For 1/5 of the days in November Neil wore a <u>blue shirt</u>. How many days is this?

Q16 What fraction of 1 hour is:

a) 5 minutes

b) 15 minutes

c) 40 minutes?

Q17 If a TV programme lasts 40 minutes, what fraction of the programme is left after:

a) 10 minutes

b) 15 minutes

c) 35 minutes?

Q18 The Sandwich Club of Great Britain are going on their annual picnic.

a) If one sandwich is $\frac{5}{8}$ " thick, how many <u>layers</u> of sandwiches can be stacked in a box 10" high?

b) How tall would the box need to be if <u>40 layers</u> of sandwiches were to be stacked inside?

1.6 Questions on Fractions with a Calculator

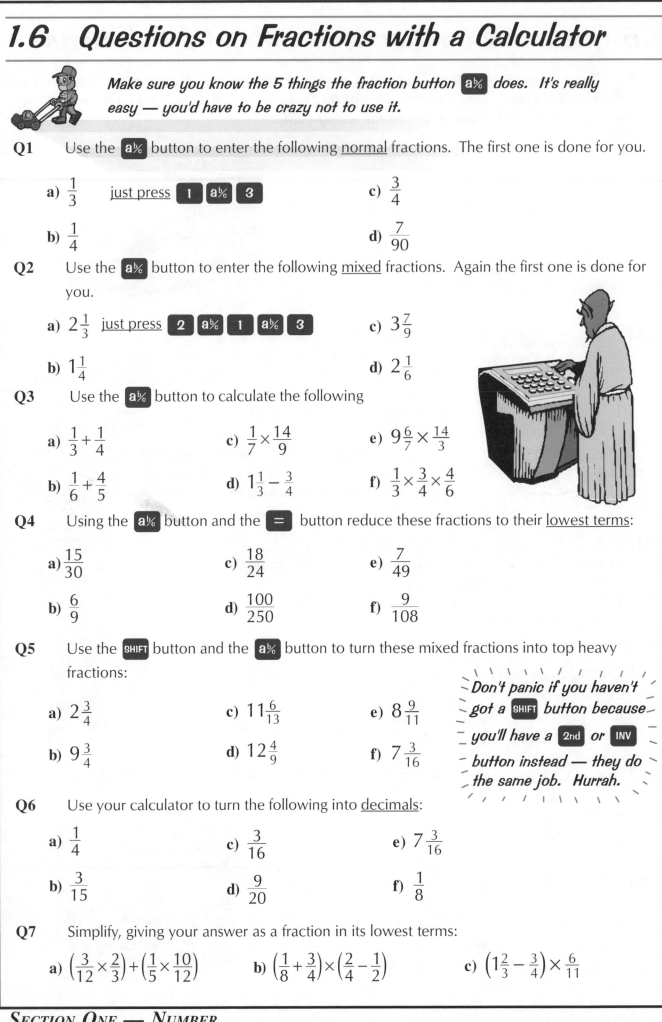

Make sure you know the 5 things the fraction button $a\frac{b}{c}$ *does. It's really easy — you'd have to be crazy not to use it.*

Q1 Use the $a\frac{b}{c}$ button to enter the following <u>normal</u> fractions. The first one is done for you.

a) $\frac{1}{3}$ <u>just press</u> **1** $a\frac{b}{c}$ **3**

b) $\frac{1}{4}$

c) $\frac{3}{4}$

d) $\frac{7}{90}$

Q2 Use the $a\frac{b}{c}$ button to enter the following <u>mixed</u> fractions. Again the first one is done for you.

a) $2\frac{1}{3}$ <u>just press</u> **2** $a\frac{b}{c}$ **1** $a\frac{b}{c}$ **3**

b) $1\frac{1}{4}$

c) $3\frac{7}{9}$

d) $2\frac{1}{6}$

Q3 Use the $a\frac{b}{c}$ button to calculate the following

a) $\frac{1}{3}+\frac{1}{4}$

b) $\frac{1}{6}+\frac{4}{5}$

c) $\frac{1}{7}\times\frac{14}{9}$

d) $1\frac{1}{3}-\frac{3}{4}$

e) $9\frac{6}{7}\times\frac{14}{3}$

f) $\frac{1}{3}\times\frac{3}{4}\times\frac{4}{6}$

Q4 Using the $a\frac{b}{c}$ button and the **=** button reduce these fractions to their <u>lowest terms</u>:

a) $\frac{15}{30}$

b) $\frac{6}{9}$

c) $\frac{18}{24}$

d) $\frac{100}{250}$

e) $\frac{7}{49}$

f) $\frac{9}{108}$

Q5 Use the **SHIFT** button and the $a\frac{b}{c}$ button to turn these mixed fractions into top heavy fractions:

a) $2\frac{3}{4}$

b) $9\frac{3}{4}$

c) $11\frac{6}{13}$

d) $12\frac{4}{9}$

e) $8\frac{9}{11}$

f) $7\frac{3}{16}$

Don't panic if you haven't got a **SHIFT** *button because you'll have a* **2nd** *or* **INV** *button instead — they do the same job. Hurrah.*

Q6 Use your calculator to turn the following into <u>decimals</u>:

a) $\frac{1}{4}$

b) $\frac{3}{15}$

c) $\frac{3}{16}$

d) $\frac{9}{20}$

e) $7\frac{3}{16}$

f) $\frac{1}{8}$

Q7 Simplify, giving your answer as a fraction in its lowest terms:

a) $\left(\frac{3}{12}\times\frac{2}{3}\right)+\left(\frac{1}{5}\times\frac{10}{12}\right)$

b) $\left(\frac{1}{8}+\frac{3}{4}\right)\times\left(\frac{2}{4}-\frac{1}{2}\right)$

c) $\left(1\frac{2}{3}-\frac{3}{4}\right)\times\frac{6}{11}$

1.6 Questions on Fractions with a Calculator

Don't get put off by all the padding in the questions — you've just got to pick out the important stuff. (And, don't forget to answer the right question — it sounds pretty dumb, but it's frightening how many people don't do it.)

Q8 At a college, two fifths of students are female, and three sevenths of these are part-time. If there are 2100 students altogether:

a) How many of these are <u>female</u> students?

b) How many are <u>part-time</u> female students?

c) If there are 1400 students altogether, how many are <u>full-time female</u> students?

Don't forget to cancel your answer to its lowest terms. Just press the [=] button — yeah, it really is that easy.

Q9 After a school fundraising event, a quarter of the money raised was spent on CD ROMs for the Learning Resource Centre and two thirds was spent on books. The remaining money, all £49.47 of it, was paid into the bank. How much money was raised at the fundraiser?

Q10 In the summer three friends ran a car cleaning service. They divided up the profits at the end of the summer according to the <u>proportion of cars</u> each had cleaned. Ali had washed 200 cars, Brenda had washed 50 and Chay had washed 175. The profits were £1700. How much did each person get?

Q11 The wage bill at an office is £2400 in total. Fred gets one sixth, Greg gets a fifth of the remainder and Hillary gets what is left. How much money are each of them paid?

Q12 If I pay my gas bill within seven days, I can have a <u>reduction</u> of an eighth of the price. If my bill is for £120, how much can I save?

Q13 Jody sold her drum kit for £360 when she decided to buy a stereo. She <u>lost a fifth</u> of her money, but then needed to save only the remaining <u>one tenth</u> of the stereo's price. How much was the drum kit originally, and how much was the stereo?

Phew, thank goodness, that's the last page on fractions — but make sure you did all the questions — it's all on the Syllabus.

1.7 Questions on Percentages

Take it from me, there are three distinct types of percentage question — and one is easier than the other two. Basically, if you can see the % symbol you're onto a winner. Try these questions and you'll see what I mean.

Top Tips

1) "OF" means "×".	Example: 30% of 150 would be translated as $\dfrac{30}{100} \times 150 = 45$.
2) "PER CENT" means "OUT OF 100".	

Q1 Calculate

a) 50% of £25.00

b) 20% of £5.25

c) 5% of £3.60

d) 36% of 400 kg

e) 12% of 75 g

f) 7% of 50 g

g) 12% of 300 rabbits

h) 18% of 150 cars

i) 0.5% of 89 m.

Q2 Terry has earnt £56 by washing cars. Whilst shopping he spent <u>20%</u> of his earnings on a CD, <u>5%</u> on his lunch and paid the rest into the bank.

a) How much money did Terry spend on food?

b) How much money did the CD cost?

Q3 John bought a new PC. The tag in the shop said it cost <u>£890+VAT</u>.

If VAT is charged at 17½%, how much did he pay?

Finding "something %" of "something-else" is really quite simple — so you'd better be sure you know how.

Q4 The admission price at Wonder World is <u>£18 for adults</u>. A child's ticket costs <u>60%</u> of the adult price.

a) How much will it cost for one adult and 4 children to enter Wonder World?

b) How much will two adults and three children spend on entrance tickets?

Q5 A double glazing salesman is paid 10% commission on every sale he makes. In addition he is paid a £50 bonus if the sale is over £500.

a) If a customer buys £499 worth of windows from the salesman, what is his <u>commission</u>?

b) How much extra will he earn if he can persuade the customer in part **a)** to spend an extra £20?

c) How much does he earn if he sells £820 worth of windows?

Q6 Daphne earns an annual wage of £18900. She doesn't pay tax on the first £3400 that she earns. How much income tax does she pay when the rate of tax is:

a) 25% ?

b) 40% ?

1.7 Questions on Percentages

Make mighty sure you can see the difference between the two types of question on this page — if you're struggling have a gander at P.14 of The Revision Guide.

Q7 Keith wanted a dark green carpet for his lounge. A local carpet shop had just what he was looking for - and for only £82.00+VAT. Keith had £96 pounds in his bank account. If VAT was charged at 17½% could Keith afford the carpet?

Q8 Terence paid £4700 for his new motorcycle. <u>Each year</u> its value decreased by 12%.
a) How much was it worth when it was one year old?
b) How much was it worth when it was two years old?

Q9

> *Bed and breakfast £37 per person*
> *Evening meal £15 per person*

Two people stay at The Pickled Parrot for two nights and they have an evening meal each night. How much is the total cost, if VAT is added at 17½%?

THE PICKLED PARROT

Look for the word "percentage" to spot the second type of percentage question. It's not as bad as it looks — well not once you know the method:

<u>Fraction</u> — <u>Decimal</u> — <u>Percentage</u>	Express <u>25p</u> as a percentage of <u>£1.25</u>
1) Put the two numbers together as a <u>fraction</u>. 2) <u>Divide</u> them to make a <u>decimal</u>. 3) <u>Multiply by 100</u> to make a <u>percentage</u>.	1) $\dfrac{25}{125}$ 2) $25 \div 125 = \underline{0.2}$ 3) $0.2 \times 100 = \underline{20\%}$

Q10 A boat manufacturer reduces the price of its small rubber dinghy from £42.00 to £31.50 what is the <u>percentage reduction</u>?

Q11 During a rain storm a water butt increased its weight from 10.4 kg to 13.52 kg. What was the <u>percentage increase</u>?

Q12 A software company reduces the price of its CD-ROMS from £27.50 to £22.00. What is the percentage reduction?

Q13 At birth, a certain African elephant measured 1.2 m tall. When the elephant was fully grown she was 3.5 m tall. Calculate the percentage increase in height over her lifetime.

Q14 Rockwood School's results for A-Level biology are given in the table.

A-Level Biology Results

Grade	A	B	C	D	E
Frequency	7	10	15	12	5

a) What percentage of candidates achieved grade A?
b) What percentage of candidates achieved grade A, B or C?
c) What percentage of candidates didn't achieve grade A, B or C?

1.7 *Questions on Percentages*

Don't forget, there are three distinct types of percentage question. Basically, if they haven't given you the original value you're in Type 3 territory.

Q15 There are approximately 9000 burger bars in the UK. Every day about 320 people visit each one. Given that the population of the UK is roughly 60 million approximately what percentage of the population visit a burger bar each day?

Most people get the third type wrong — but only because they don't recognise them and use the simple method:

Example: A house <u>rose</u> in value by <u>25%</u> to £62,000 over the past year. What was its value a year ago?

Method: £62,000 = <u>125%</u>
(÷125)   £496   = <u>1%</u>
(×100)   £49,600 = <u>100%</u>
So the value a year ago was <u>£49,600</u>.

An <u>increase</u> of 25% means that £62,000 represents <u>125%</u> of the original value.
(If it had been a <u>reduction</u>, £62,000 would have represented <u>75%</u> of the original value.)

Q16 A pair of jeans shrunk in length by 20% after washing.
a) If the jeans are now 32 inches long, how long were they <u>originally</u>?
b) If the jeans are now 28 inches long, how long were they originally?

Q17 Janet bought a new hat in the sales for £42.00. The original price had been reduced by 25%. What was the original price?

Q18 An antiques expert estimates that his collection of fine Victorian table mats is increasing in value at a rate of 9% every year. Today the collection is worth £436.
a) How much was his collection worth a year ago?
b) How much will his collection be worth one year from now?

Q19 A sign in a bike shop window advertised a new XLS bicycle and after negotiating with the shop manager, I managed to get a 5% reduction in the price. I paid £142.50 for my new XLS bicycle - what was the original price?

Q20 In the new year sales Geoff bought a baseball cap for £17.85. The original price had been reduced by 15%.
What was the original price?

1.8   Questions on Fractions and Decimals

Remember, decimals are just a simple way of writing fractions — so it's easy to convert between the two. It's even easier if you get your calculator to do the hard work — so use it.

To convert *decimals to fractions*, write the number as a fraction of 10, 100 etc, then cancel down.	To convert *fractions to decimals* just use your calculator and divide.
Eg: $0.6 = \dfrac{6}{10} = \dfrac{3}{5}$ $0.15 = \dfrac{15}{100} = \dfrac{3}{20}$ $0.025 = \dfrac{25}{1000} = \dfrac{1}{40}$	Eg: $\dfrac{2}{3} = 2 \div 3 = 0.667$ $\dfrac{75}{100} = 75 \div 100 = 0.75$ $\dfrac{120}{150} = 120 \div 150 = 0.8$

Q1 Write the following fractions as decimals, giving your answer to 4 dp.

a) $\dfrac{1}{2}$ e) $\dfrac{1}{16}$ i) $\dfrac{6}{7}$ m) $\dfrac{42}{51}$

b) $\dfrac{1}{4}$ f) $\dfrac{1}{25}$ j) $\dfrac{8}{15}$ n) $\dfrac{17}{19}$

c) $\dfrac{1}{10}$ g) $\dfrac{3}{4}$ k) $\dfrac{4}{21}$ o) $\dfrac{1}{11}$

d) $\dfrac{1}{20}$ h) $\dfrac{19}{20}$ l) $\dfrac{7}{18}$ p) $\dfrac{0}{100}$

Q2 Write the following decimals as fractions:

a) 0.1   e) 0.19   i) 0.25   m) 0.125
b) 0.2   f) 0.473   j) 0.3   n) 0.72
c) 0.34   g) 0.101   k) 0.4   o) 0.8764
d) 0.9   h) 0.16   l) 0.86   p) 1.2

Sometimes they put in extra details to confuse you. Just ignore it — simply write down the fraction or decimal then carry out the conversion. Go on, outsmart them.

Q3 During the football season, Chris collected 0.45 of his favourite team's stickers. Write this decimal as a fraction.

Q4 In the following conversion table fill in the gaps:

Q5 Over the course of a formula one motor race, 8/22 of the cars did not finish. Write this fraction as a decimal.

FRACTION	DECIMAL
$^1\!/_{10}$	
	0.15
	0.9
$^1\!/_8$	
$^3\!/_{16}$	
	0.375
	0.15
$^9\!/_{20}$	
	0.625
$^9\!/_8$	

1.9 Questions on Decimals and Percentages

I reckon that converting decimals to percentages is about as easy as it gets — so make the most of it.

All you're doing is multiplying by 100 — it really couldn't be easier.

DECIMALS TO PERCENTAGES	Eg
Move the <u>decimal point</u> <u>2 places</u> to the <u>right</u>.	0.5 = 50% 0.62 = 62% 0.359 = 35.9%

Q1 Express each of the following as a percentage
a) 0.25   **e)** 1.0   **i)** 0.221   **m)** 0.4152
b) 0.5   **f)** 0.2   **j)** 0.546   **n)** 0.8406
c) 0.75   **g)** 0.11   **k)** 0.227   **o)** 0.3962
d) 0.1   **h)** 0.51   **l)** 0.713   **p)** 0.2828

PERCENTAGES TO DECIMALS	Eg
Move the <u>decimal point</u> <u>2 places</u> to the <u>left</u>.	20% = 0.2 75% = 0.75 33.3% = 0.333

Now you're dividing by 100 — so just move the decimal point the other way. It's as simple as that.

Q2 Express each percentage as a decimal
a) 50%   **e)** 62%   **i)** 60.2%   **m)** 75.16%
b) 12%   **f)** 17%   **j)** 54.9%   **n)** 44.02%
c) 40%   **g)** 16%   **k)** 43.1%   **o)** 98.25%
d) 34%   **h)** 77%   **l)** 78.8%   **p)** 82.65%

Q3 Harold estimates that 0.24 of his collection of racing snails are from Great Britain and Northern Ireland. Write this decimal as a percentage.

Q4 In the following conversion table fill in the gaps:

Q5 Jane reads in a newspaper that 34% of the population regularly watch soap operas on TV. Write this percentage as a decimal.

DECIMAL	PERCENTAGE
0.15	
	72%
0.6	
	18%
0.78	
	0.9%
0.33	
0.295	
	11.2%
	110%

1.10 Questions on Fractions and Percentages

For these, you'll need to use a combination of the methods on the last couple of pages.

Express 1/5 as a percentage	Express 60% as a fraction
1) Fraction to Decimal: 1 ÷ 5 = 0.2 2) Decimal to Percentage: (move the decimal point) <u>20%</u>	1) Percentage to Decimal: (move the decimal point) 0.6 2) Decimal to Fraction: 6/10 = 3/5

Q1 Express each percentage as a fraction in its lowest terms
a) 25%   e) 51%   i) 98%   m) 8.2%
b) 60%   f) 20%   j) 8%   n) 49.6%
c) 45%   g) 76%   k) 65%   o) 88.6%
d) 30%   h) 94%   l) 90%   p) 32.4%

Q2 Express each of the following as a percentage

a) $\frac{1}{2}$ e) $\frac{1}{25}$ i) $\frac{33}{100}$ m) $\frac{1}{13}$

b) $\frac{1}{4}$ f) $\frac{2}{3}$ j) $\frac{9}{23}$ n) $\frac{2}{5}$

c) $\frac{1}{8}$ g) $\frac{4}{15}$ k) $\frac{6}{7}$ o) $\frac{3}{7}$

d) $\frac{3}{4}$ h) $\frac{2}{7}$ l) $\frac{3}{8}$ p) $\frac{2}{21}$

Yet more fractions and percentages. They really want you to know this stuff, so you need to practise.

Q3 119 out of 140 houses on an estate have video recorders. What percentage is this?

Q4 In a general knowledge quiz Tina scored 13/20. What percentage is this?

Q5 In the following conversion table fill in the gaps:

Q6 In a Physics exam Tony scored 78/120. What percentage is this?

Q7 In a survey 46/72 people said they had been on holiday to Spain. What percentage is this?

FRACTION	PERCENTAGE
	25%
	30%
7/10	
	33 ⅓%
1/4	
5/8	
3/8	
	82%
	43.5%

Bye!

1.11   *Questions on Rounding Off*

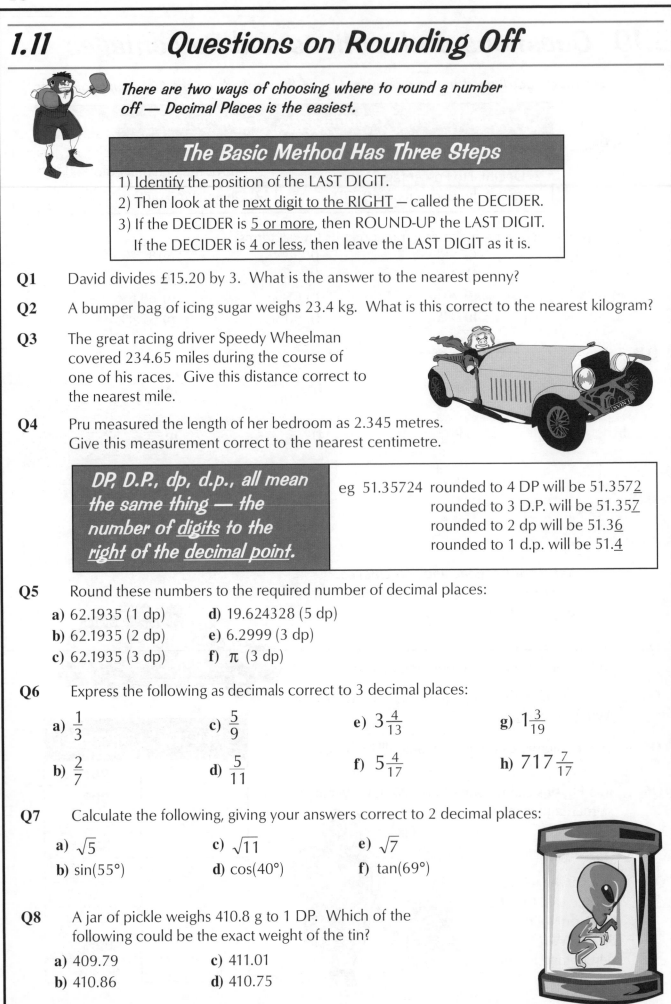

There are two ways of choosing where to round a number off — Decimal Places is the easiest.

The Basic Method Has Three Steps

1) <u>Identify</u> the position of the LAST DIGIT.
2) Then look at the <u>next digit to the RIGHT</u> — called the DECIDER.
3) If the DECIDER is <u>5 or more</u>, then ROUND-UP the LAST DIGIT.
    If the DECIDER is <u>4 or less</u>, then leave the LAST DIGIT as it is.

Q1   David divides £15.20 by 3. What is the answer to the nearest penny?

Q2   A bumper bag of icing sugar weighs 23.4 kg. What is this correct to the nearest kilogram?

Q3   The great racing driver Speedy Wheelman covered 234.65 miles during the course of one of his races. Give this distance correct to the nearest mile.

Q4   Pru measured the length of her bedroom as 2.345 metres. Give this measurement correct to the nearest centimetre.

> *DP, D.P., dp, d.p., all mean the same thing — the number of <u>digits</u> to the <u>right</u> of the <u>decimal point</u>.*

> eg 51.35724   rounded to 4 DP will be 51.357<u>2</u>
>   rounded to 3 D.P. will be 51.35<u>7</u>
>   rounded to 2 dp will be 51.3<u>6</u>
>   rounded to 1 d.p. will be 51.<u>4</u>

Q5   Round these numbers to the required number of decimal places:

     a) 62.1935 (1 dp)   **d)** 19.624328 (5 dp)
     b) 62.1935 (2 dp)   **e)** 6.2999 (3 dp)
     c) 62.1935 (3 dp)   **f)** π (3 dp)

Q6   Express the following as decimals correct to 3 decimal places:

     a) $\frac{1}{3}$ **c)** $\frac{5}{9}$ **e)** $3\frac{4}{13}$ **g)** $1\frac{3}{19}$

     b) $\frac{2}{7}$ **d)** $\frac{5}{11}$ **f)** $5\frac{4}{17}$ **h)** $717\frac{7}{17}$

Q7   Calculate the following, giving your answers correct to 2 decimal places:

     a) $\sqrt{5}$ **c)** $\sqrt{11}$ **e)** $\sqrt{7}$
     b) sin(55°)   **d)** cos(40°)   **f)** tan(69°)

Q8   A jar of pickle weighs 410.8 g to 1 DP. Which of the following could be the exact weight of the tin?

     a) 409.79   **c)** 411.01
     b) 410.86   **d)** 410.75

1.11 Questions on Rounding Off

Significant Figures are just like Decimal Places, but a bit tricky — now you need to worry about the evil zeros.

SIGNIFICANT FIGURES

1) The 1st significant figure of any number is simply THE FIRST DIGIT WHICH ISN'T ZERO.
2) The 2nd, 3rd, 4th, etc. significant figures follow immediately after the 1st, REGARDLESS OF BEING ZEROS OR NOT ZEROS.
3) After Rounding Off the LAST DIGIT, end ZEROS must be filled in up to, BUT NOT BEYOND, the decimal point.

Q9 Round these numbers to the required number of significant figures.

a) 1329.62 (3 SF)
b) 1329.62 (4 SF)
c) 1329.62 (5 SF)
d) 120 (1 SF)
e) 0.024687 (1 SF)
f) 0.024687 (4 SF)

Whenever a measurement is rounded off to a given unit, the actual measurement can be anything up to half a unit bigger or smaller.

1) 90 m to the nearest 10 metres could be anything between 85 m and 95 m. (But not exactly equal to 95 m, or it would be rounded up to 100 m).
2) 700 people to the nearest 10 people could be anything between 695 people and 704 people. (Because this only involves whole numbers.)

Q10 At a golf club, a putting green is given as being 5 m long to the nearest metre. Give the range of values that the actual length of the green could be.

Q11 A rectangular rug is 1.6 m long and 0.6 m wide. Both measurements are given correct to one decimal place.
a) State the maximum possible length of the rug.
b) Calculate the maximum possible area of the rug.

If you want to move a piece of heavy furniture into a small space, you need to know how big its measurements could really be.

Q12 Carlo weighs himself on some scales that are accurate to the nearest 10 g. The digital display shows his weight as 142.46 kg.
a) What is the maximum that he could weigh?
b) What is the minimum that he could weigh?

Q13 Claudia ran a 100 m race in 11.6 seconds. If the time was measured to the nearest 0.1 seconds and the distance to the nearest metre, what is the maximum value of his average speed, in metres per second?

1.12   Questions on Accuracy and Estimating

We're back to Significant Figures — I hope you enjoyed P.19.
Still, it's all good practice, and practice makes...

1) For fairly CASUAL MEASUREMENTS, 2 SIGNIFICANT FIGURES are most appropriate.

Cooking — 250 g (2 sig fig) of sugar, not 253 g (3 SF) or 300 g (1 SF)

2) For IMPORTANT OR TECHNICAL THINGS, 3 SIGNIFICANT FIGURES are essential.

A length that will be cut to fit, eg you'd measure a shelf as 25.6 cm long, not 26 cm or 25.63 cm.

3) Only for REALLY SCIENTIFIC WORK would you need over 3 SIGNIFICANT FIGURES.

Only someone really keen would want to know the length of a piece of
string to the nearest tenth of a millimetre — like 34.46 cm, for example.

Q1   A village green is roughly rectangular with a length of 33 m 48 cm and is 24 m and 13 cm
wide. Calculate the area of the green in m² to:
a) 2 DP
b) 3 SF.
c) State which of parts a) and b) would be the more reasonable value to use.

Just think casual, technical or really scientific...

Q2   Round each of the following to an appropriate degree of accuracy:
a) 42.798 g of sugar used to make a cake
b) a hall carpet of length 7.216 m
c) 3.429 g of $C_{12}H_{22}O_{11}$ (sugar) for a scientific experiment
d) 1.132 litres of lemonade used in a fruit punch
e) 0.541 miles from Jeremy's house to the nearest shop
f) 28.362 miles per gallon.

Q3   Decide on an appropriate degree of accuracy for the following:
a) the total dry weight, 80872 kg, of the space shuttle OV-102 Columbia
with its 3 main engines
b) the distance of 3.872 miles from Mel's house to Bryan's house
c) 1.563 m of fabric required to make a bedroom curtain
d) 152.016 kg of coal delivered to Jeff's house
e) 6 buses owned by the Partridge Flight Bus Company
f) the maximum night temperature of 11.721° forecast for
Birmingham by a TV weather presenter.

Q4   Calculate, giving your answer to an
appropriate degree of accuracy:

a) $\dfrac{41.75 \times 0.9784}{22.3 \times 2.54}$

b) $\dfrac{12.54 + 7.33}{12.54 - 7.22}$

*The important thing here is to give
your answer to one less significant
figure than the question.*

1.12 Questions on Accuracy and Estimating

This is very easy — as long as you realise what's expected.

ESTIMATING the ANSWER to a CALCULATION

1) ROUND EVERYTHING OFF to nice easy CONVENIENT NUMBERS
2) Then WORK OUT THE ANSWER using those nice easy numbers.

Q5 Showing all your working, estimate the value of the following:

a) $\dfrac{244.5 + 49.1}{53.2 - 41.2}$

b) $\dfrac{21.2 \times 9.7}{\sqrt{406.6}}$

c) $\dfrac{3019.23 \times 3.0433}{19.33 \times 5.102}$

d) $\dfrac{(19.2)^2 \div 20.3}{4.3 \times 5.011}$

If you don't show your working you'll lose easy marks so I guess it's worth doing.

ESTIMATING AREAS and VOLUMES

1) Draw or imagine a RECTANGLE OR CUBOID of similar size to the object in question.
2) ROUND OFF ALL LENGTHS to the NEAREST WHOLE, and work it out.

Q6 Estimate the areas of the following:

a)

b)

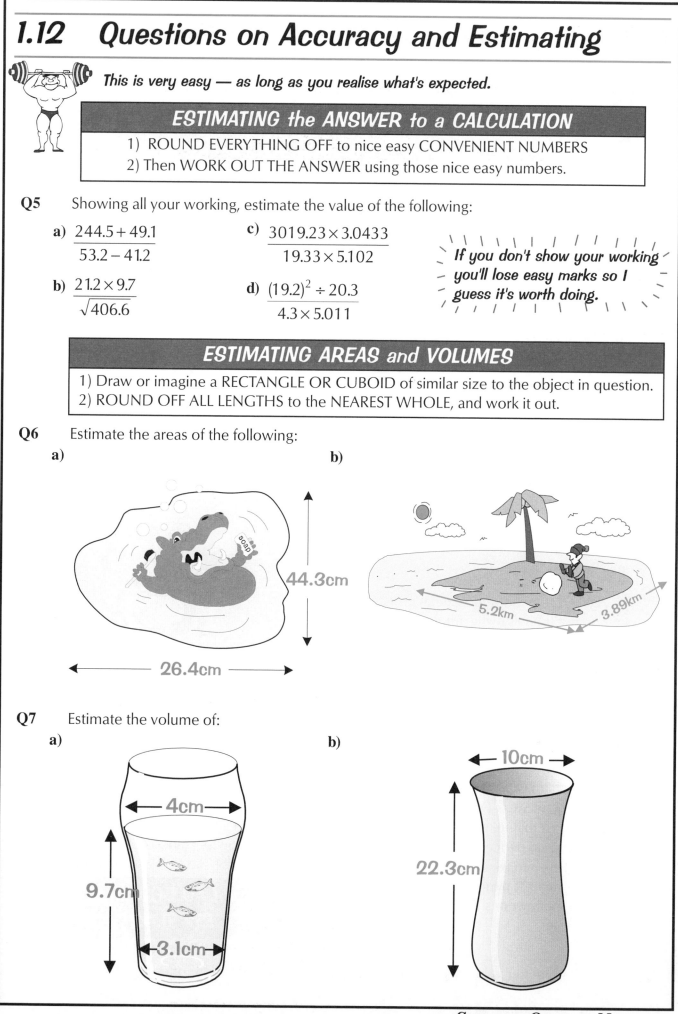

44.3cm

26.4cm

5.2km   **3.89km**

Q7 Estimate the volume of:

a)

4cm

9.7cm

3.1cm

b)

10cm

22.3cm

1.13   Questions on Conversion Factors

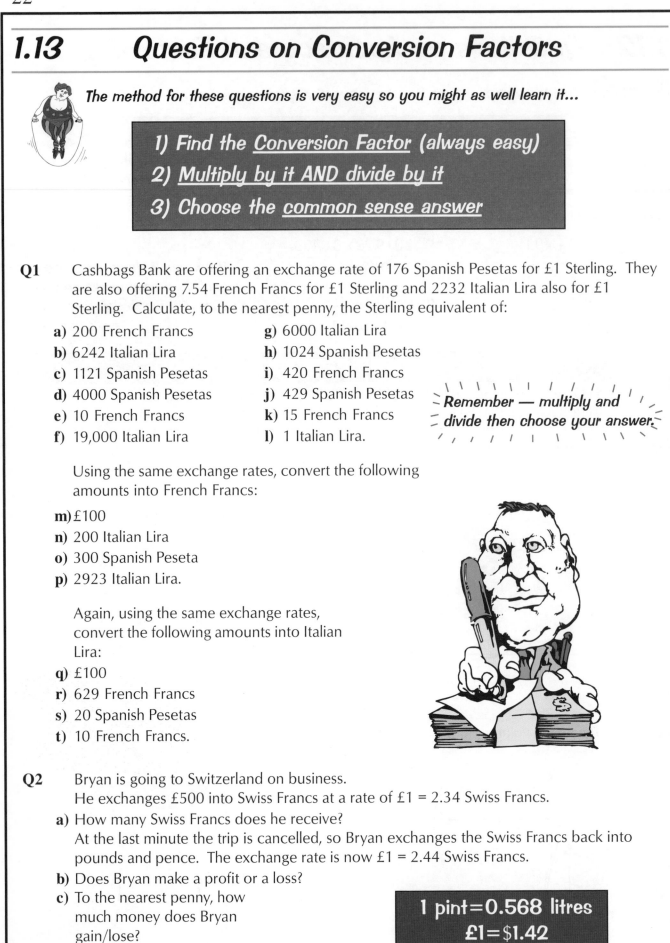

The method for these questions is very easy so you might as well learn it...

> 1) Find the <u>Conversion Factor</u> (always easy)
> 2) <u>Multiply by it AND divide by it</u>
> 3) Choose the <u>common sense answer</u>

Q1   Cashbags Bank are offering an exchange rate of 176 Spanish Pesetas for £1 Sterling. They are also offering 7.54 French Francs for £1 Sterling and 2232 Italian Lira also for £1 Sterling. Calculate, to the nearest penny, the Sterling equivalent of:

a) 200 French Francs

b) 6242 Italian Lira

c) 1121 Spanish Pesetas

d) 4000 Spanish Pesetas

e) 10 French Francs

f) 19,000 Italian Lira

g) 6000 Italian Lira

h) 1024 Spanish Pesetas

i) 420 French Francs

j) 429 Spanish Pesetas

k) 15 French Francs

l) 1 Italian Lira.

Remember — multiply and divide then choose your answer.

Using the same exchange rates, convert the following amounts into French Francs:

m) £100

n) 200 Italian Lira

o) 300 Spanish Peseta

p) 2923 Italian Lira.

Again, using the same exchange rates, convert the following amounts into Italian Lira:

q) £100

r) 629 French Francs

s) 20 Spanish Pesetas

t) 10 French Francs.

Q2   Bryan is going to Switzerland on business.
He exchanges £500 into Swiss Francs at a rate of £1 = 2.34 Swiss Francs.

a) How many Swiss Francs does he receive?
At the last minute the trip is cancelled, so Bryan exchanges the Swiss Francs back into pounds and pence. The exchange rate is now £1 = 2.44 Swiss Francs.

b) Does Bryan make a profit or a loss?

c) To the nearest penny, how much money does Bryan gain/lose?

> 1 pint = 0.568 litres
> £1 = $1.42

Q3   Which is better value, 2 pints of orange juice for $0.72 or 1 litre of orange juice for 49p?

1.13   *Questions on Conversion Factors*

Q4   Use the conversion graph below to find:

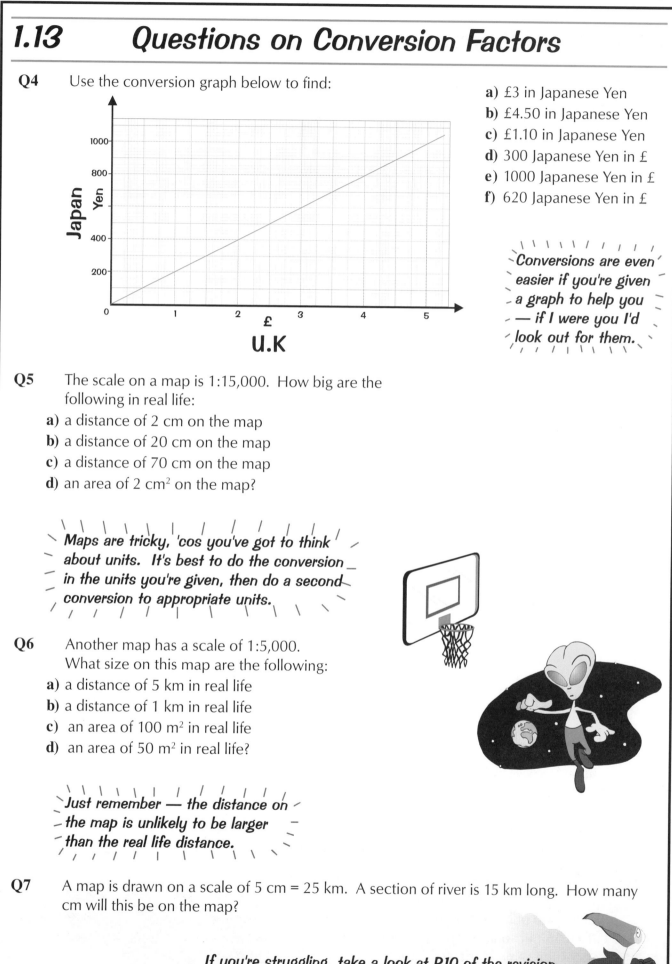

a) £3 in Japanese Yen
b) £4.50 in Japanese Yen
c) £1.10 in Japanese Yen
d) 300 Japanese Yen in £
e) 1000 Japanese Yen in £
f) 620 Japanese Yen in £

Conversions are even easier if you're given a graph to help you — if I were you I'd look out for them.

Q5   The scale on a map is 1:15,000. How big are the following in real life:

a) a distance of 2 cm on the map
b) a distance of 20 cm on the map
c) a distance of 70 cm on the map
d) an area of 2 cm² on the map?

Maps are tricky, 'cos you've got to think about units. It's best to do the conversion in the units you're given, then do a second conversion to appropriate units.

Q6   Another map has a scale of 1:5,000.
What size on this map are the following:

a) a distance of 5 km in real life
b) a distance of 1 km in real life
c) an area of 100 m² in real life
d) an area of 50 m² in real life?

Just remember — the distance on the map is unlikely to be larger than the real life distance.

Q7   A map is drawn on a scale of 5 cm = 25 km. A section of river is 15 km long. How many cm will this be on the map?

If you're struggling, take a look at P.10 of the revision guide to see how it's done.

SECTION ONE — NUMBER

1.14 Questions on Metric and Imperial Units

You're probably wondering whether you really need to learn these, well you do.

Approximate Conversions	
1 kg = 2¼ lbs	1 gallon = 4.5 litres
1 m = 1 yard (+10%)	1 foot = 30 cm
1 litre = 1¾ pints	1 metric *tonne* = 1 imperial *ton*
1 inch = 2.5 cm	1 mile = 1.6 km or 5 miles = 8 km

Q1   The water butt in my garden holds 20 gallons of rain-water. How many litres is this?

Q2   Convert 192 g into ounces.

Q3   Tom walked 17 km in one day, while Dave walked 10 miles. Who walked further?

Q4   Some scrap metal weighs 11 <u>tonnes</u>, how many <u>tons</u> is this?

Q5   A carpenter needs to cut a 7 inch piece of wood.
  a) How many cm is this?
  b) How many mm is this?

If you haven't done the questions on Conversion Factors yet, then have a quick look.

Q6   At the gym, Karen can lift a barbell weighing 40 kg.
  a) Convert this into pounds.
  b) How many ounces is this?
      Sara can lift a barbell weighing 0.041 tonnes.
  c) Who can lift the most?

Q7   One local garage prices its unleaded petrol at £3.30 per gallon. A supermarket garage prices its unleaded petrol at 70.9 pence per litre. Which is cheaper?

Q8   David is throwing a party for 15 of his friends. He decides that it would be nice to make a bowl of fruit punch and carefully follows a recipe for 24 pints worth.
  a) How many litres of fruit punch is this?
  b) If divided equally, how many pints of fruit punch is this per person at the party?
  c) How many litres of fruit punch is this per person at the party?

Q9   A recipe for a gigantic chocolate cake requires 9 lb of sugar. How many 1 kg bags of sugar does Sarah need to buy so that she can make the cake?

Q10 George is going to buy some fabric for a new pair of trousers that he is going to make. A local shop prices the fabric that he would like at £6.56 per square yard. A fabric superstore prices the same fabric at £7.20 per square metre. According to price, where should George buy his fabric?

1.14 Questions on Metric and Imperial Units

You should have no problems here, you've even been given all the conversion factors.

Q11 A tree in my garden is 15 feet tall.
    a) How many inches is this?   **d)** How many cm is this?
    b) How many yards is this?   **e)** How many mm is this?
    c) How many metres is this?   **f)** How many km is this?

I'm sure you know the difference between 12 and 24 hour clocks, but just so there's no excuses...

Q12 The times below are given using the 24 hour system. Using am or pm, give the equivalent time for a 12 hour clock.
    a) 0400   **c)** 0215   **e)** 2130
    b) 1712   **d)** 1522   **f)** 0001

Q13 The times below are taken from a 12 hour clock. Give the equivalent 24 hour readings.
    a) 10.30 pm   **c)** 12.30 am   **e)** 9.15 am
    b) 11.22 am   **d)** 12.30 pm   **f)** 3.33 pm

Q14 Find the time elapsed between the following pairs of times:
    a) 0920 on 1 November 1999 and 1720 on the same day.
    b) 11.22 pm on 1 November 1999 and 9.15 am the next day.
    c) 3.18 am on 1 November 1999 and 3.14 pm later the same day.
    d) 0410 on 1 November 1999 and 0358 on 3 November 1999.

Q15 Convert the following into hours and minutes
    a) 3.75 hours   **b)** 0.2 hours   **c)** 5.8 hours.

Q16 Convert the following into just hours:
    a) 4 hours and 30 minutes
    b) 1 hour and 6 minutes
    c) 15 minutes.

Q17 This timetable refers to three trains that travel from Asham to Derton.
    a) Which train is quickest from Asham to Derton?
    b) Which train is quickest from Cottingham to Derton?
    c) I live in Bordhouse. It takes me 8 minutes to walk to the train station. At what time must I leave the house by to arrive in Derton before 2.30 pm?

Asham – Derton			
	Train 1	Train 2	Train 3
Asham	0832	1135	1336
Bordhouse	0914	1216	1414
Cottingham	1002	1259	1456
Derton	1101	1404	1602

1.15 Questions on Special Number Sequences

There are five special sequences: EVEN, ODD, SQUARE, CUBE and TRIANGLE NUMBERS. You really need to know them and their nth terms.

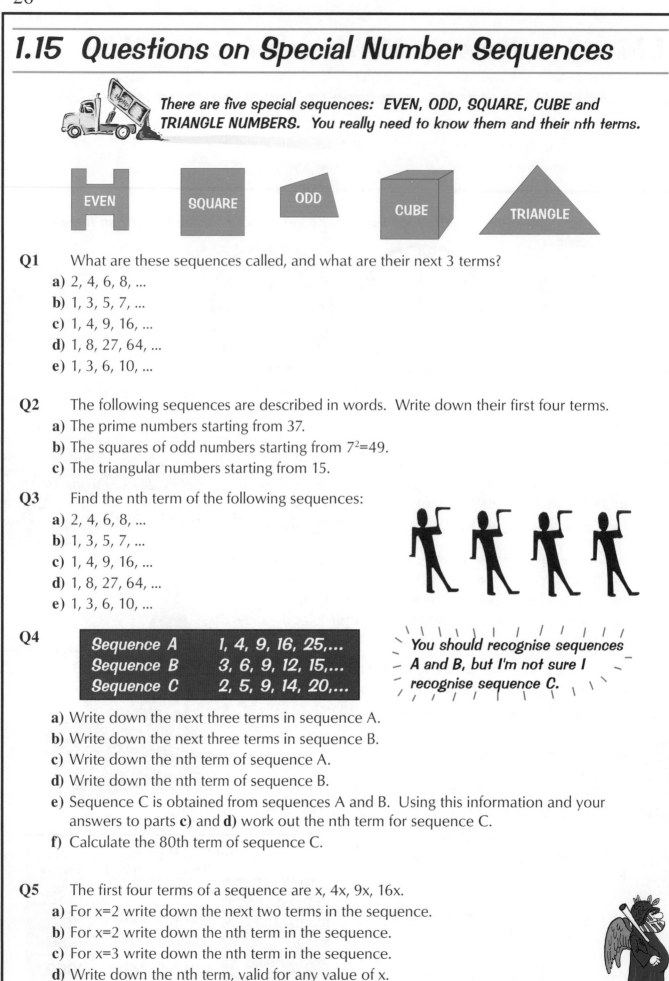

Q1 What are these sequences called, and what are their next 3 terms?
a) 2, 4, 6, 8, ...
b) 1, 3, 5, 7, ...
c) 1, 4, 9, 16, ...
d) 1, 8, 27, 64, ...
e) 1, 3, 6, 10, ...

Q2 The following sequences are described in words. Write down their first four terms.
a) The prime numbers starting from 37.
b) The squares of odd numbers starting from $7^2=49$.
c) The triangular numbers starting from 15.

Q3 Find the nth term of the following sequences:
a) 2, 4, 6, 8, ...
b) 1, 3, 5, 7, ...
c) 1, 4, 9, 16, ...
d) 1, 8, 27, 64, ...
e) 1, 3, 6, 10, ...

Q4

Sequence A	1, 4, 9, 16, 25,...
Sequence B	3, 6, 9, 12, 15,...
Sequence C	2, 5, 9, 14, 20,...

You should recognise sequences A and B, but I'm not sure I recognise sequence C.

a) Write down the next three terms in sequence A.
b) Write down the next three terms in sequence B.
c) Write down the nth term of sequence A.
d) Write down the nth term of sequence B.
e) Sequence C is obtained from sequences A and B. Using this information and your answers to parts c) and d) work out the nth term for sequence C.
f) Calculate the 80th term of sequence C.

Q5 The first four terms of a sequence are x, 4x, 9x, 16x.
a) For x=2 write down the next two terms in the sequence.
b) For x=2 write down the nth term in the sequence.
c) For x=3 write down the nth term in the sequence.
d) Write down the nth term, valid for any value of x.
e) For x=½ calculate the 75th term in the sequence.

1.16 Questions on Number Patterns

Number sequences are fun — they're often nothing more than pretty pictures.

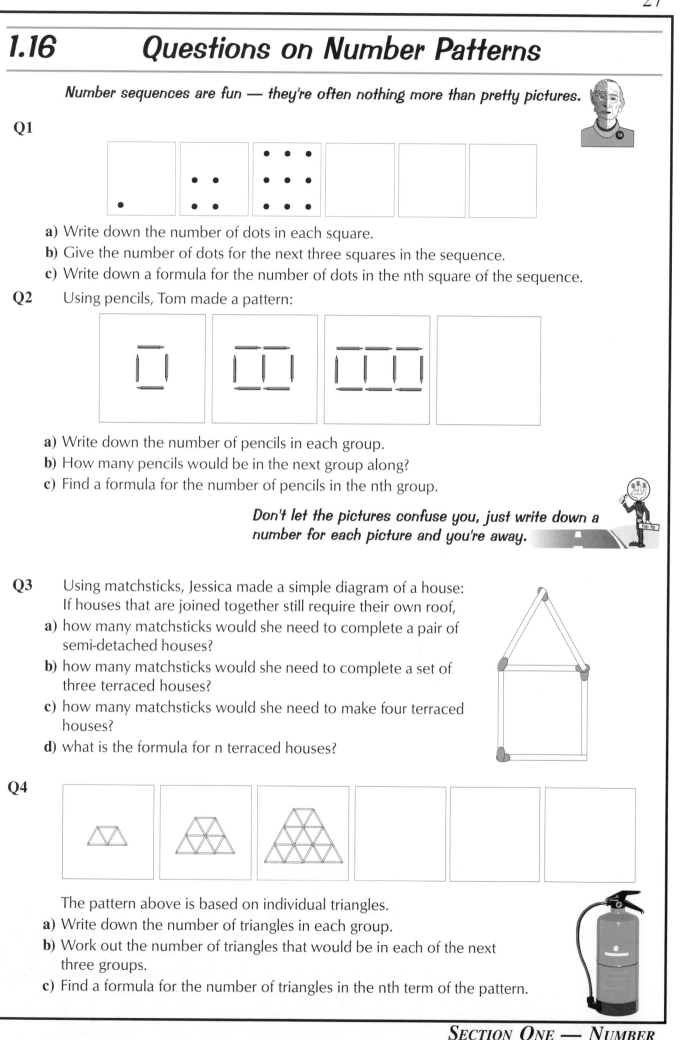

Q1

a) Write down the number of dots in each square.

b) Give the number of dots for the next three squares in the sequence.

c) Write down a formula for the number of dots in the nth square of the sequence.

Q2 Using pencils, Tom made a pattern:

a) Write down the number of pencils in each group.

b) How many pencils would be in the next group along?

c) Find a formula for the number of pencils in the nth group.

Don't let the pictures confuse you, just write down a number for each picture and you're away.

Q3 Using matchsticks, Jessica made a simple diagram of a house:
If houses that are joined together still require their own roof,

a) how many matchsticks would she need to complete a pair of semi-detached houses?

b) how many matchsticks would she need to complete a set of three terraced houses?

c) how many matchsticks would she need to make four terraced houses?

d) what is the formula for n terraced houses?

Q4

The pattern above is based on individual triangles.

a) Write down the number of triangles in each group.

b) Work out the number of triangles that would be in each of the next three groups.

c) Find a formula for the number of triangles in the nth term of the pattern.

1.16　Questions on Number Patterns

In the Exam you'll probably have to find the nth term of a sequence. To get full marks you need to know how to handle the "Common Difference Type" and the "Changing Difference Type". Have a look at P.21 of the revision guide if you need a hand.

Q5　A square tile pattern is formed with black and white tiles. In the centre there is always a
black tile. The rest of the pattern is made up of black
and white tiles, with the four corner tiles of the
square always being black.
The first term of the pattern is shown.
Work out the formula for:

a) the number of black tiles

b) the number of white tiles

c) the total number of tiles.

This is what you need to know to find the nth
term of a "Common Difference Type" sequence:

Common Difference Type: nth term = dn + (a−d)
1) "a" is the <u>FIRST TERM</u> in the sequence.   2) "d" is the <u>COMMON DIFFERENCE.</u>

Q6　In the following sequences, write down the next 3 terms and the nth term:

a) 2, 5, 8, 11,...

b) 7, 12, 17, 22,...

c) 1, 11, 21, 31,...

d) 49, 56, 63, 70,...

Q7　Jeff is collecting the post for his grandmother while she is
away on holiday. On the first day she was away she
received 3 letters. On the second day the pile of letters had
grown to 6. By the third day, Jeff had 9 letters in all.
This pattern continued while his grandmother was away,
and she returned from her holiday on the ninth day.

a) How many letters were waiting for her?

b) How many letters would have been waiting if she had
returned on the nth day?

Changing Difference Type: nth term = a + (n−1)d + ½(n−1)(n−2)C
1) "a" is the <u>first term</u> in the sequence,   2) "d" is the <u>first difference</u> and   3) "C" is the <u>change between one difference and the next.</u>

Q8　Write down the next three terms and nth
term of:

a) 2, 5, 9, 14,...

b) 3, 6, 11, 18,...

c) 6, 9, 16, 27,...

d) 11, 16, 24, 35,...

*Another type, another formula. Use this
for "Changing Difference" Sequences. It
looks like a nightmare, I admit, but all
you have to do is pop in the values of a,
d and C and you're away.*

1.16 Questions on Number Patterns

There are six main types of number sequence, but you'll only be asked to find the nth term for two. That means only two formulas, can't say fairer than that.

Q9 The nth term of a sequence is n(n+1).

  a) Write down the first 3 terms (n=1,2,3...).

  b) Explain why every term in the sequence is even.

  c) Write down the nth term of another sequence in which every term is even.

  d) Write down the nth term of a sequence in which every term is odd.

COMMON MULTIPLIER	COMMON DIVIDER
This type of number pattern has a <u>common multiplier</u> linking each pair of numbers. eg 5, 10, 20, 40,... In this case the <u>common multiplier</u> is 2.	This type has a <u>common divider</u> linking each pair of numbers. eg 189, 63, 21, 7,... In this case the <u>common divider</u> is 3.

Q10 For each of the following sequences, write down the next three terms:

  a) 1, 4, 16, 64,...   **c)** 6, 12, 24, 48,...

  b) 3, 15, 75, 375,...   **d)** 9, 27, 81, 243,...

Q11 Bryan collects stamps. In order to increase his collection he placed an advert in a national newspaper asking members of the public to send him stamps. On the 1st day he received 2 stamps. On the 2nd day he had received 6 stamps in total. By the end of third day he had received 18 stamps in total. How many stamps had Bryan received by the end of the:

  a) 4th day

  b) 6th day

  c) 10th day

  d) nth day.

Q12 For each of the following sequences, write down the next three terms:

  a) 729, 243, 81, 27,...

  b) 31250, 6250, 1250, 250,...

  c) 12288, 3072, 768, 192,...

  d) 5103, 1701, 567, 189,...

Q13 In order to work out the evaporation rate, Joanna measured the area of a puddle of water every hour on the hour. At 1300 the area of the puddle was 128 cm². 1 hour later the area of the puddle was 64 cm². At 1500 the area was 32 cm².

  a) What was the area of the puddle of water at 1600?

  b) What was the area of the puddle at 1800?

2.1   Questions on Regular Polygons

The one thing they're __guaranteed__ to ask you about is __Interior and Exterior Angles__ — you'd better get learning those formulas...

A **POLYGON** is a many sided shape. A **REGULAR** polygon is one where **ALL THE SIDES AND ANGLES ARE THE SAME.**

You need to know these two formulas:

1) EXTERIOR ANGLE = 360° ÷ No. of Sides

2) INTERIOR ANGLE = 180° — EXTERIOR ANGLE

Q1   Describe what a __regular__ polygon is.

Q2   What sort of triangles occur in a __regular hexagon__ when each vertex is joined to the centre by a straight line?

Q3   What sort of triangles occur in every regular polygon (__except__ a hexagon), when each vertex is joined to the centre by a straight line?

Q4   Using a __compass__, construct a regular hexagon with sides equal to 3 cm.

These compass ones are a bit fiddly — the only way to make sure you can do them is to keep trying. If you can't do them in the comfort of your own home, you'll stand no chance in the Exam.

Q5   What are the names given to the two types of angles associated with regular polygons?

Q6   What formula links interior with exterior angles?

Q7   What formula could be used to work out the __exterior__ angle of a regular polygon if the number of sides of the regular polygon is known?

Q8   What formula could be used to work out the __interior__ angle of a regular polygon if the number of sides of the regular polygon is known?

Q9   Using a compass, construct an __equilateral__ triangle with sides 3 cm. What angle is at each vertex?

Q10   Sketch a regular hexagon and draw in all its lines of symmetry. State the order of __rotational__ symmetry.

Remember, an octopus has eight tentacles — it's an octagon that has eight sides.

If you feel like doing a few more of these, have a look at P.73...

Q11   Do regular octagons __tessellate__?
What shape do you need to put with octagons to form a __tiling__ pattern?

Q12   Draw in all the lines of symmetry on this pentagon.
State the order of __rotational__ symmetry.

Q13   Which British coins in regular use have the same number of sides as a __regular heptagon__?

2.1   Questions on Regular Polygons

Once you've got all the answers to Q14, look at the pattern and *learn it* — it's dead easy and it'll save you time if you remember it.

Q14   Complete the following table:

Name	Sides	Lines of Symmetry	Order of Rotational Symmetry
Equilateral Triangle			
Square		4	
Regular Pentagon			
Regular Hexagon	6		
Regular Heptagon	7		
Regular Octagon			7
Regular Decagon	10		

Q15   In each of the pentagons, all the sides are of equal length, two of the angles are 90° and the other interior angles are m, m, and r degrees.

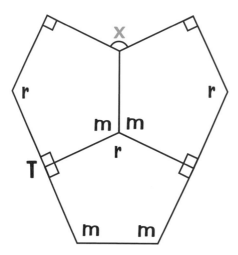

a) Explain in <u>two</u> different ways why 2m + r = 360°.

b) What is the exterior angle x?

c) Copy the diagram and add two more pentagons (by tracing through) so that the point T is completely surrounded and the whole figure forms part of a tessellation. Label all the angles of the new pentagons.

Q16   A square and a regular hexagon are placed adjacent to each other.

a) What is the <u>size</u> of ∠PQW?

b) What is the <u>size</u> of ∠PRW?

c) How many sides has the <u>regular polygon</u> that has ∠PQW as one of its angles?

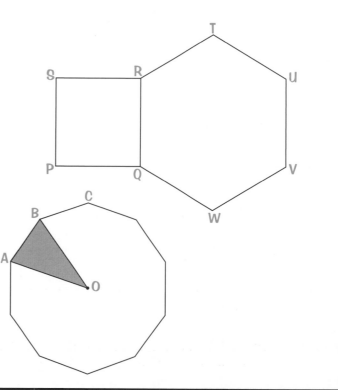

Q17   Here is a <u>regular decagon</u>. Calculate:

a) ∠AOB

b) ∠OBA

c) ∠ABC

2.1   Questions on Regular Polygons

Q18   In a regular <u>7 sided</u> polygon, what is the size of one interior angle, is it
    a) $128\frac{4}{7}°$ **b)** 135°   **c)** 120°   **d)** $112\frac{2}{7}°$ or   **e)** 140°?

You'll need to brush up on your Trigonometry for this one — yeah, bit dull innit. Still, you've got to do these things for the Exam, so turn to Section 3 and get scribbling...

Q19   A <u>regular hexagon</u> has a perimeter of 48cm. What is the distance between two of the opposite sides, is it

    a) 13.9 cm   **b)** 18.5 cm   **c)** 12.2 cm   **d)** 15.7 cm   or   **e)** 14.2 cm?

Q20   What is the size of an interior angle of a <u>dodecagon</u> (a 12 sided polygon)?

Q21   An <u>irregular pentagon</u> has interior angles of 100°, 104°, 120°. If the other two angles are equal, what is their size?

Q22   A regular polygon has an <u>interior</u> angle of 160°. Calculate
    a) the size of each exterior angle
    b) how many sides it has.

Q23   The <u>exterior</u> angle of a <u>regular</u> polygon is 24°. How many sides does it have?

Q24 a) Find the size of the interior angles of a <u>regular</u> 24 sided polygon.

    b) From this answer calculate one <u>exterior</u> angle and show that the <u>sum</u> of the exterior angles equals 360°.

Q25   Complete the table, then write a sentence to describe what is happening to the values of the interior/exterior angles as the number of sides increases.

Number of sides	Name	Interior angle	Exterior angle
5			
6			
7	Heptagon		
8			
9	Nonagon	140°	
10		144°	
11	Hendecagon	147.2727°	
12			
15			
18			
24			

Look at question 19

Look at question 20

2.2 Questions on Symmetry

They do say that bad things happen in threes... and now you've got to learn three types of symmetry — but don't worry, I reckon their names pretty much give the game away.

There are **THREE** types of symmetry:	
1) LINE SYMMETRY	You can draw a mirror line across the object and both sides will fold together exactly.
2) PLANE SYMMETRY	This applies to 3-D solids. You can draw a plane mirror surface through the solid to make the shape exactly the same on both sides of the plane.
3) ROTATIONAL SYMMETRY	You can rotate the shape or drawing into different positions that all look exactly the same.

Q1 Draw <u>all</u> the lines of symmetry for each of the following shapes. (Some shapes may have no lines of symmetry)

a) b) c) d) e) f)

These questions are a piece of cake if you use tracing paper — and remember you can use it in the Exam, so take some with you or ask for it.

Q2 What is the <u>order of rotational symmetry</u> for each of the following shapes ?

a) b) c) d)

Q3 Mark in the <u>lines of symmetry</u> of the following letters. State the <u>order</u> of rotational symmetry for each one.

MHVBAKSZ

2.2 Questions on Symmetry

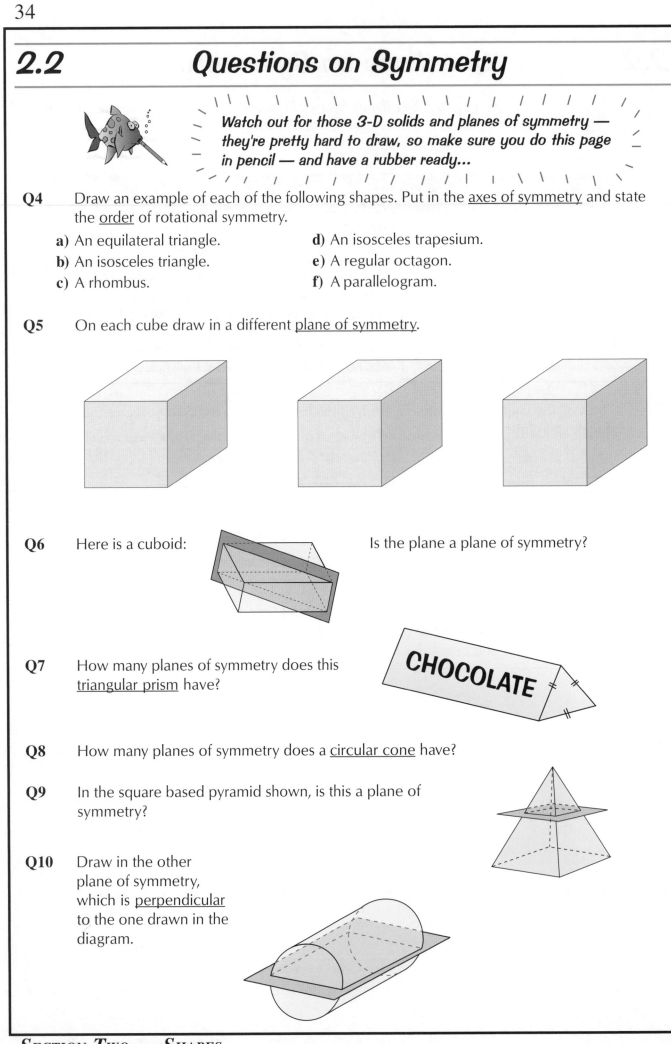

Watch out for those 3-D solids and planes of symmetry — they're pretty hard to draw, so make sure you do this page in pencil — and have a rubber ready...

Q4 Draw an example of each of the following shapes. Put in the <u>axes of symmetry</u> and state the <u>order</u> of rotational symmetry.

a) An equilateral triangle. **d)** An isosceles trapesium.

b) An isosceles triangle. **e)** A regular octagon.

c) A rhombus. **f)** A parallelogram.

Q5 On each cube draw in a different <u>plane of symmetry</u>.

Q6 Here is a cuboid: Is the plane a plane of symmetry?

Q7 How many planes of symmetry does this <u>triangular prism</u> have?

CHOCOLATE

Q8 How many planes of symmetry does a <u>circular cone</u> have?

Q9 In the square based pyramid shown, is this a plane of symmetry?

Q10 Draw in the other plane of symmetry, which is <u>perpendicular</u> to the one drawn in the diagram.

2.2 Questions on Symmetry

Q11   How many planes of symmetry does a <u>tetrahedron</u> have?

Q12   Would all the planes of symmetry of a cube meet in a <u>line</u>, <u>point</u> or <u>plane</u>?

Q13   This is a description of <u>which 3-D solid</u>?
This solid has faces, edges and vertices.
All the faces have the same shape and all the edges have the same length.
There are 4 vertices.
Is the solid:

    a) a cube,   **b)** a cuboid,   **c)** a square based pyramid or **d)** a tetrahedron?

There are a few different shapes creeping in here — just checking you're awake...

Q14   How many <u>planes of symmetry</u> does a blackboard rubber like the one shown have?

And don't think they won't try this in the Exam...

Q15   A roofing tile is shown.
  a) How many planes of symmetry does this have?
  b) What <u>angle</u> do they meet at?
  c) <u>How</u> do they meet, line, point or plane?

Q16   Bert the mathematical ant crawls from X to Y by the <u>shortest route</u> on the surface of the cuboid.
Is the length of his journey:
  a) $2+\sqrt{34}$ cm,
  b) $\sqrt{50}$ cm, or
  c) 10 cm ?

Q17   The diagram shows a <u>square-based pyramid</u> of height X with a square base of side 2x. P is the centre of the base, whilst T is the mid-point of AB, and S is the midpoint of CD.
  a) How many planes of symmetry does the square-based pyramid have?
  b) Is it true that $\angle$TVS is a <u>right angle</u>?

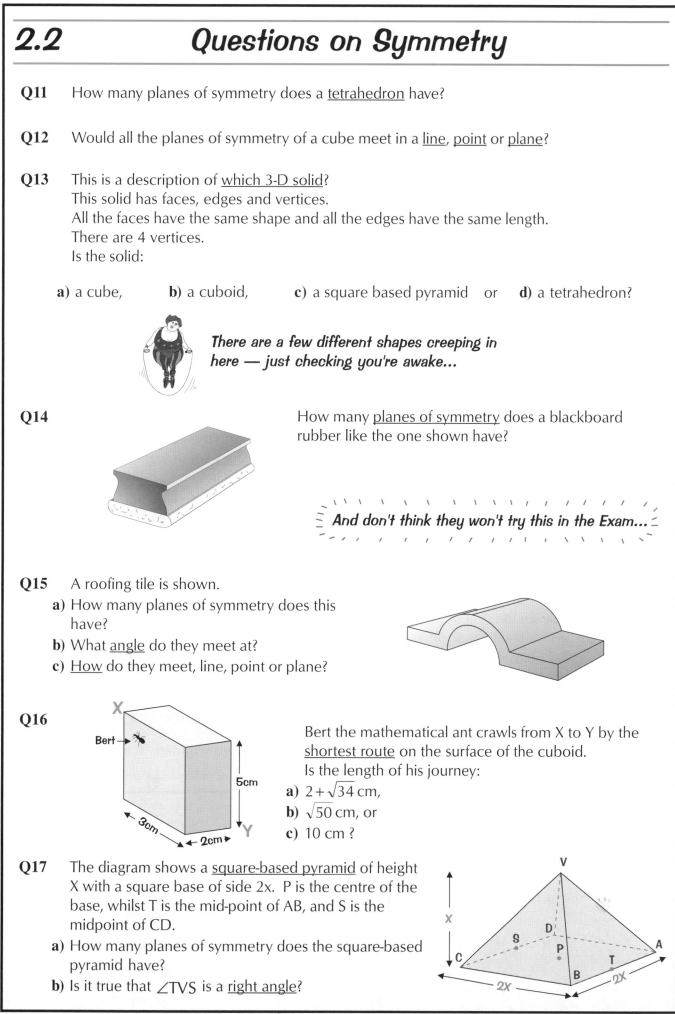

2.3 Questions on Shapes You Need To Know

You need to know about __all__ of the following shapes __and__ their symmetries.

Eeeek.

2-D Shapes	3-D Solids
1) SQUARE	1) REGULAR TETRAHEDRON
2) RECTANGLE	2) CYLINDER
3) RHOMBUS	3) CUBE
4) PARALLELOGRAM	4) CUBOID
5) TRAPEZIUM	5) SPHERE
6) KITE	6) TRIANGULAR PRISM
7) EQUILATERAL TRIANGLE	7) CONE
8) RIGHT-ANGLED TRIANGLE	8) SQUARE-BASED PYRAMID
9) ISOSCELES TRIANGLE	

Q1 Solve these simple riddles to find the names of 6 common shapes:

a) I have 4 sides of the same length but my two pairs of __parallel__ sides are not at right angles to each other, although my __diagonals__ bisect each other at 90°.

b) I am a shape that likes to fly. My two __isosceles__ triangles form the four-sided shape, but if I am split down my line of symmetry I will show two __congruent__ triangles instead.

c) I have four sides, 2 pairs of parallel sides, each pair of equal length but different from the other pair. I have no line of symmetry because of this and the fact that my sides don't meet at 90°.

d) I am related to a square – but I am not one.
I am related to a parallelogram – but I am not one.
I have two symmetries of __order 2__.

e) I can be one of three.
I can look like the roof of a house with a line of symmetry.
I can be one even if you join my pair of parallel sides, by any old straight lines.

f) My order of rotational symmetry = My number of lines of symmetry = My number of sides = My number of right angles.

Q2 Name 4 different triangles and draw a sketch for each one, showing appropriate, relevant differences.

Q3 Name each of the following solids. Draw in a single __plane__ of symmetry if any exist:

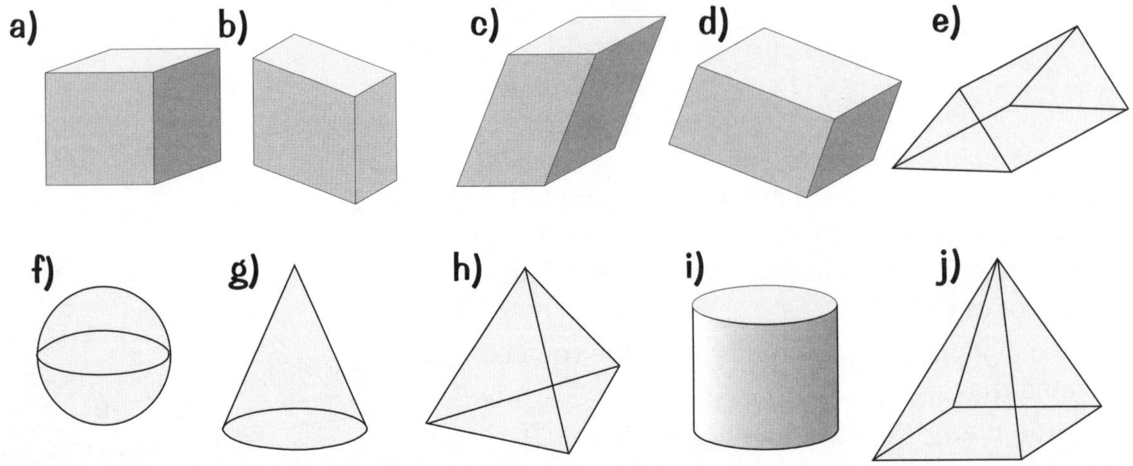

a)   b)   c)   d)   e)

f)   g)   h)   i)   j)

2.4 Questions on Length, Area and Volume

Time to get your brain in gear

— these can get pretty confusing, believe me.

You need to know these three facts:

1) LENGTH FORMULAS always have LENGTHS OCCURING SINGLY
2) AREA FORMULAS always have lengths MULTIPLIED IN PAIRS
3) VOLUME FORMULAS always have lengths multiplied in GROUPS OF THREE

Q1 p, q and r are lengths. State for each of the following, whether the formula gives a <u>length</u>, an <u>area</u>, a <u>volume</u> or <u>none of these</u>:

a) $p + q$

b) $pq - rq$

c) $p^2q^2 + pr^2$

d) pr/q

e) $5pqr/10$

f) $\pi pqr/2$

g) $p^3 + q^3 + r^3$

h) $9pr^2 - 2q$

Q2 w, x, y and z are lengths. State for each of the following, whether the formula gives a <u>length</u>, an <u>area</u> or a <u>volume</u>, when numbers are substituted in for the dummy variables:

a) $\dfrac{xy}{w}$

b) $\dfrac{xy^2 - w^2y}{z^2}$

c) $\dfrac{x^3}{y} - 14wz$

d) $\dfrac{x^2}{w} + \dfrac{w^2}{y} + \dfrac{y^2}{z} + \dfrac{z^4}{x^3}$

Q3 a, b, and c are lengths, r is the radius, $\pi = 3.14$.
State whether the formula gives a <u>perimeter</u>, <u>area</u> or <u>neither</u> of these.

a) $3\pi r^2 + abc$

b) $6\pi r + a - 6c$

c) $17ab + \pi r^2$

d) $\dfrac{16abc}{8b}$

Q4 If r is a length, is $\frac{4}{3}\pi r^2$ a volume formula?

Q5 If b and h are lengths, is ½bh an area formula?

Q6 Is $\dfrac{h}{2}(x + y)$ an area formula, if x, y and h are lengths?

Q7 If x and h are lengths, could this be a perimeter formula?
$x + x + h + h + h$

Q8 Could ½Dd be a volume formula, given that D and d are lengths?

Q9 The following statements are <u>incomplete</u>. For each one, find out what is missing and rewrite the formula correctly:

a) Volume of a cube = l   (where l is the length)
b) Area of a circle = $\pi\dfrac{d}{2}$ (where d is the diameter)
c) Perimeter of a circle = πr (where r is the radius)

Remember :-

if r is a length, then r^2 is an area and r^3 is a volume.

If you ever see something like r^6 then rub your eyes because it's gone wrong — unless you're an alien from a 6-dimensional universe, in which case you'll feel right at home.

2.5   *Questions on Areas*

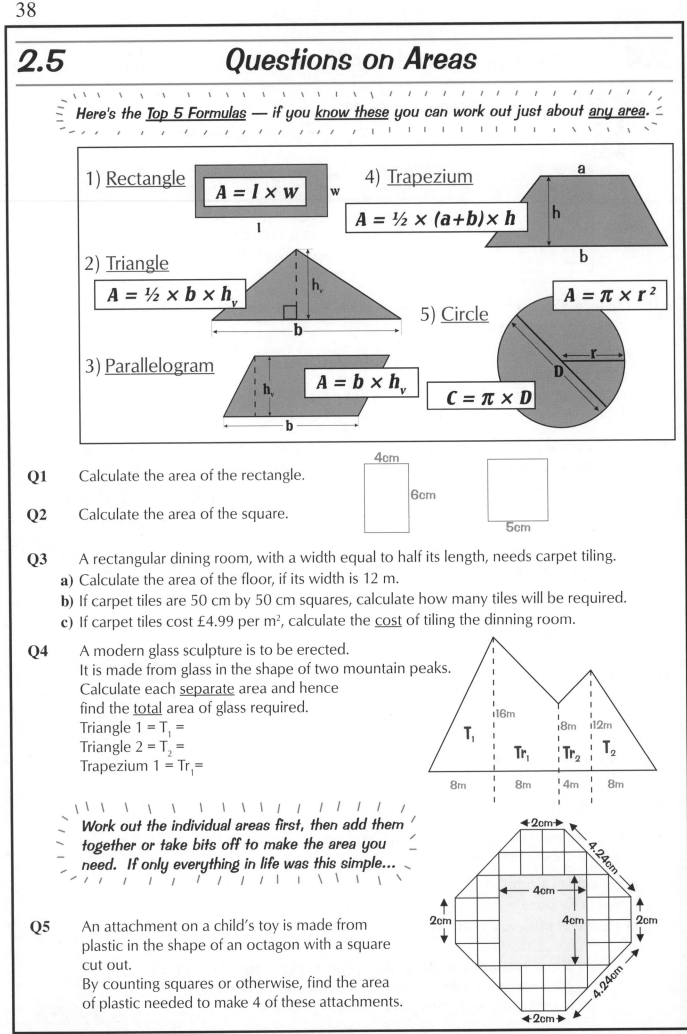

1) <u>Rectangle</u>

$$A = l \times w$$

2) <u>Triangle</u>

$$A = \tfrac{1}{2} \times b \times h_v$$

3) <u>Parallelogram</u>

$$A = b \times h_v$$

4) <u>Trapezium</u>

$$A = \tfrac{1}{2} \times (a+b) \times h$$

5) <u>Circle</u>

$$A = \pi \times r^2$$

$$C = \pi \times D$$

Q1   Calculate the area of the rectangle.

4cm

6cm

Q2   Calculate the area of the square.

5cm

Q3   A rectangular dining room, with a width equal to half its length, needs carpet tiling.
      a) Calculate the area of the floor, if its width is 12 m.
      b) If carpet tiles are 50 cm by 50 cm squares, calculate how many tiles will be required.
      c) If carpet tiles cost £4.99 per m², calculate the <u>cost</u> of tiling the dinning room.

Q4   A modern glass sculpture is to be erected.
      It is made from glass in the shape of two mountain peaks.
      Calculate each <u>separate</u> area and hence
      find the <u>total</u> area of glass required.
      Triangle 1 = T_1 =
      Triangle 2 = T_2 =
      Trapezium 1 = Tr_1 =

16m   8m   12m

T_1 Tr_1 Tr_2 T_2

8m   8m   4m   8m

2cm

4.24cm

4cm

2cm   4cm   2cm

4.24cm

2cm

Q5   An attachment on a child's toy is made from
      plastic in the shape of an octagon with a square
      cut out.
      By counting squares or otherwise, find the area
      of plastic needed to make 4 of these attachments.

2.5   *Questions on Areas*

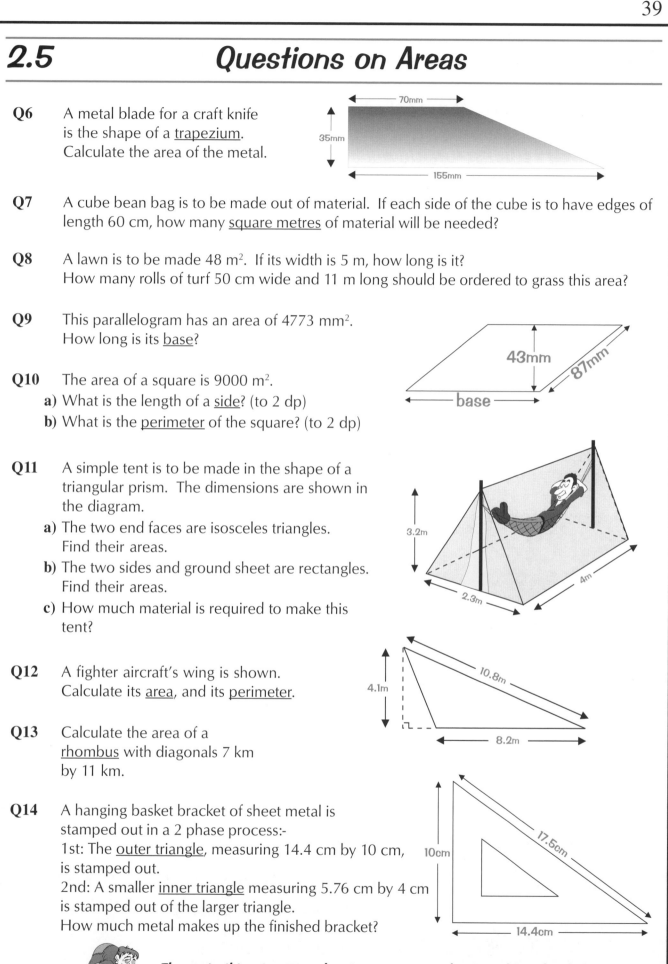

Q6   A metal blade for a craft knife is the shape of a <u>trapezium</u>. Calculate the area of the metal.

Q7   A cube bean bag is to be made out of material. If each side of the cube is to have edges of length 60 cm, how many <u>square metres</u> of material will be needed?

Q8   A lawn is to be made 48 m². If its width is 5 m, how long is it? How many rolls of turf 50 cm wide and 11 m long should be ordered to grass this area?

Q9   This parallelogram has an area of 4773 mm². How long is its <u>base</u>?

Q10   The area of a square is 9000 m².
     a) What is the length of a <u>side</u>? (to 2 dp)
     b) What is the <u>perimeter</u> of the square? (to 2 dp)

Q11   A simple tent is to be made in the shape of a triangular prism. The dimensions are shown in the diagram.
     a) The two end faces are isosceles triangles. Find their areas.
     b) The two sides and ground sheet are rectangles. Find their areas.
     c) How much material is required to make this tent?

Q12   A fighter aircraft's wing is shown. Calculate its <u>area</u>, and its <u>perimeter</u>.

Q13   Calculate the area of a <u>rhombus</u> with diagonals 7 km by 11 km.

Q14   A hanging basket bracket of sheet metal is stamped out in a 2 phase process:-
1st: The <u>outer triangle</u>, measuring 14.4 cm by 10 cm, is stamped out.
2nd: A smaller <u>inner triangle</u> measuring 5.76 cm by 4 cm is stamped out of the larger triangle.
How much metal makes up the finished bracket?

The <u>main thing</u> to remember is — you can <u>always</u> split up hard shapes into easy ones... like the "Top Five" on the other page, which you've already learnt.

2.6 Questions on Perimeters and Areas

For perimeters, the <u>Big Blob Method</u> is the <u>best way</u> to be sure you've got all the sides.

<u>PERIMETER</u> is the distance all the way around the outside of a 2D shape

Always use the <u>BIG BLOB</u> method :
1) Put a <u>BIG BLOB</u> at one corner, then go around the shape.
2) Write down the length of every side as you go.
3) Even sides that seem to have no length given — you must work them out.
4) Keep going until you get back to the <u>BIG BLOB</u>. Then add up all the sides.

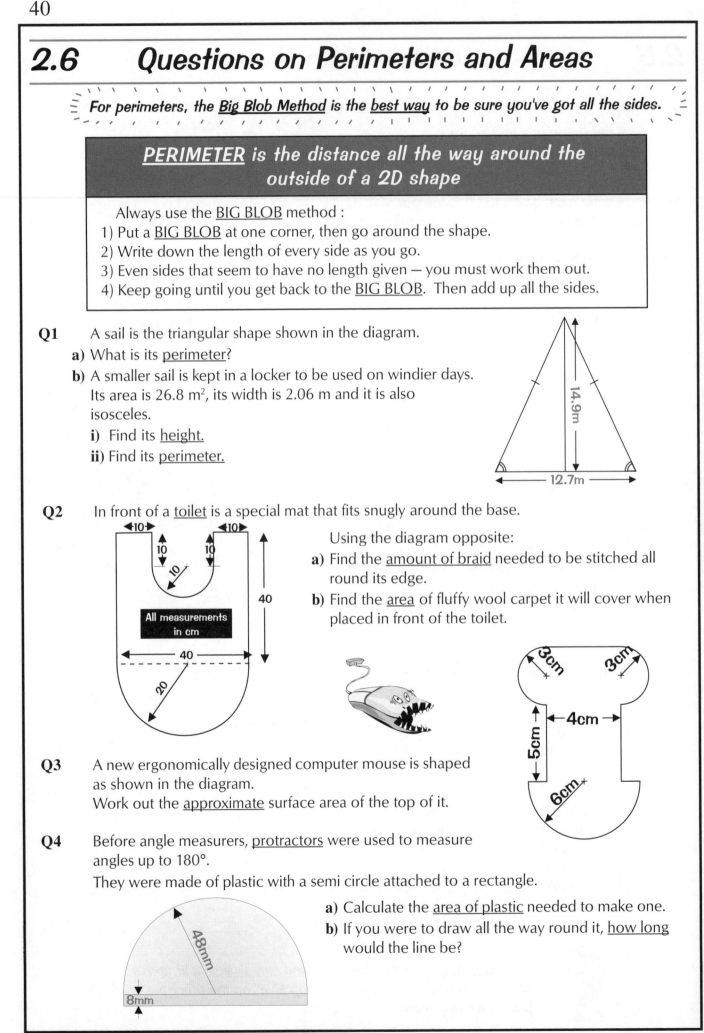

Q1 A sail is the triangular shape shown in the diagram.
a) What is its <u>perimeter</u>?
b) A smaller sail is kept in a locker to be used on windier days.
Its area is 26.8 m², its width is 2.06 m and it is also
isosceles.
i) Find its <u>height.</u>
ii) Find its <u>perimeter.</u>

14.9m

12.7m

Q2 In front of a <u>toilet</u> is a special mat that fits snugly around the base.

10   10
10   10
10
40
All measurements
in cm
40
20

Using the diagram opposite:
a) Find the <u>amount of braid</u> needed to be stitched all
round its edge.
b) Find the <u>area</u> of fluffy wool carpet it will cover when
placed in front of the toilet.

3cm   3cm
4cm
5cm
6cm

Q3 A new ergonomically designed computer mouse is shaped
as shown in the diagram.
Work out the <u>approximate</u> surface area of the top of it.

Q4 Before angle measurers, <u>protractors</u> were used to measure
angles up to 180°.
They were made of plastic with a semi circle attached to a rectangle.

48mm

8mm

a) Calculate the <u>area of plastic</u> needed to make one.
b) If you were to draw all the way round it, <u>how long</u>
would the line be?

2.6 Questions on Perimeters and Areas

Keep using __Good Reliable Methods__ — they won't let you down, I guarantee it. You'll soon find you can do them in your sleep... not that I'd recommend it.

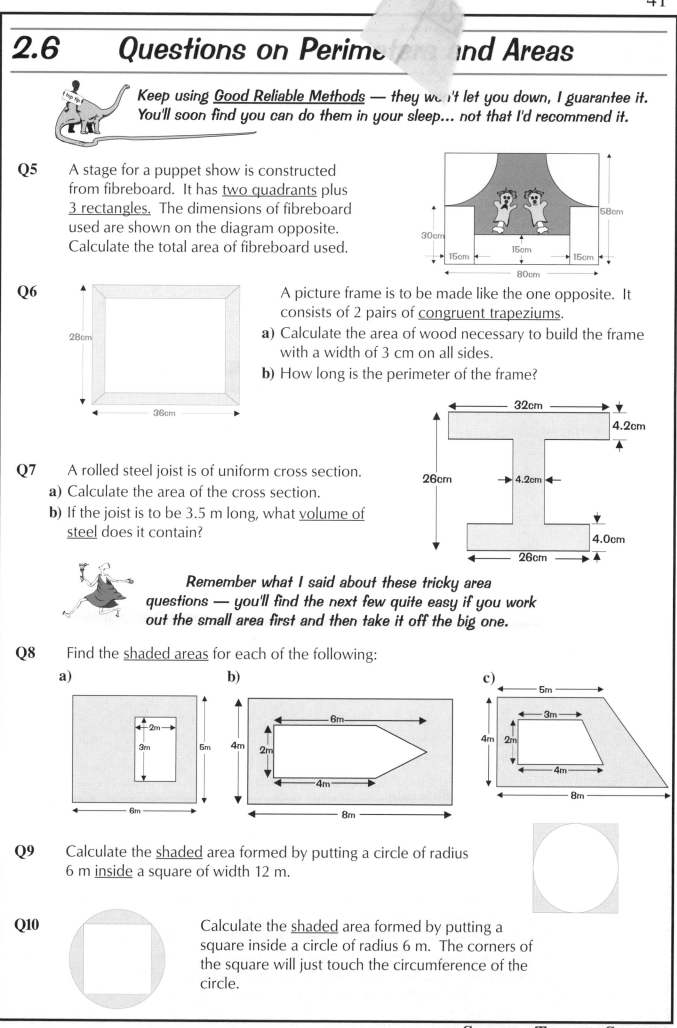

Q5 A stage for a puppet show is constructed from fibreboard. It has __two quadrants__ plus __3 rectangles.__ The dimensions of fibreboard used are shown on the diagram opposite. Calculate the total area of fibreboard used.

Q6 A picture frame is to be made like the one opposite. It consists of 2 pairs of __congruent trapeziums__.
a) Calculate the area of wood necessary to build the frame with a width of 3 cm on all sides.
b) How long is the perimeter of the frame?

Q7 A rolled steel joist is of uniform cross section.
a) Calculate the area of the cross section.
b) If the joist is to be 3.5 m long, what __volume of steel__ does it contain?

Remember what I said about these tricky area questions — you'll find the next few quite easy if you work out the small area first and then take it off the big one.

Q8 Find the __shaded areas__ for each of the following:
a)
b)
c)

Q9 Calculate the __shaded__ area formed by putting a circle of radius 6 m __inside__ a square of width 12 m.

Q10 Calculate the __shaded__ area formed by putting a square inside a circle of radius 6 m. The corners of the square will just touch the circumference of the circle.

2.7 Questions on Solids and Nets

Before you go any further — make sure you know these 4 facts...

Surface Area and Nets

1) <u>SURFACE AREA</u> only applies to solid 3-D objects. It's the <u>TOTAL AREA</u> of all the <u>OUTER SURFACES</u> added together.
2) There is no simple formula for surface area — you have to work out each side in turn and then <u>ADD THEM ALL TOGETHER</u>.
3) A <u>NET</u> is just A <u>SOLID SHAPE</u> folded out <u>FLAT</u>.
4) SURFACE AREA OF SOLID = AREA OF NET.

Q1 <u>Match</u> these three names with the 2-dimensional drawings of the 3-D shapes.

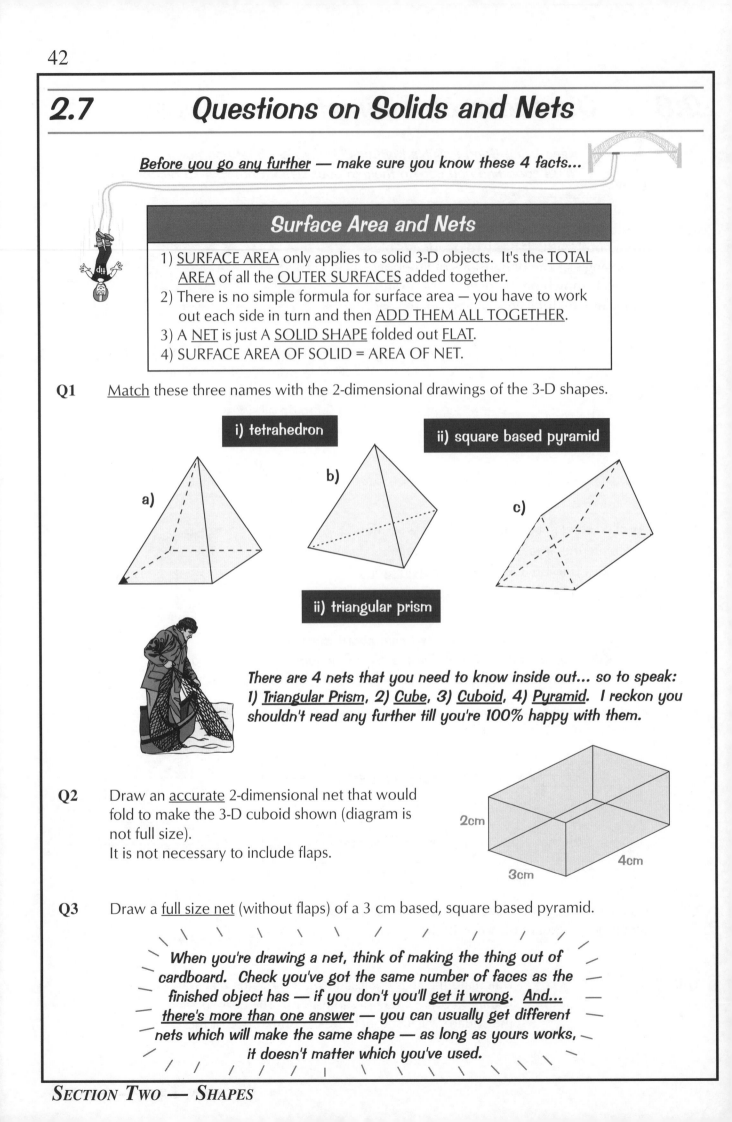

i) tetrahedron

ii) square based pyramid

a)

b)

c)

ii) triangular prism

There are 4 nets that you need to know inside out... so to speak:
1) <u>Triangular Prism</u>, 2) <u>Cube</u>, 3) <u>Cuboid</u>, 4) <u>Pyramid</u>. I reckon you
shouldn't read any further till you're 100% happy with them.

Q2 Draw an <u>accurate</u> 2-dimensional net that would fold to make the 3-D cuboid shown (diagram is not full size).
It is not necessary to include flaps.

2cm

3cm

4cm

Q3 Draw a <u>full size net</u> (without flaps) of a 3 cm based, square based pyramid.

When you're drawing a net, think of making the thing out of
cardboard. Check you've got the same number of faces as the
finished object has — if you don't you'll <u>get it wrong</u>. <u>And...</u>
<u>there's more than one answer</u> — you can usually get different
nets which will make the same shape — as long as yours works,
it doesn't matter which you've used.

2.7 Questions on Solids and Nets

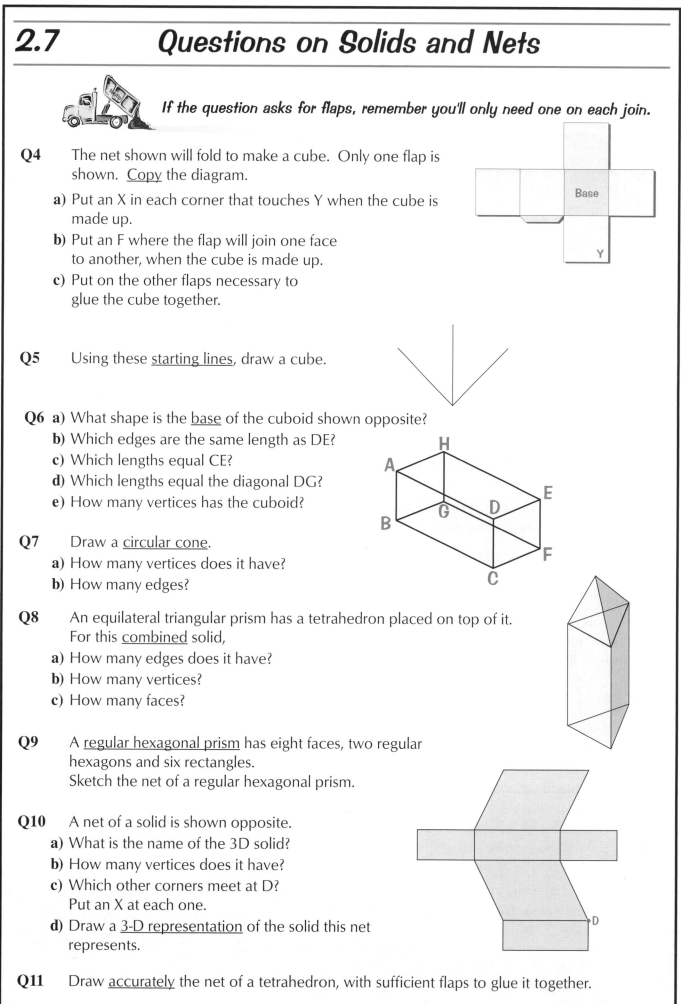

If the question asks for flaps, remember you'll only need one on each join.

Q4 The net shown will fold to make a cube. Only one flap is shown. <u>Copy</u> the diagram.

  a) Put an X in each corner that touches Y when the cube is made up.

  b) Put an F where the flap will join one face to another, when the cube is made up.

  c) Put on the other flaps necessary to glue the cube together.

Base

Y

Q5 Using these <u>starting lines</u>, draw a cube.

Q6 a) What shape is the <u>base</u> of the cuboid shown opposite?

  b) Which edges are the same length as DE?

  c) Which lengths equal CE?

  d) Which lengths equal the diagonal DG?

  e) How many vertices has the cuboid?

Q7 Draw a <u>circular cone</u>.

  a) How many vertices does it have?

  b) How many edges?

Q8 An equilateral triangular prism has a tetrahedron placed on top of it. For this <u>combined</u> solid,

  a) How many edges does it have?

  b) How many vertices?

  c) How many faces?

Q9 A <u>regular hexagonal prism</u> has eight faces, two regular hexagons and six rectangles. Sketch the net of a regular hexagonal prism.

Q10 A net of a solid is shown opposite.

  a) What is the name of the 3-D solid?

  b) How many vertices does it have?

  c) Which other corners meet at D? Put an X at each one.

  d) Draw a <u>3-D representation</u> of the solid this net represents.

Q11 Draw <u>accurately</u> the net of a tetrahedron, with sufficient flaps to glue it together.

2.8 Questions on Volume and Capacity

Capacity is exactly the same thing as volume — simple as that. And things will get even simpler once you've learnt the two formulas below.

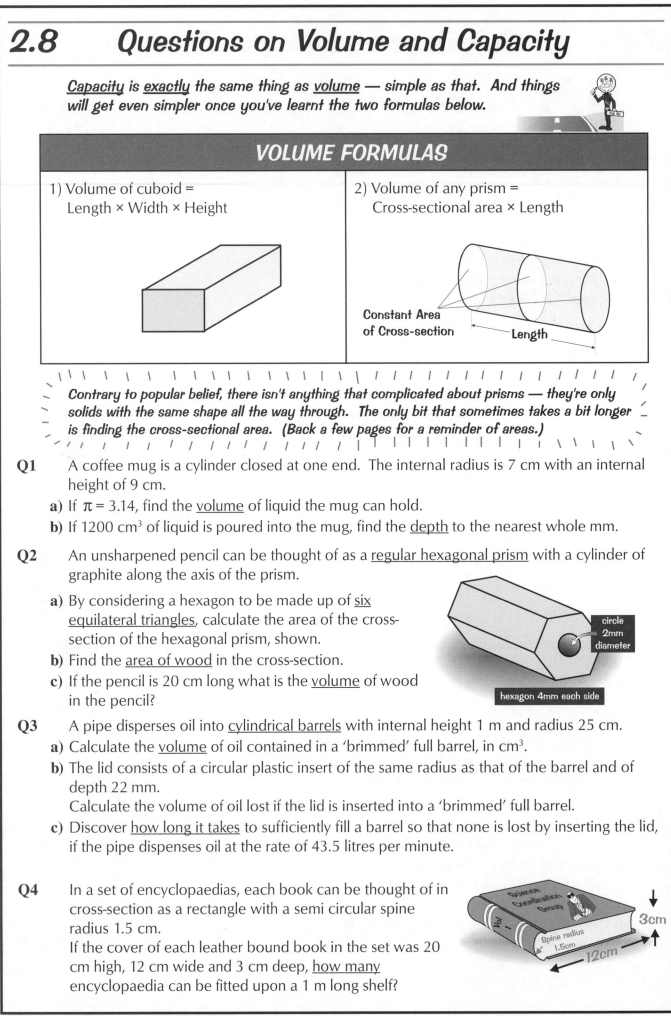

VOLUME FORMULAS

1) Volume of cuboid =
   Length × Width × Height

2) Volume of any prism =
   Cross-sectional area × Length

Constant Area
of Cross-section   Length

Contrary to popular belief, there isn't anything that complicated about prisms — they're only solids with the same shape all the way through. The only bit that sometimes takes a bit longer is finding the cross-sectional area. (Back a few pages for a reminder of areas.)

Q1   A coffee mug is a cylinder closed at one end. The internal radius is 7 cm with an internal height of 9 cm.

a) If π = 3.14, find the <u>volume</u> of liquid the mug can hold.

b) If 1200 cm³ of liquid is poured into the mug, find the <u>depth</u> to the nearest whole mm.

Q2   An unsharpened pencil can be thought of as a <u>regular hexagonal prism</u> with a cylinder of graphite along the axis of the prism.

a) By considering a hexagon to be made up of <u>six equilateral triangles</u>, calculate the area of the cross-section of the hexagonal prism, shown.

b) Find the <u>area of wood</u> in the cross-section.

c) If the pencil is 20 cm long what is the <u>volume</u> of wood in the pencil?

circle
2mm
diameter

hexagon 4mm each side

Q3   A pipe disperses oil into <u>cylindrical barrels</u> with internal height 1 m and radius 25 cm.

a) Calculate the <u>volume</u> of oil contained in a 'brimmed' full barrel, in cm³.

b) The lid consists of a circular plastic insert of the same radius as that of the barrel and of depth 22 mm.
Calculate the volume of oil lost if the lid is inserted into a 'brimmed' full barrel.

c) Discover <u>how long it takes</u> to sufficiently fill a barrel so that none is lost by inserting the lid, if the pipe dispenses oil at the rate of 43.5 litres per minute.

Q4   In a set of encyclopaedias, each book can be thought of in cross-section as a rectangle with a semi circular spine radius 1.5 cm.
If the cover of each leather bound book in the set was 20 cm high, 12 cm wide and 3 cm deep, <u>how many</u> encyclopaedia can be fitted upon a 1 m long shelf?

Science
Coordination
Group

Vol

3cm

Spine radius
1.5cm

12cm

2.8   Questions on Volume and Capacity

*This prism stuff doesn't seem too bad to me — yeah,
OK it's true there's a never ending supply of the darn
things, but you're only really worrying about the cross-
sectional area... then multiplying by the length.*

Q5   A special offer "YARD of CHOCOLATE" has to have the weight stamped upon the outside of the packet. The cross section of the chocolate bar is an <u>equilateral triangle</u> with sides of 6 cm. If a yard is approximated by 36", with <u>each inch ≈ 2.5 cm</u>,

   a) calculate the <u>volume of chocolate</u> in the yard (to 2 dp).

   b) If the chocolate has a <u>density of 14 g/cm³</u>, calculate the <u>weight</u> of the bar that should be stamped on the packet, rounded to the nearest g.

Q6   Beans are sold either in "standard" 12 cm high, 7 cm diameter cans or in "individual" 5 cm high, 7 cm diameter cans. The "standard" cans hold 410 g of beans when full. What <u>weight</u> of beans will the "individual" cans hold if filled to the same density?

Q7   Nosher's Xmas Hamper is a wicker basket in the shape of a <u>regular pentagonal prism</u>. The hamper has internal dimensions of 40 cm long sides and a depth of 40 cm. What volume of <u>delicious</u> seasonal food could be fitted within this space?

Q8   A tree trunk can be thought of as a circular prism with a height of 1.7 m. If the trunk has diameter 60 cm what <u>volume of wood</u> is this in m³?   *(Units...)*

Q9   A cylindrical copper pipe has insulation in the form of a foam tube placed around the outside of it. The pipe has external dimensions of 10 cm diameter and 10 m length. The foam tubing is 25 mm thick

   a) Find the <u>cross-sectional area</u> of the pipe.

   b) Find the <u>cross-sectional area</u> of insulation.

   c) Find the <u>volume</u> of the insulation over the 10 m length.

Q10   Rubber chocks are put under the wheels of aeroplanes to stop them moving when on the ground.

   A typical chock for a large aircraft is shown opposite.

   a) Calculate the <u>volume of rubber</u>.

   b) Calculate the <u>mass of the chock</u> if rubber compound
   of density 1.7 g/cm³ was used.

   c) Would a <u>person</u> be able to lift this into position?

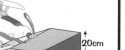

20cm
35cm
50cm   40cm

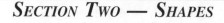

2.9 Questions on Three Letter Angle Notation

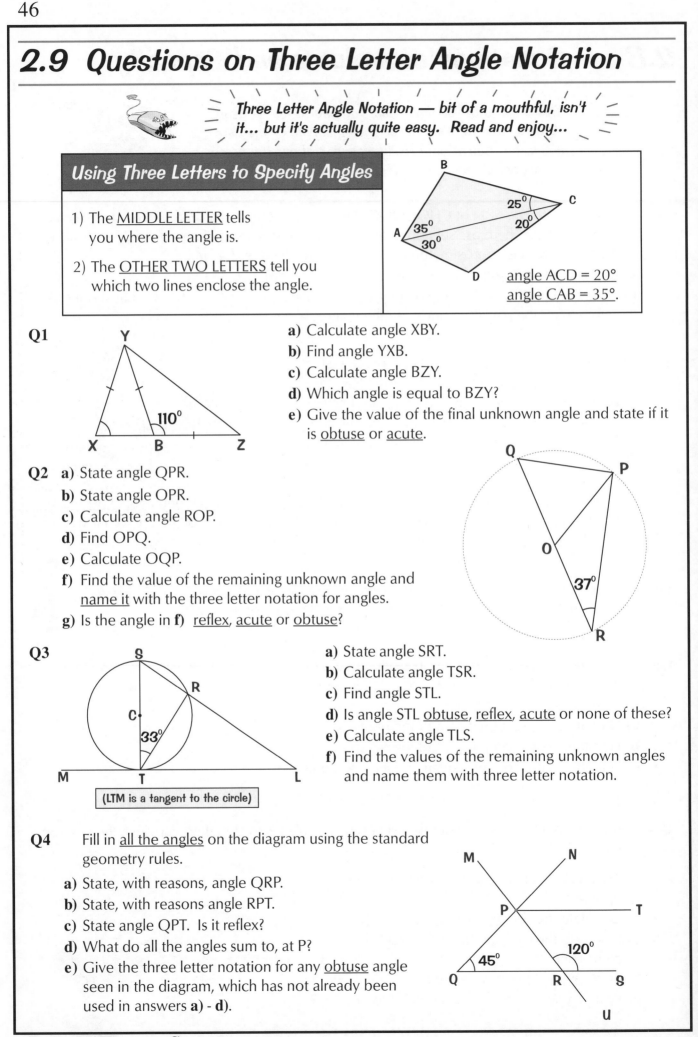

Three Letter Angle Notation — bit of a mouthful, isn't it... but it's actually quite easy. Read and enjoy...

Using Three Letters to Specify Angles

1) The <u>MIDDLE LETTER</u> tells you where the angle is.

2) The <u>OTHER TWO LETTERS</u> tell you which two lines enclose the angle.

angle ACD = 20°
angle CAB = 35°.

Q1

a) Calculate angle XBY.
b) Find angle YXB.
c) Calculate angle BZY.
d) Which angle is equal to BZY?
e) Give the value of the final unknown angle and state if it is <u>obtuse</u> or <u>acute</u>.

Q2 a) State angle QPR.

b) State angle OPR.
c) Calculate angle ROP.
d) Find OPQ.
e) Calculate OQP.
f) Find the value of the remaining unknown angle and <u>name it</u> with the three letter notation for angles.
g) Is the angle in **f)** <u>reflex</u>, <u>acute</u> or <u>obtuse</u>?

Q3

a) State angle SRT.
b) Calculate angle TSR.
c) Find angle STL.
d) Is angle STL <u>obtuse</u>, <u>reflex</u>, <u>acute</u> or none of these?
e) Calculate angle TLS.
f) Find the values of the remaining unknown angles and name them with three letter notation.

(LTM is a tangent to the circle)

Q4 Fill in <u>all the angles</u> on the diagram using the standard geometry rules.

a) State, with reasons, angle QRP.
b) State, with reasons angle RPT.
c) State angle QPT. Is it reflex?
d) What do all the angles sum to, at P?
e) Give the three letter notation for any <u>obtuse</u> angle seen in the diagram, which has not already been used in answers **a) - d)**.

2.10   Questions on Geometry

Angle Rules — you've already met a couple of these in the Polygons bit... and here are another 7 to go at. You can't get away without knowing these, I'm afraid, so get learning.

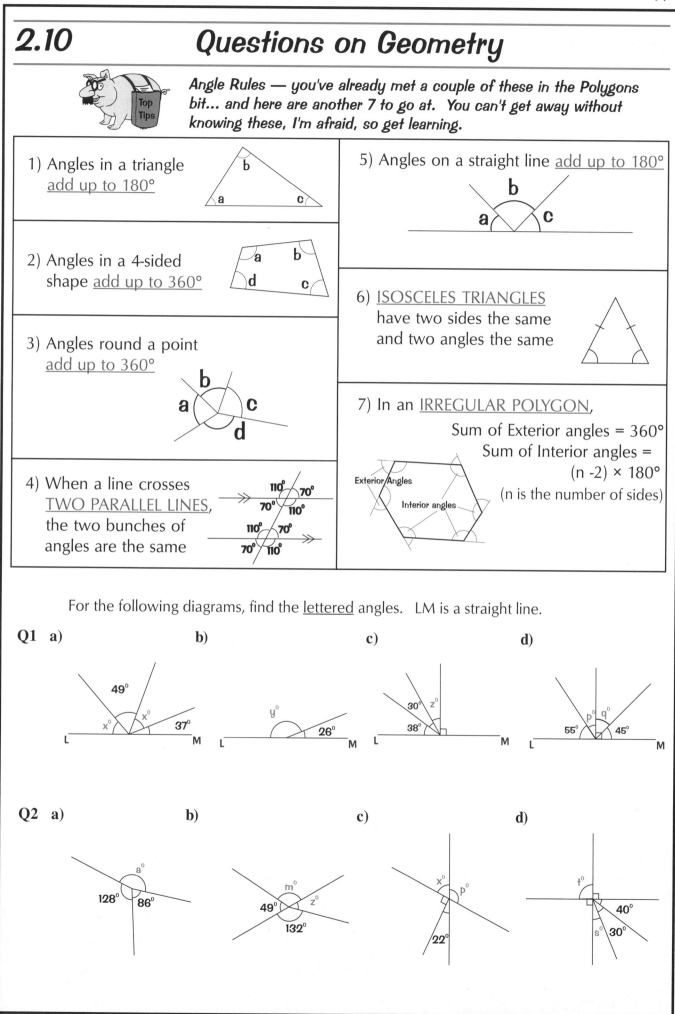

1) Angles in a triangle <u>add up to 180°</u>

2) Angles in a 4-sided shape <u>add up to 360°</u>

3) Angles round a point <u>add up to 360°</u>

4) When a line crosses <u>TWO PARALLEL LINES</u>, the two bunches of angles are the same

5) Angles on a straight line <u>add up to 180°</u>

6) <u>ISOSCELES TRIANGLES</u> have two sides the same and two angles the same

7) In an <u>IRREGULAR POLYGON</u>,
Sum of Exterior angles = 360°
Sum of Interior angles = (n -2) × 180°
(n is the number of sides)

Exterior Angles

Interior angles

For the following diagrams, find the <u>lettered</u> angles. LM is a straight line.

Q1 a) 49° x° x° 37° L M

b) y° 26° L M

c) 30° z° 38° L M

d) p° q° 55° 45° L M

Q2 a) a° 128° 86°

b) m° 49° z° 132°

c) x° p° 22°

d) t° 40° s° 30°

SECTION TWO — SHAPES

2.10 Questions on Geometry

This page is a bit dull — just lots of boring angles... still, that's geometry for you. Oh and by the way, you've got to work the angles out — don't try and sneakily measure them, they're probably drawn wrong anyway...

For the following diagrams, find the <u>lettered</u> angles.   LM is a straight line.

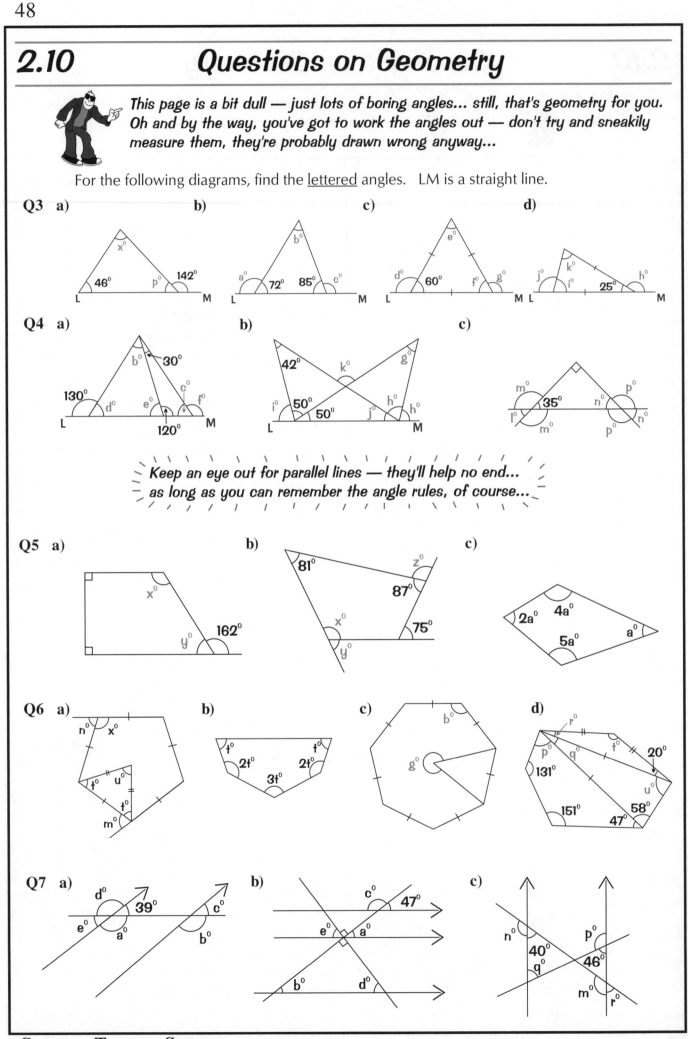

Keep an eye out for parallel lines — they'll help no end... as long as you can remember the angle rules, of course...

2.10   *Questions on Geometry*

Don't forget — with geometry, the more you do it, the easier it gets... honestly.

For the following diagrams, find the <u>lettered</u> angles.   LM is a straight line.

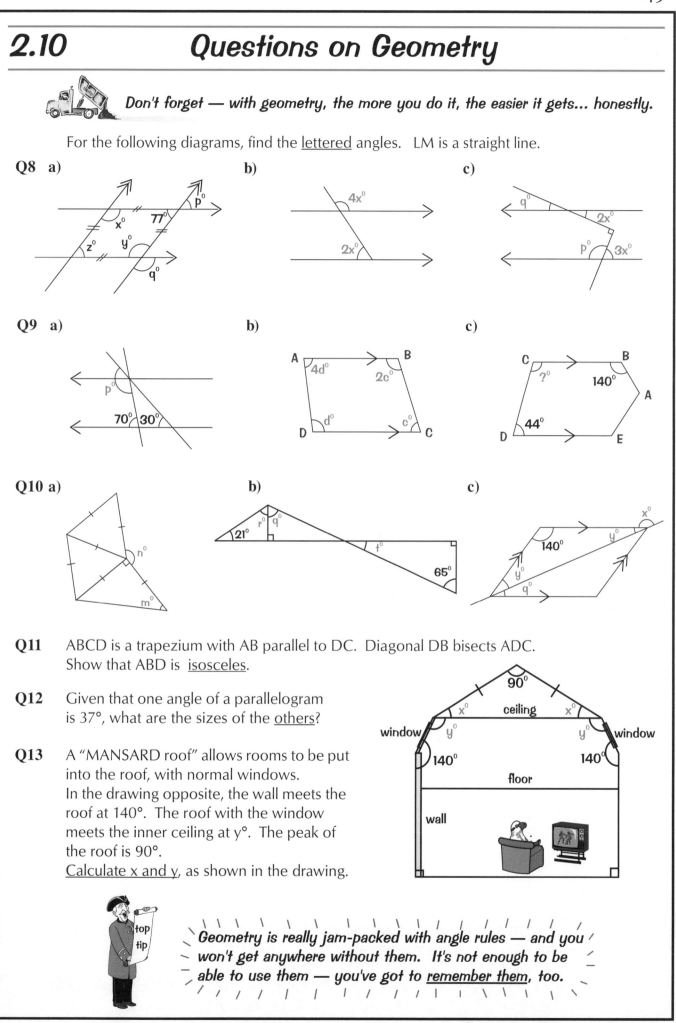

Q8 a)   **b)**   **c)**

Q9 a)   **b)**   **c)**

Q10 a)   **b)**   **c)**

Q11   ABCD is a trapezium with AB parallel to DC. Diagonal DB bisects ADC.
Show that ABD is <u>isosceles</u>.

Q12   Given that one angle of a parallelogram
is 37°, what are the sizes of the <u>others</u>?

Q13   A "MANSARD roof" allows rooms to be put
into the roof, with normal windows.
In the drawing opposite, the wall meets the
roof at 140°. The roof with the window
meets the inner ceiling at y°. The peak of
the roof is 90°.
<u>Calculate x and y</u>, as shown in the drawing.

*Geometry is really jam-packed with angle rules — and you
won't get anywhere without them. It's not enough to be
able to use them — you've got to <u>remember them</u>, too.*

2.11 Questions on Circles

You'll have no problems here if you learn these two formulas. Remember r stands for radius, D for Diameter and π for an annoying number slightly bigger than 3.

Circle Formulas

1) The <u>Area A</u> of a circle is $A = \pi \times r^2$

2) The <u>Circumference C</u> of a circle is $C = \pi \times D$

Q1 Find the <u>circumference</u> of each of the circles to 1 dp, using π = 3.14,
a) diameter = 20 m
b) diameter = 12 m
c) radius = 6 m
d) radius = 10 m.

Q2 Find the <u>area</u> of each of the circles <u>to 3 dp</u>, using π = 3.142,
a) diameter = 13.2 cm
b) diameter = 16.4 cm
c) radius = 3.56 m
d) radius = 6.15 m.

Q3 Using π = 3.14, find:
a) The area of a circle with radius = 6.12 m. Give your answer <u>to 3 dp</u>.
b) The circumference of a circle with radius = 7.2 m. Give your answer <u>to 2 sf</u>.
c) The circumference of a circle with diameter = 14.8 m. Give your answer <u>to 1 dp</u>.
d) The area of a circle with diameter = 4.246 cm. Give answer your <u>to 3 dp</u>.

Q4 Taking π as the value given by your calculator, find the <u>radius</u> of the following circles. All answers to 4 dp.
a) Circumference of 10 m.
b) Circumference of 0.02 mm.
c) Area of 36 cm².

Q5 Find the <u>area and the perimeter</u> of each of the shapes drawn here. Use π = 3.14.

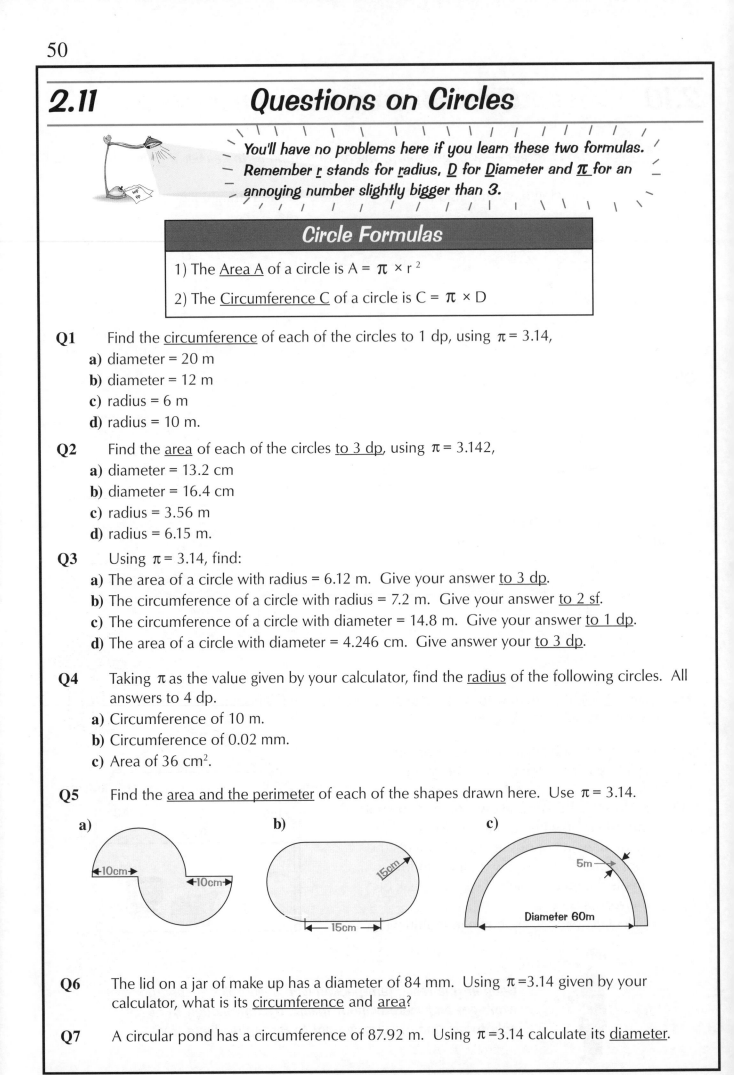

a)

◄10cm►

◄10cm►

b)

15cm

◄— 15cm —►

c)

5m

Diameter 60m

Q6 The lid on a jar of make up has a diameter of 84 mm. Using π =3.14 given by your calculator, what is its <u>circumference</u> and <u>area</u>?

Q7 A circular pond has a circumference of 87.92 m. Using π =3.14 calculate its <u>diameter</u>.

2.12 Questions on Area and Circumference

If you're having trouble remembering which formula is which, look at the r term — something with an r² in it has got to be an area, because it's a length timesed by a length.

Q8 A car wheel plus tyre has a diameter of 58 cm. Using π =3.14 what is the <u>circumference</u> of the tyre? How many <u>revolutions</u> (to the nearest whole number) will the tyre make in travelling 1000 m?

Q9 The pond in Question 7 has a 1 m wide concrete path around its circumference. Calculate the <u>area of the path</u>.

Q10 A rug in front of a fire is in the shape of a semicircle. It has a diameter equal to the width of the fire hearth, which is 1.8 m wide. using π =3.14 calculate the <u>area of the rug</u>, to 3 sf.

Q11 The rug in Q10 is to have non-slip braid attached around its perimeter to stop it moving. How many <u>metres of braid</u> will be required to do the job? (Give answer to 3 sf.)

Q12 A child's sandpit is circular, and made from hard PVC. It has a depth of 10 cm and a diameter of 450 mm. (π = 3.14)

  a) Calculate the <u>surface area</u> of the sandpit's floor both in mm² and m² to 2 dp.

  b) A red stripe is to be painted all of the way round the inside face of the sandpit. <u>How long</u> would the stripe be in mm?

  c) If the stripe were to be 20 mm wide, what <u>area</u> of red paint would be visible?

Q13 A yo-yo is made up of two identical halves. Each half is circular with a circular spindle protruding format. The two spindles are glued together and the string is tied on and wrapped around it 50 times.

  a) The central spindle has a diameter of 1.2 cm. What is its <u>circumference</u>?

  b) Using your answer from **a)**, find approximately <u>how long</u> the yo-yo's string should be if 6 cm is allowed for a finger loop, and 5cm is allowed to tie it to the spindle.

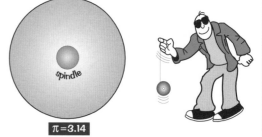

Q14 A Big Wheel at a fairground has a diameter of 36 m.

  a) How far does a passenger travel in <u>one revolution</u>?

  b) If the wheel at full capacity has a speed of 6 revolutions per minute, and a ride lasts for 4 minutes, how far does a passenger travel? (π = 3.14)

Q15 The <u>base</u> of a triangle is equal in length to the <u>circumference</u> of a circle which has a radius of 5 cm. The triangle and the circle also have an <u>equal area</u>. What is the height of the triangle? (Again, π = 3.14)

Q16 The diagram shows the spool on a cassette with recording tape wrapped around it. The ring of tape has an internal radius of 11 mm and external radius 23 mm.

  a) Find the area of the <u>side view</u> of tape in cm².

  b) If the recording tape is 50 m long, how <u>thick</u> is it?

  c) If half of the cassette is played, half of the tape is unwound from one spool to the other. Calculate the external radius of the tape now occupying the <u>original</u> spool.

2.12   Questions on Circle Geometry

Just when you thought circles were getting easy... you've now got four more vital things to know about them.

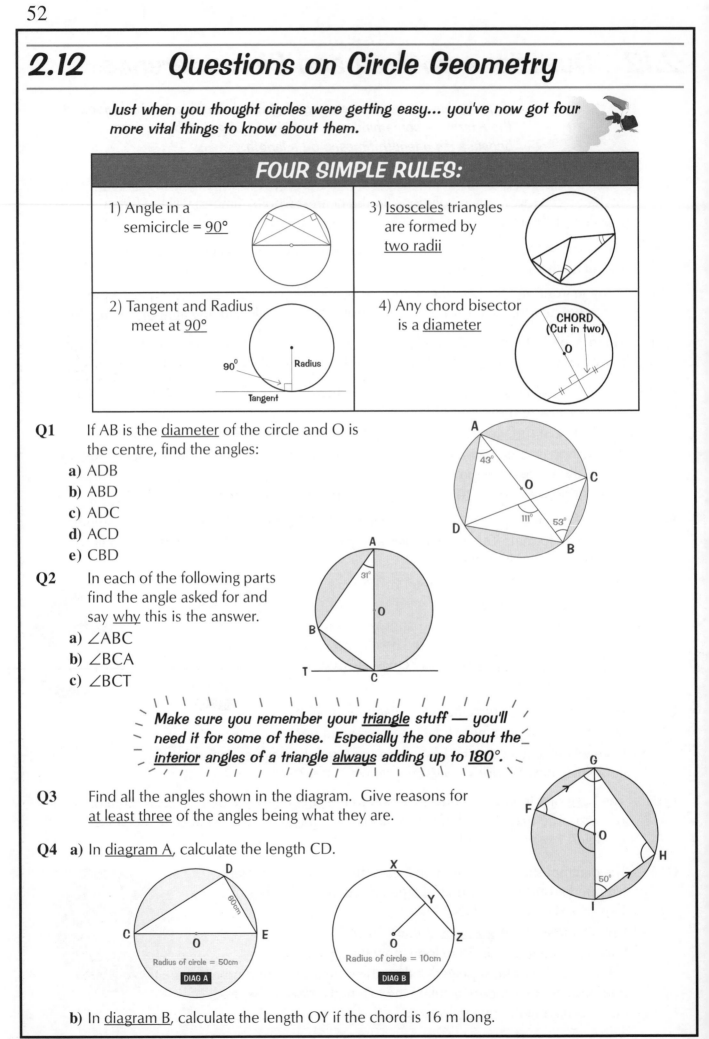

FOUR SIMPLE RULES:

1) Angle in a semicircle = <u>90°</u>

2) Tangent and Radius meet at <u>90°</u>

3) <u>Isosceles</u> triangles are formed by <u>two radii</u>

4) Any chord bisector is a <u>diameter</u>

Q1 If AB is the <u>diameter</u> of the circle and O is the centre, find the angles:

a) ADB

b) ABD

c) ADC

d) ACD

e) CBD

Q2 In each of the following parts find the angle asked for and say <u>why</u> this is the answer.

a) ∠ABC

b) ∠BCA

c) ∠BCT

Make sure you remember your <u>triangle</u> stuff — you'll need it for some of these. Especially the one about the <u>interior</u> angles of a triangle <u>always</u> adding up to <u>180°</u>.

Q3 Find all the angles shown in the diagram. Give reasons for <u>at least three</u> of the angles being what they are.

Q4 a) In <u>diagram A</u>, calculate the length CD.

b) In <u>diagram B</u>, calculate the length OY if the chord is 16 m long.

2.13 Questions on Similarity and Enlargement

You must remember the important difference between similarity and congruence.

Similarity and Congruence

1) Two shapes are <u>similar</u> if they're the <u>same shape</u> but different size. The lengths of the two shapes are related to the scale factor by this very important formula triangle:

2) Two shapes are <u>congruent</u> if they're the <u>same size</u> and <u>same shape</u>

NEW LENGTH

SCALE FACTOR **X** OLD LENGTH

Q1 Two picture frames are shown. One picture is <u>similar</u> to the other. Calculate L cm, the length of the smaller frame.

Q2 For each of the following pairs:
 a) Decide if the shapes are similar or not.
 b) Give a reason for your answer.

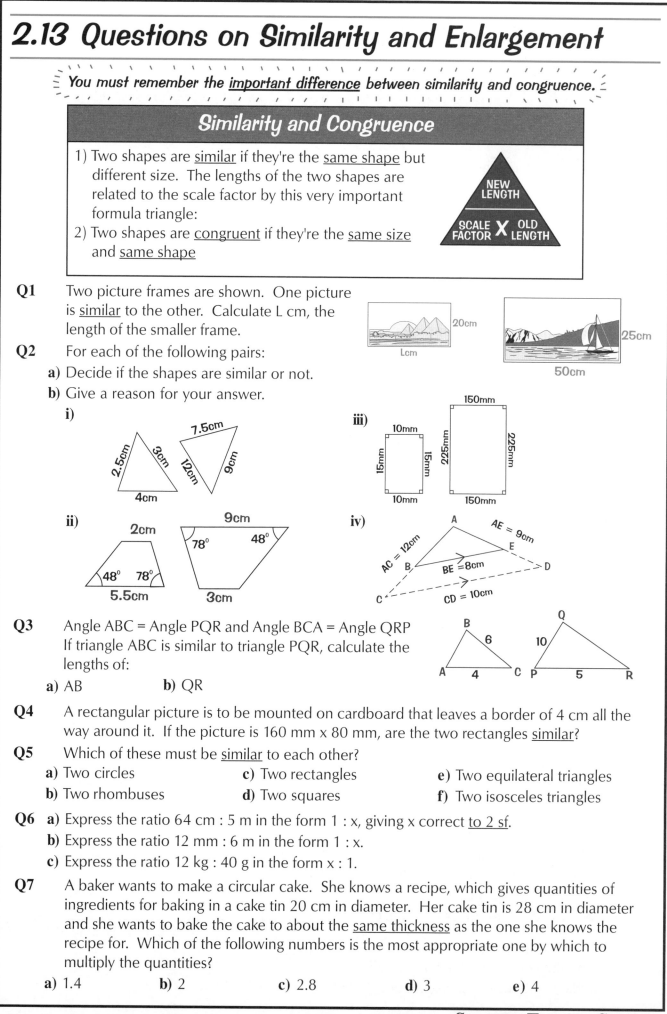

20cm
Lcm

25cm
50cm

i)
7.5cm
2.5cm
3cm
12cm
9cm
4cm

iii)
150mm
10mm
15mm
15mm
225mm
225mm
10mm
150mm

ii)
2cm
9cm
78° 48°
48° 78°
5.5cm
3cm

iv)
A
AE = 9cm
AC = 12cm
B
E
D
BE = 8cm
C
CD = 10cm

Q3 Angle ABC = Angle PQR and Angle BCA = Angle QRP
If triangle ABC is similar to triangle PQR, calculate the lengths of:
 a) AB **b)** QR

B
6
A 4 C

Q
10
P 5 R

Q4 A rectangular picture is to be mounted on cardboard that leaves a border of 4 cm all the way around it. If the picture is 160 mm x 80 mm, are the two rectangles <u>similar</u>?

Q5 Which of these must be <u>similar</u> to each other?
 a) Two circles **c)** Two rectangles **e)** Two equilateral triangles
 b) Two rhombuses **d)** Two squares **f)** Two isosceles triangles

Q6 a) Express the ratio 64 cm : 5 m in the form 1 : x, giving x correct <u>to 2 sf</u>.
 b) Express the ratio 12 mm : 6 m in the form 1 : x.
 c) Express the ratio 12 kg : 40 g in the form x : 1.

Q7 A baker wants to make a circular cake. She knows a recipe, which gives quantities of ingredients for baking in a cake tin 20 cm in diameter. Her cake tin is 28 cm in diameter and she wants to bake the cake to about the <u>same thickness</u> as the one she knows the recipe for. Which of the following numbers is the most appropriate one by which to multiply the quantities?
 a) 1.4 **b)** 2 **c)** 2.8 **d)** 3 **e)** 4

SECTION TWO — SHAPES

2.13 Questions on Similarity and Enlargement

Congruence — a funny word I agree. It just means that things are exactly the same — the same size and the same shape.

Q1 Enlarge square S by a scale factor of 4, using the <u>ray technique</u> or other method. The centre of enlargement is (2, 12). Label the new square K' L' M' N'. What are the <u>coordinates</u> of these new points?

Q2 Enlarge rectangle Z by a scale factor of 3 using any method. The centre of enlargement is (2,0). Label the new rectangle W'X'Y'V'. What are the <u>coordinates</u> of these new points?

Q3 Enlarge triangle T by a scale factor of 2 about (18,0). Label this triangle T'. Reduce T' by a scale factor of ½ about a centre of enlargement (12,0). Label this triangle T''.

a) Give the three coordinates of T''.

b) What <u>single</u> transformation would map T onto T''?

c) What <u>single</u> transformation would map T'' back onto T?

Similar, that's a bit more obvious... it means <u>nearly the same</u> — <u>same shape</u>, but a <u>different size</u>.

Q4 Square A1 is an enlargement of square A. By using ray diagrams or otherwise, find the centre of enlargement. What is the scale factor of enlargement?

Q5 Square A2 is an <u>enlargement</u> of square A.
Find the centre of enlargement. What are its coordinates?
What is the scale factor of enlargement mapping A onto A2?

Q6 B1 is an <u>enlargement</u> of B. What are the coordinates of the centre of enlargement? What scale factor maps B onto B1?

Q7 C0 is a <u>reduction</u> of C1. Find the centre of reduction to 1 dp. What is the scale factor of reduction that maps C1 onto C0, to 1 dp?

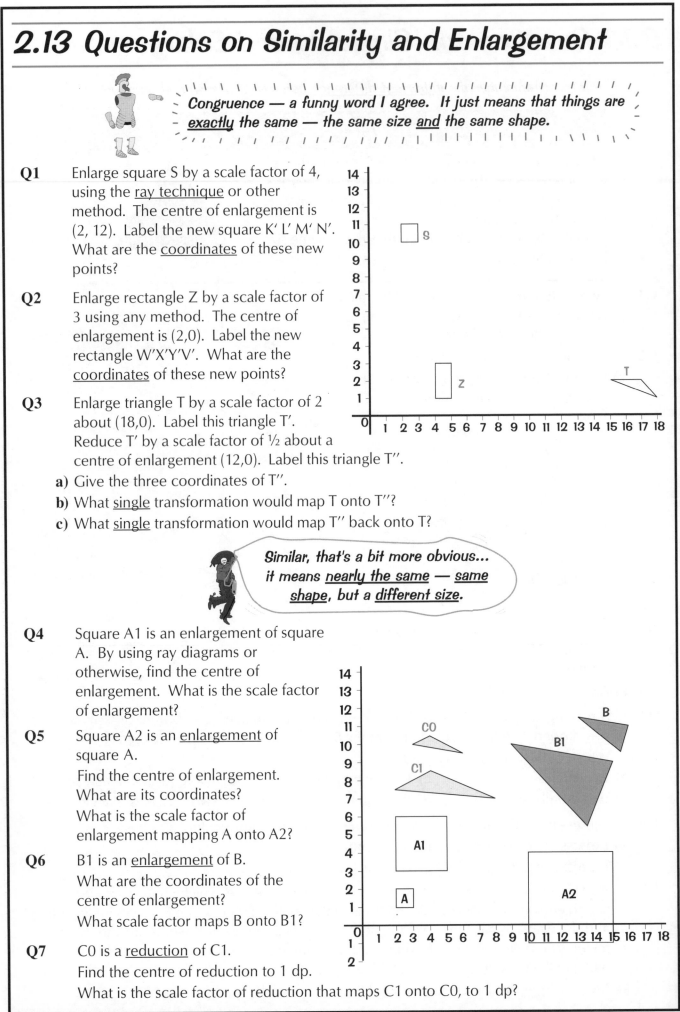

2.14   *Questions on Transformations*

You've got to be able to give all the details for each type — and it <u>will</u> be in the Exam.

Use the word <u>TERRY</u> to remember the 4 transformations :	Always specifiy <u>ALL</u> the details:
T ranslation	1) VECTOR OF TRANSLATION
E nlargement	1) SCALE FACTOR 2) CENTRE OF ENLARGEMENT
R otation	1) MIRROR LINE
R eflection	1) ANGLE TURNED 2) DIRECTION 3) CENTRE OF ROTATION
Y	

Q1   Write down the <u>translation vectors</u> for the translations shown.

The Y doesn't stand for anything, in case you're wondering...

a)   **b)**   **c)**

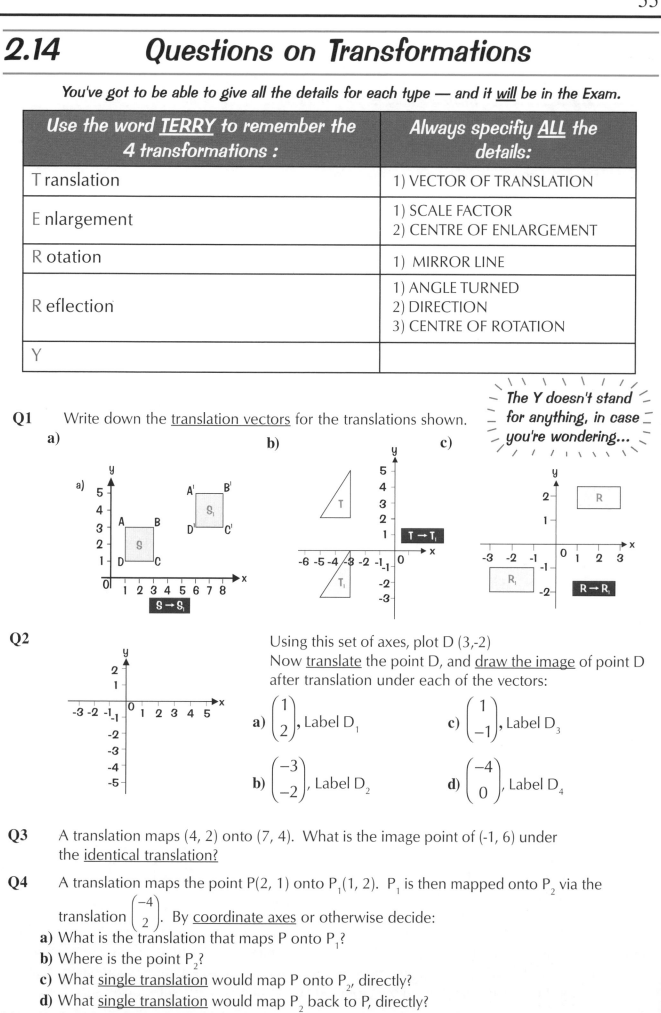

Q2   Using this set of axes, plot D (3,-2)

Now <u>translate</u> the point D, and <u>draw the image</u> of point D after translation under each of the vectors:

a) $\begin{pmatrix} 1 \\ 2 \end{pmatrix}$, Label D_1 **c)** $\begin{pmatrix} 1 \\ -1 \end{pmatrix}$, Label D_3

b) $\begin{pmatrix} -3 \\ -2 \end{pmatrix}$, Label D_2 **d)** $\begin{pmatrix} -4 \\ 0 \end{pmatrix}$, Label D_4

Q3   A translation maps (4, 2) onto (7, 4). What is the image point of (-1, 6) under the <u>identical translation?</u>

Q4   A translation maps the point P(2, 1) onto P_1(1, 2). P_1 is then mapped onto P_2 via the translation $\begin{pmatrix} -4 \\ 2 \end{pmatrix}$. By <u>coordinate axes</u> or otherwise decide:

a) What is the translation that maps P onto P_1?
b) Where is the point P_2?
c) What <u>single translation</u> would map P onto P_2, directly?
d) What <u>single translation</u> would map P_2 back to P, directly?

2.14 Questions on Transformations

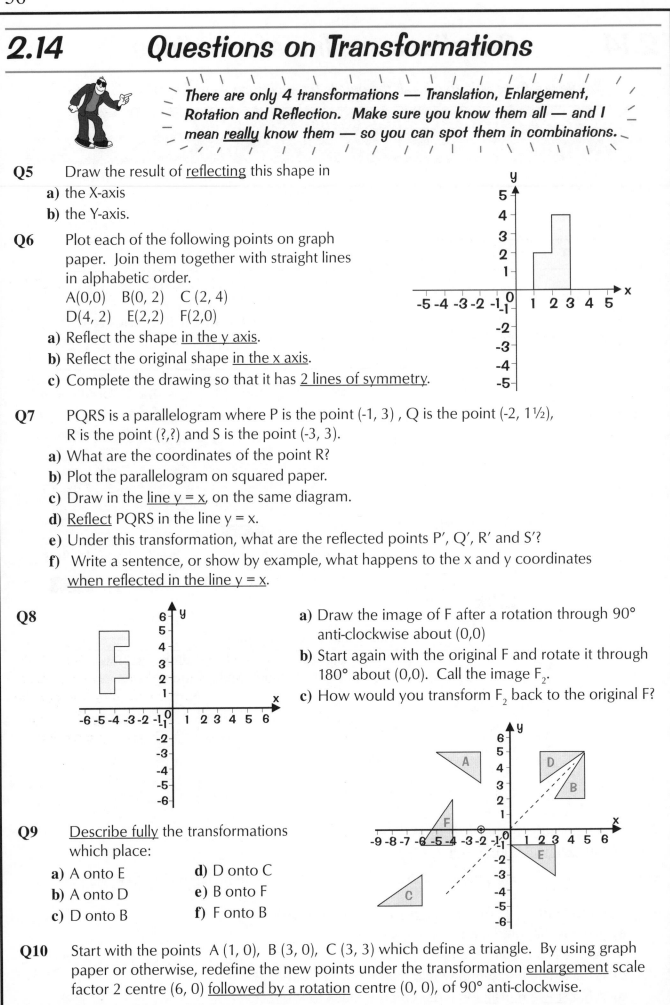

There are only 4 transformations — Translation, Enlargement, Rotation and Reflection. Make sure you know them all — and I mean really know them — so you can spot them in combinations.

Q5   Draw the result of <u>reflecting</u> this shape in
   a) the X-axis
   b) the Y-axis.

Q6   Plot each of the following points on graph paper. Join them together with straight lines in alphabetic order.
   A(0,0)   B(0, 2)   C (2, 4)
   D(4, 2)   E(2,2)   F(2,0)
   a) Reflect the shape <u>in the y axis</u>.
   b) Reflect the original shape <u>in the x axis</u>.
   c) Complete the drawing so that it has <u>2 lines of symmetry</u>.

Q7   PQRS is a parallelogram where P is the point (-1, 3) , Q is the point (-2, 1½), R is the point (?,?) and S is the point (-3, 3).
   a) What are the coordinates of the point R?
   b) Plot the parallelogram on squared paper.
   c) Draw in the <u>line y = x</u>, on the same diagram.
   d) <u>Reflect</u> PQRS in the line y = x.
   e) Under this transformation, what are the reflected points P′, Q′, R′ and S′?
   f) Write a sentence, or show by example, what happens to the x and y coordinates <u>when reflected in the line y = x</u>.

Q8
   a) Draw the image of F after a rotation through 90° anti-clockwise about (0,0)
   b) Start again with the original F and rotate it through 180° about (0,0). Call the image F_2.
   c) How would you transform F_2 back to the original F?

Q9   <u>Describe fully</u> the transformations which place:
   a) A onto E   **d)** D onto C
   b) A onto D   **e)** B onto F
   c) D onto B   **f)** F onto B

Q10   Start with the points A (1, 0), B (3, 0), C (3, 3) which define a triangle. By using graph paper or otherwise, redefine the new points under the transformation <u>enlargement</u> scale factor 2 centre (6, 0) <u>followed by a rotation</u> centre (0, 0), of 90° anti-clockwise.

2.14 Questions on Transformations

△ ABC means "the triangle with vertices A, B and C". And you'd never have worked that one out if I hadn't told you...

Q11 In the diagram △ K″L″M″ is the image of △ KLM <u>after</u> it has been rotated about (0,0) 90° anti-clockwise and then translated by $\begin{pmatrix} -3 \\ -1 \end{pmatrix}$.

By using <u>inverse transformations</u>,

a) Find △ K'L'M' after the inverse translation has been applied to △ K″L″M″. Draw it on the diagram.

b) Find △ KLM the original triangle after applying the inverse rotation to △ K'L'M'. Draw it on the diagram.

c) <u>Check</u> by doing the complete joint transformation on △ KLM to see that you end up at △ K″L″M″.

Q12 The points L(3, 1), M(5, 4), N(8, 4), P(8, 1) define a <u>trapezium</u> LMNP.

L' (-1,-5), M' (-3,-8), N'(-6,-8), P'(-6,-5) define the image of the original trapezium under a rotation through 180° about C(x,y).
By plotting L'M'N'P' on the diagram opposite, <u>determine the point C</u> and state the values of x and y.

There are a few <u>vectors</u> sneaking in here as well — <u>urghh</u>. Make sure you get the coordinates the right way round — <u>top</u> for <u>x</u> direction, <u>bottom</u> for <u>y</u> direction.

Q13 a) Determine the centre of enlargement and scale factor that maps PRQ onto P' R' Q'.

b) Are triangles PRQ and P' R' Q' similar or congruent?

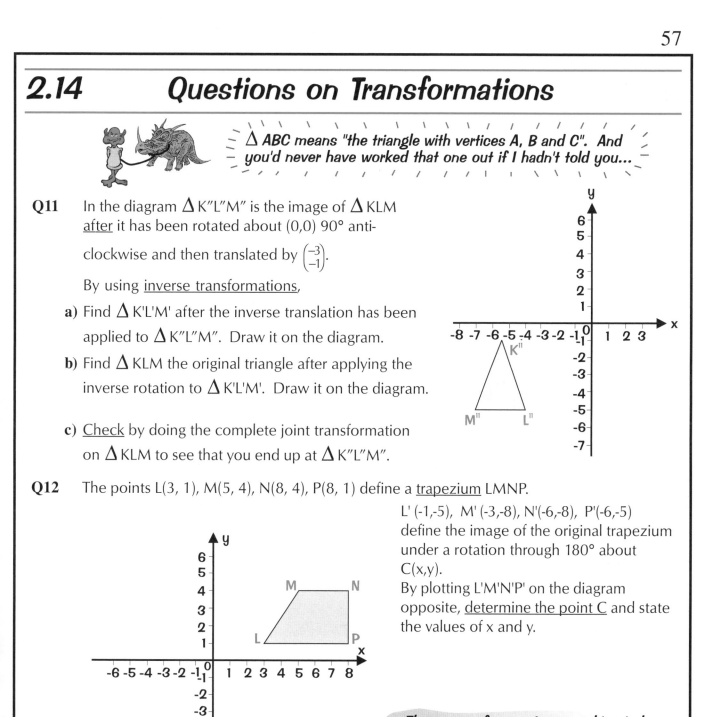

3.1 Questions on Trigonometry

You really need to know your <u>trigonometric formulas</u> — you'll struggle without them.

An <u>EASY WAY</u> to remember the <u>THREE</u> formulas is to write <u>"SOH CAH TOA"</u> before you start — then turn the most suitable into a <u>FORMULA TRIANGLE</u>.

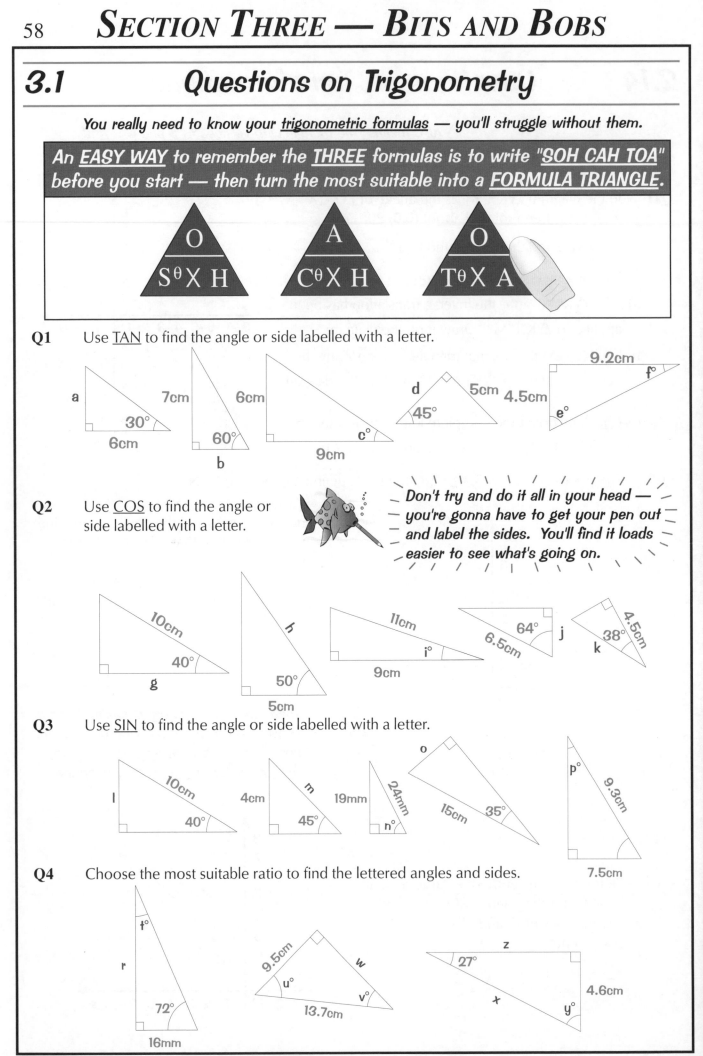

Q1 Use <u>TAN</u> to find the angle or side labelled with a letter.

Q2 Use <u>COS</u> to find the angle or side labelled with a letter.

Don't try and do it all in your head — you're gonna have to get your pen out and label the sides. You'll find it loads easier to see what's going on.

Q3 Use <u>SIN</u> to find the angle or side labelled with a letter.

Q4 Choose the most suitable ratio to find the lettered angles and sides.

3.1 Questions on Trigonometry

Don't worry, these questions are just more of the same — except they've got prettier pictures. Don't forget to label the sides, though.

Q5 Mary was lying on the floor looking up at the star on top of her Christmas tree. She looked up through an angle of 55° when she was 1.5 m from the base of the tree. How high was the star?

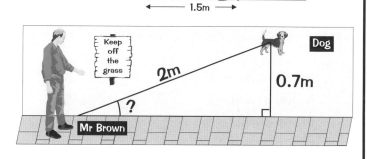

Q6 Mr Brown took his dog for a walk in the park. The dog's lead was 2 m long. The dog ran 0.7 m from the path Mr Brown was walking on.

What angle did the lead make with the path?

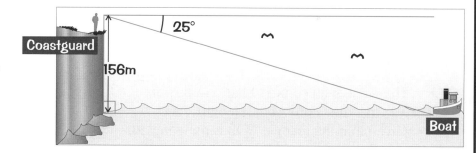

Q7 A coastguard on a cliff top saw a boat in trouble at sea. The cliff was 156 m high. The angle of depression that the coastguard looked along was 25°.

What distance was the boat from:
a) the base of the cliff?
b) the coastguard?

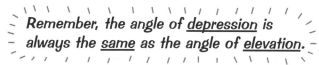

Remember, the angle of <u>depression</u> is always the <u>same</u> as the angle of <u>elevation</u>.

Q8 A boy walked diagonally across a rectangular field and measured the distance as 95 m. The line he walked on made an angle of 40° with the longer edge of the field.
a) Draw a <u>rough sketch</u> of the field and the boy's path across it.
b) Calculate the length and width of the field.
c) Calculate the area of the field.

Q9 A window cleaner with an extending ladder has to clean windows on two levels of a building. For the lower level his ladder must reach to 3.5 m. For the higher level it must reach 7 m. If the base of the ladder is always 2.5 m from the wall what angle is made with the horizontal when used for:
a) the lower level?
b) the upper level?

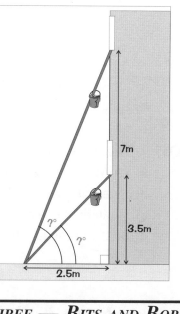

SECTION THREE — BITS AND BOBS

3.1   Questions on Trigonometry

These darn triangles seem to get __everywhere__, including the Exam —
so make sure you can do __everything__ on the last three pages, because
you're gonna need it all.

Q10   Two fell tops are 1.5 km apart
horizontally. One is 720 m high and the
other is 340 m high. Find:

     a) the difference in height between them

     b) the angle of elevation looking from the
lower to the higher fell.

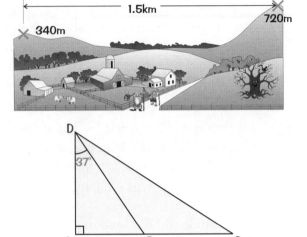

Q11   If the angle of elevation of D from C is
27°, calculate:

     a) the angle BDC

     b) the length AD

     c) the angle DBC

     d) the length BC.

Q12   The points P(1,2), Q(4,2) and R(4,-3) when joined together form a right-angled triangle.

     a) Draw a rough sketch of the triangle, labelling the length of each side.

     b) __Without measuring__, calculate the angle RPQ.

     c) __Deduce__ angle PRQ.

Q13   The circle with centre O has a radius of
10 cm. The chord AB has length $\sqrt{200}$.
Given that the triangle AOB is right-angled,
calculate the angle ABO.

Don't let that __circle__ put you off — it's a __normal question__ really.
Draw in the rest of the triangle and label the sides O, A and H.
You've got all the sides, so all you need to do is __choose the__
__formula__. How nice.

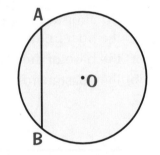

Q14   A right-angled triangle XYZ has sides measuring 30 m, 40 m and 50 m.

     a) Draw a __rough sketch__ of the triangle, clearly labelling the hypotenuse.

     b) Calculate the size of the smallest angle.

Q15   The points A(1,-2), B(4,-1) and C(1, 3) are the vertices of the triangle ABC.

     a) On graph paper, __plot__ the points A, B and C.

     b) By adding a suitable horizontal line, or otherwise, calculate the angle CAB.

     c) Similarly calculate the angle ACB.

     d) By using the fact that the interior angles of a triangle add up to 180° work out the angle
ABC.

3.1 Questions on Trigonometry

If you want to get full marks, you'll need a good diagram. If they've been mean and haven't provided one then draw your own and don't forget to label the sides O, A, and H.

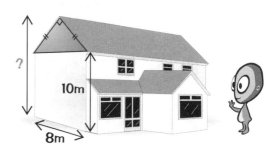

Q16 David wants to work out the height of his house. By counting rows of bricks he estimates that the bottom of the roof is 10 m above the ground. The width of the house is 8 m. Also, the angle made at the top of the roof is 90°.
<u>What is the height</u> of David's house?

Q17 A girl walked diagonally across a rectangular field and measured the distance as 220 m. The line she walked on made an angle of 30° with the longer edge of the field.

    a) Draw a <u>rough sketch</u> of the field and the girl's path across it.

    b) Calculate the length and width of the field.

    c) Calculate the area of the field.

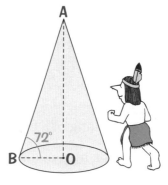

Q18 The base of a cone has a radius of 7 cm. The angle ABO is 72°.

    a) Work out the <u>height</u> of the cone OA.

    b) A similar cone has a base radius of 14 cm. What is the height of this cone?

Remember to check that your answer is <u>sensible</u>.

Q19 John runs in a north west direction from X for six miles to point Y. He then turns and runs in a south west direction for eight miles to point Z.

    a) Draw a <u>rough sketch</u> of John's route.

    b) Write down the size of angle XYZ.

    c) Calculate the length XZ.

Q20 A <u>regular octagon</u> is shown on the right. The centre O is 5 cm from the vertex P. Q is a point in the centre of one side.

    a) By considering the angles at the centre of the octagon, find the size of the angle QOP.

    b) Calculate the length of one side of the octagon.

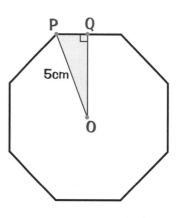

Q21 P is the point (10, 15), O is the origin.

    a) Calculate the angle between OP and the positive Y-axis.

    b) Using your answer to part **a)** work out the distance from O to P.

3.2 Questions on Bearings

A compass always points North...
*It's easy to get lost here so always follow these **2 easy rules.***

1) **BEARINGS** are always measured clockwise **FROM** the northline.

2) You should give all bearings as **3 FIGURES**, even the small ones.

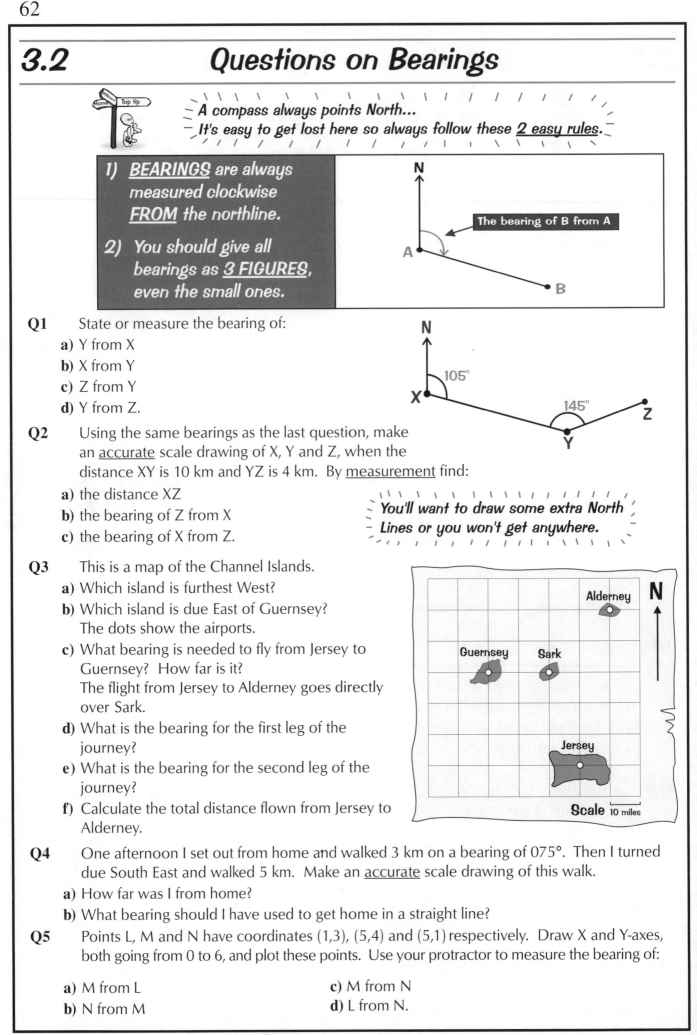

The bearing of B from A

Q1 State or measure the bearing of:
a) Y from X
b) X from Y
c) Z from Y
d) Y from Z.

Q2 Using the same bearings as the last question, make an <u>accurate</u> scale drawing of X, Y and Z, when the distance XY is 10 km and YZ is 4 km. By <u>measurement</u> find:
a) the distance XZ
b) the bearing of Z from X
c) the bearing of X from Z.

You'll want to draw some extra North Lines or you won't get anywhere.

Q3 This is a map of the Channel Islands.
a) Which island is furthest West?
b) Which island is due East of Guernsey? The dots show the airports.
c) What bearing is needed to fly from Jersey to Guernsey? How far is it?
The flight from Jersey to Alderney goes directly over Sark.
d) What is the bearing for the first leg of the journey?
e) What is the bearing for the second leg of the journey?
f) Calculate the total distance flown from Jersey to Alderney.

Scale 10 miles

Q4 One afternoon I set out from home and walked 3 km on a bearing of 075°. Then I turned due South East and walked 5 km. Make an <u>accurate</u> scale drawing of this walk.
a) How far was I from home?
b) What bearing should I have used to get home in a straight line?

Q5 Points L, M and N have coordinates (1,3), (5,4) and (5,1) respectively. Draw X and Y-axes, both going from 0 to 6, and plot these points. Use your protractor to measure the bearing of:

a) M from L
b) N from M

c) M from N
d) L from N.

3.2   *Questions on Bearings*

Q6   Mr Brown is standing on the riverbank watching a cricket match on the other side. The bowler is on a bearing of 210° from Mr Brown and the batsman 190° from Mr Brown. When the batsman looks at the bowler he is looking along a bearing of 310°.

a) Draw a <u>rough sketch</u> to show this and put in all the angles given.

b) Calculate the bearing of the batsman from the bowler.

c) Calculate the bearing of Mr Brown from the batsman.

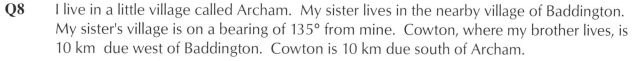

The word "<u>from</u>" is the most important word in a bearings question — so look out for it — it tells you where to start <u>from</u>.

Q7   A lighthouse keeper spots a boat on a bearing of 123°. A woman, due South of the lighthouse, sees the boat on a bearing of 065°. If the woman is 12 miles from the lighthouse, make an <u>accurate scale drawing</u> showing this information. Measure the distance of the boat from:

a) the lighthouse

b) the woman.

Q8   I live in a little village called Archam. My sister lives in the nearby village of Baddington. My sister's village is on a bearing of 135° from mine. Cowton, where my brother lives, is 10 km due west of Baddington. Cowton is 10 km due south of Archam.

a) Draw a rough sketch showing the relative positions of Archam, Baddington and Cowton.

b) What sort of shape is defined by the lines joining the three villages?

c) Calculate the area of the shape in part **b)**.

By the time you've finished this section, you'll never be able to get lost. No matter how many times people tell you to.

Q9   Geoff spent the day walking in Flatlands. In an effort not to get lost, he only walked in <u>straight lines</u> and every time he changed direction he noted the new bearing in his notebook. When it became dark he retraced his footsteps back to his starting position.

a) Draw a rough sketch of the path that Geoff took.

b) Given that one of Geoff's strides is 0.5 m long, how far did he walk, in metres, during the day?

c) How far would he have walked during the day if he had gone directly back to his starting point rather than retracing his steps?

Start Bearing	Distance Walked
060°	5000 Steps
180°	10,000 Steps
240°	5000 Steps

64

3.3 Questions on Loci and Constructions

Don't let a silly word like <u>locus</u> put you off — there are <u>easy</u> <u>marks</u> to be had here, but you've got to do everything neatly, using a pencil, ruler and compasses.

> <u>LOCUS</u> — a line showing all points obeying the given rule.
> <u>CONSTRUCTIONS</u> — accurate drawings using pencil, ruler and compasses, often to show a locus.

Q1 On a plain piece of paper <u>mark two points A and B</u> which are 6 cm apart.
  a) Draw the locus of points which are 4 cm from A.
  b) Draw the locus of points which are 3 cm from B.
  c) There are 2 points which are both 4 cm from A and 3 cm from B, label them X and Y.

Q2 Draw a line CD which is 5 cm long.
  a) Draw the locus of points which are 2 cm from this line.
  b) Mark the points E and F which are furthest away from C and D respectively.

> *Just to be really awkward, these points don't always make a nice line — they make an area. You often need to shade the area where all the points obey the rule — that's what the next couple are like.*

Q3 In Jersey, Pierre has 2 cows which he keeps tethered on ropes 3 m long. One day they graze in a small paddock 15 m by 10 m as shown.

  a) Draw a <u>sketch</u> of the grass that the cows can graze on if the ropes are fixed to 2 stakes each 3 m from the hedge and one 3 m from the fence, the other 3 m from the wall.

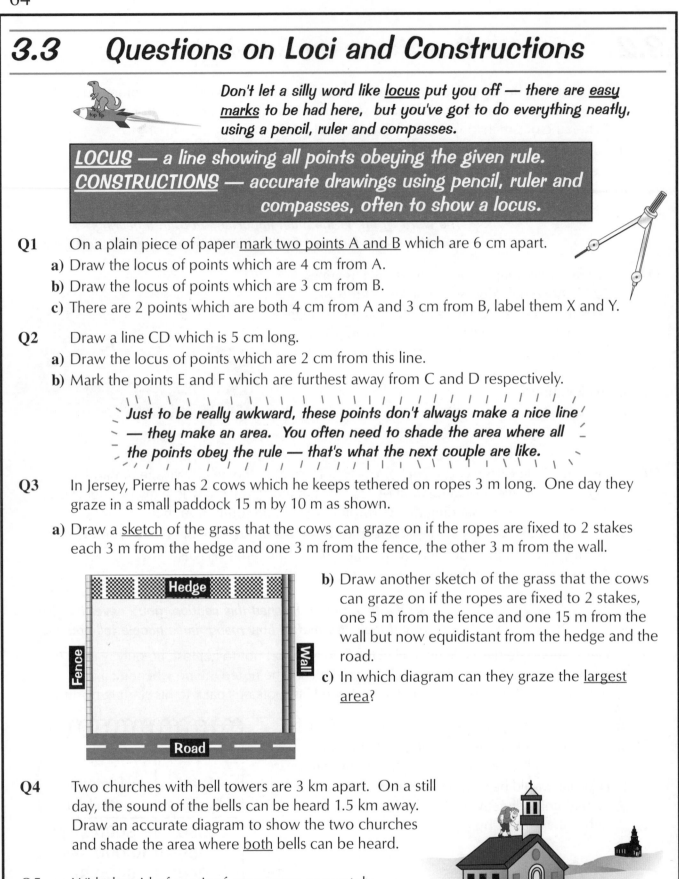

  b) Draw another sketch of the grass that the cows can graze on if the ropes are fixed to 2 stakes, one 5 m from the fence and one 15 m from the wall but now equidistant from the hedge and the road.
  c) In which diagram can they graze the <u>largest area</u>?

Q4 Two churches with bell towers are 3 km apart. On a still day, the sound of the bells can be heard 1.5 km away. Draw an accurate diagram to show the two churches and shade the area where <u>both</u> bells can be heard.

Q5 With the aid of a pair of compasses accurately draw an equilateral triangle with sides 5 cm. Now accurately draw a square with sides 6 cm.

Q6 **a)** Construct a triangle ABC in which AB is 6 cm, BC is 7.5 cm and AC is 5 cm long.
  b) Construct the perpendicular bisector of AB and where this line meets BC, label the new point D.

3.3   Questions on Loci and Constructions

Q7

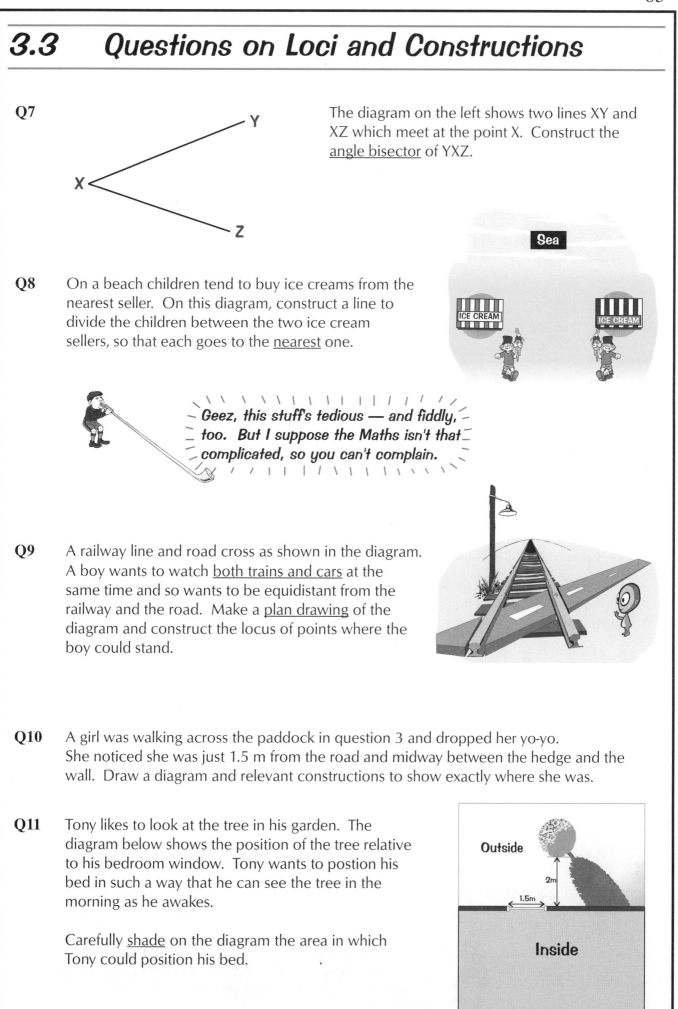

The diagram on the left shows two lines XY and XZ which meet at the point X. Construct the <u>angle bisector</u> of YXZ.

Q8   On a beach children tend to buy ice creams from the nearest seller. On this diagram, construct a line to divide the children between the two ice cream sellers, so that each goes to the <u>nearest</u> one.

Geez, this stuff's tedious — and fiddly, too. But I suppose the Maths isn't that complicated, so you can't complain.

Q9   A railway line and road cross as shown in the diagram. A boy wants to watch <u>both trains and cars</u> at the same time and so wants to be equidistant from the railway and the road. Make a <u>plan drawing</u> of the diagram and construct the locus of points where the boy could stand.

Q10   A girl was walking across the paddock in question 3 and dropped her yo-yo. She noticed she was just 1.5 m from the road and midway between the hedge and the wall. Draw a diagram and relevant constructions to show exactly where she was.

Q11   Tony likes to look at the tree in his garden. The diagram below shows the position of the tree relative to his bedroom window. Tony wants to position his bed in such a way that he can see the tree in the morning as he awakes.

Carefully <u>shade</u> on the diagram the area in which Tony could position his bed.

3.4   *Questions on Formula Triangles*

This is what you've been waiting for — perhaps the <u>most important page</u> in this section. Get the hang of this bit and you can use it to help you with <u>anything</u>... well, nearly.

You can use a formula triangle for <u>ANY FORMULA</u> with <u>THREE THINGS</u>, where two are <u>MULTIPLIED</u> to give the third.

Eg: area of a rectangle = length × height.
This will give the formula triangle:

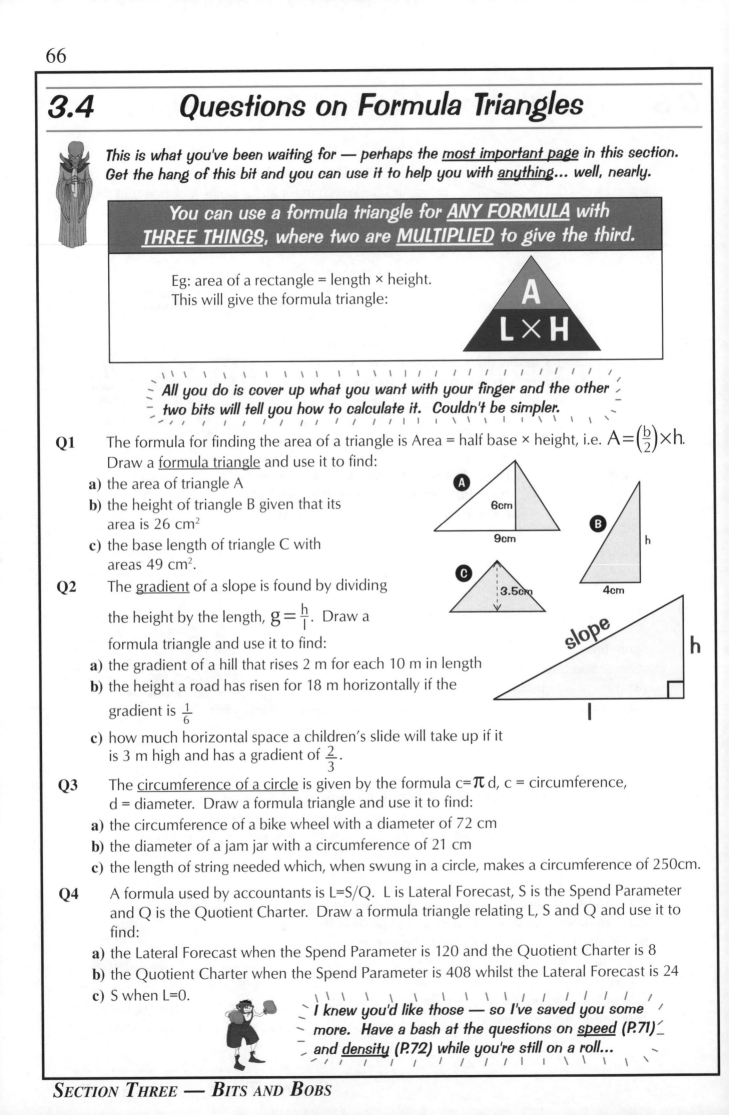

A
L × H

All you do is cover up what you want with your finger and the other two bits will tell you how to calculate it. Couldn't be simpler.

Q1 The formula for finding the area of a triangle is Area = half base × height, i.e. $A = \left(\frac{b}{2}\right) \times h$.
Draw a <u>formula triangle</u> and use it to find:

a) the area of triangle A

b) the height of triangle B given that its area is 26 cm²

c) the base length of triangle C with areas 49 cm².

Q2 The <u>gradient</u> of a slope is found by dividing the height by the length, $g = \frac{h}{l}$. Draw a formula triangle and use it to find:

a) the gradient of a hill that rises 2 m for each 10 m in length

b) the height a road has risen for 18 m horizontally if the gradient is $\frac{1}{6}$

c) how much horizontal space a children's slide will take up if it is 3 m high and has a gradient of $\frac{2}{3}$.

Q3 The <u>circumference of a circle</u> is given by the formula $c = \pi d$, c = circumference, d = diameter. Draw a formula triangle and use it to find:

a) the circumference of a bike wheel with a diameter of 72 cm

b) the diameter of a jam jar with a circumference of 21 cm

c) the length of string needed which, when swung in a circle, makes a circumference of 250cm.

Q4 A formula used by accountants is L=S/Q. L is Lateral Forecast, S is the Spend Parameter and Q is the Quotient Charter. Draw a formula triangle relating L, S and Q and use it to find:

a) the Lateral Forecast when the Spend Parameter is 120 and the Quotient Charter is 8

b) the Quotient Charter when the Spend Parameter is 408 whilst the Lateral Forecast is 24

c) S when L=0.

I knew you'd like those — so I've saved you some more. Have a bash at the questions on <u>speed</u> (P.71) and <u>density</u> (P.72) while you're still on a roll...

3.5   Questions on Pythagoras' Theorem

If you're as big a fan of Pythagoras' as me, you'll ignore him and use this method instead:

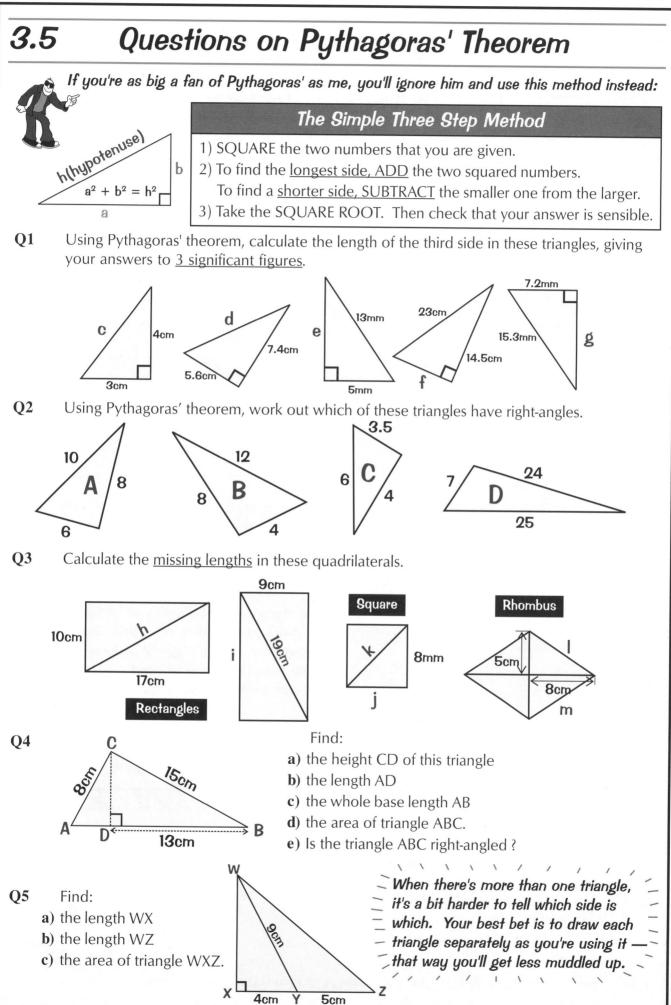

h(hypotenuse)

b

$a^2 + b^2 = h^2$

a

The Simple Three Step Method

1) SQUARE the two numbers that you are given.
2) To find the <u>longest side, ADD</u> the two squared numbers.
   To find a <u>shorter side, SUBTRACT</u> the smaller one from the larger.
3) Take the SQUARE ROOT. Then check that your answer is sensible.

Q1   Using Pythagoras' theorem, calculate the length of the third side in these triangles, giving your answers to <u>3 significant figures</u>.

c   4cm   3cm

d   7.4cm   5.6cm

e   13mm   5mm

23cm   15.3mm   14.5mm   f

7.2mm   g

Q2   Using Pythagoras' theorem, work out which of these triangles have right-angles.

10   A   8   6

12   8   B   4

3.5   6   C   4

7   D   24   25

Q3   Calculate the <u>missing lengths</u> in these quadrilaterals.

10cm   h   17cm

Rectangles

9cm   i   19cm

Square   k   8mm   j

Rhombus   5cm   l   8cm   m

Q4

C   8cm   15cm   A   D   13cm   B

Find:
a) the height CD of this triangle
b) the length AD
c) the whole base length AB
d) the area of triangle ABC.
e) Is the triangle ABC right-angled ?

Q5   Find:
a) the length WX
b) the length WZ
c) the area of triangle WXZ.

W   9cm   X   4cm   Y   5cm   Z

When there's more than one triangle, it's a bit harder to tell which side is which. Your best bet is to draw each triangle separately as you're using it — that way you'll get less muddled up.

3.5 Questions on Pythagoras' Theorem

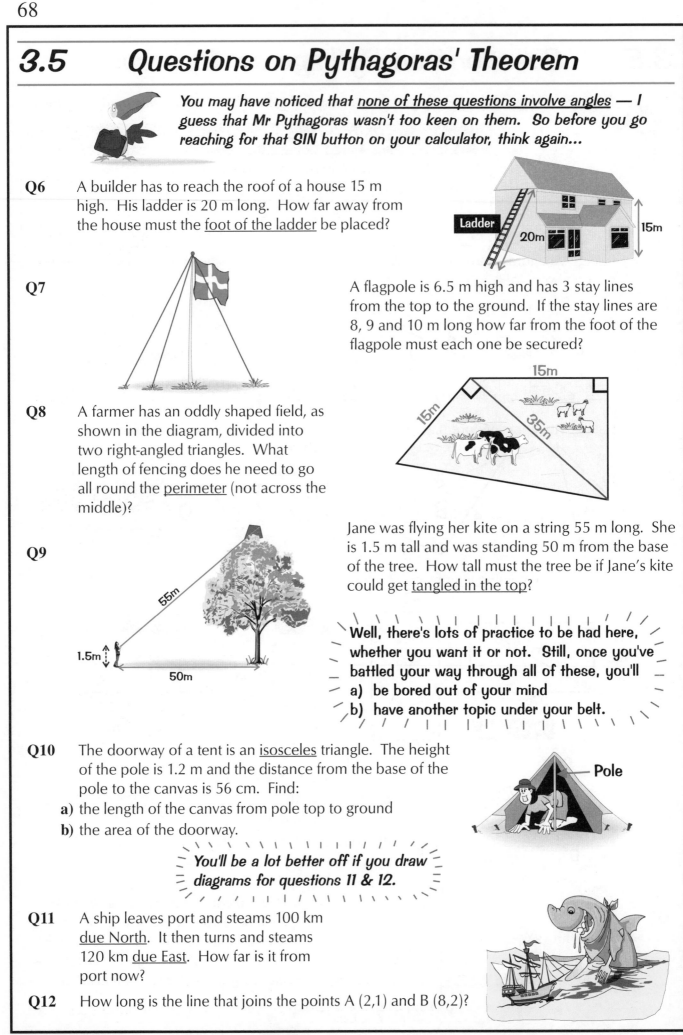

You may have noticed that none of these questions involve angles — I guess that Mr Pythagoras wasn't too keen on them. So before you go reaching for that SIN button on your calculator, think again...

Q6 A builder has to reach the roof of a house 15 m high. His ladder is 20 m long. How far away from the house must the foot of the ladder be placed?

Ladder
20m
15m

Q7 A flagpole is 6.5 m high and has 3 stay lines from the top to the ground. If the stay lines are 8, 9 and 10 m long how far from the foot of the flagpole must each one be secured?

15m
15m
35m

Q8 A farmer has an oddly shaped field, as shown in the diagram, divided into two right-angled triangles. What length of fencing does he need to go all round the perimeter (not across the middle)?

Q9 Jane was flying her kite on a string 55 m long. She is 1.5 m tall and was standing 50 m from the base of the tree. How tall must the tree be if Jane's kite could get tangled in the top?

55m
1.5m
50m

Well, there's lots of practice to be had here, whether you want it or not. Still, once you've battled your way through all of these, you'll
a) be bored out of your mind
b) have another topic under your belt.

Q10 The doorway of a tent is an isosceles triangle. The height of the pole is 1.2 m and the distance from the base of the pole to the canvas is 56 cm. Find:
a) the length of the canvas from pole top to ground
b) the area of the doorway.

Pole

You'll be a lot better off if you draw diagrams for questions 11 & 12.

Q11 A ship leaves port and steams 100 km due North. It then turns and steams 120 km due East. How far is it from port now?

Q12 How long is the line that joins the points A (2,1) and B (8,2)?

SECTION THREE — BITS AND BOBS

3.5   Questions on Pythagoras' Theorem

Make sure that you only use Pythagoras' Theorem on right-angled triangles — it doesn't work too well on anything else. In fact it doesn't work at all.

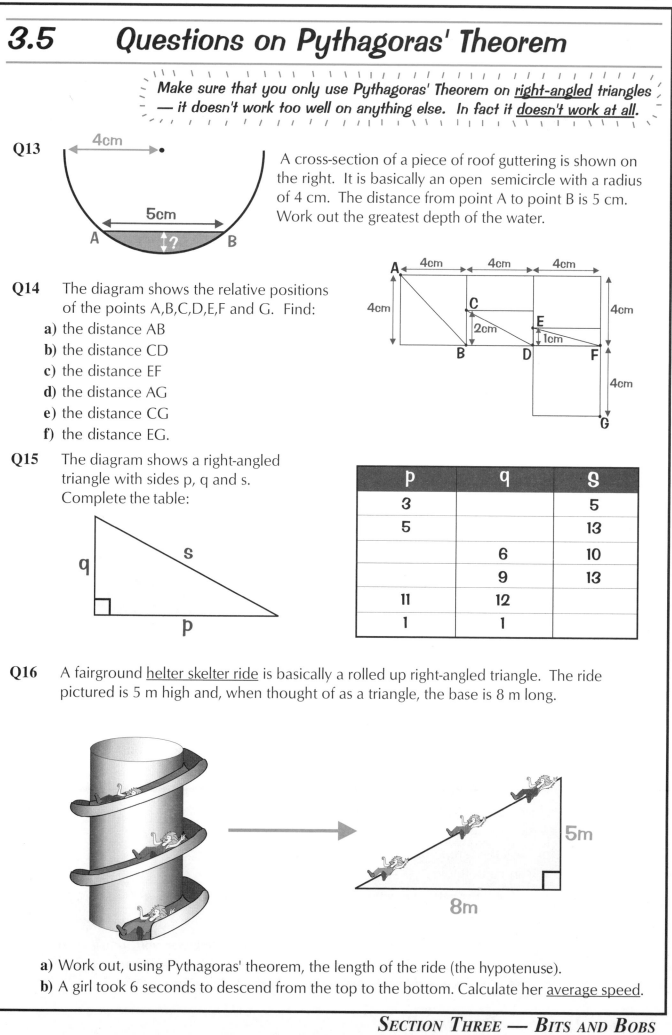

Q13 A cross-section of a piece of roof guttering is shown on the right. It is basically an open semicircle with a radius of 4 cm. The distance from point A to point B is 5 cm. Work out the greatest depth of the water.

Q14 The diagram shows the relative positions of the points A,B,C,D,E,F and G. Find:
  a) the distance AB
  b) the distance CD
  c) the distance EF
  d) the distance AG
  e) the distance CG
  f) the distance EG.

Q15 The diagram shows a right-angled triangle with sides p, q and s. Complete the table:

p	q	s
3		5
5		13
	6	10
	9	13
11	12	
1	1	

Q16 A fairground <u>helter skelter ride</u> is basically a rolled up right-angled triangle. The ride pictured is 5 m high and, when thought of as a triangle, the base is 8 m long.

  a) Work out, using Pythagoras' theorem, the length of the ride (the hypotenuse).
  b) A girl took 6 seconds to descend from the top to the bottom. Calculate her <u>average speed</u>.

3.6   Questions on Using Formulas

It's really important you get your units right — if you get them wrong you'll <u>lose marks</u>.

> ### The <u>UNITS you get OUT</u> of a formula
> ### <u>DEPEND ENTIRELY</u> upon the <u>UNITS you put INTO IT</u>

> Example. "A boy runs 1500 m in 6 minutes. Find his speed in km/h"
> *ANSWER:* First you must CONVERT INTO KM AND HOURS.
>   1500 m = <u>1.5 km</u>   6 mins = <u>0.1 hours</u> (mins÷60)
>   So the boy's speed is 1.5 km divided by 0.1 hours, which gives <u>15 km/h</u>

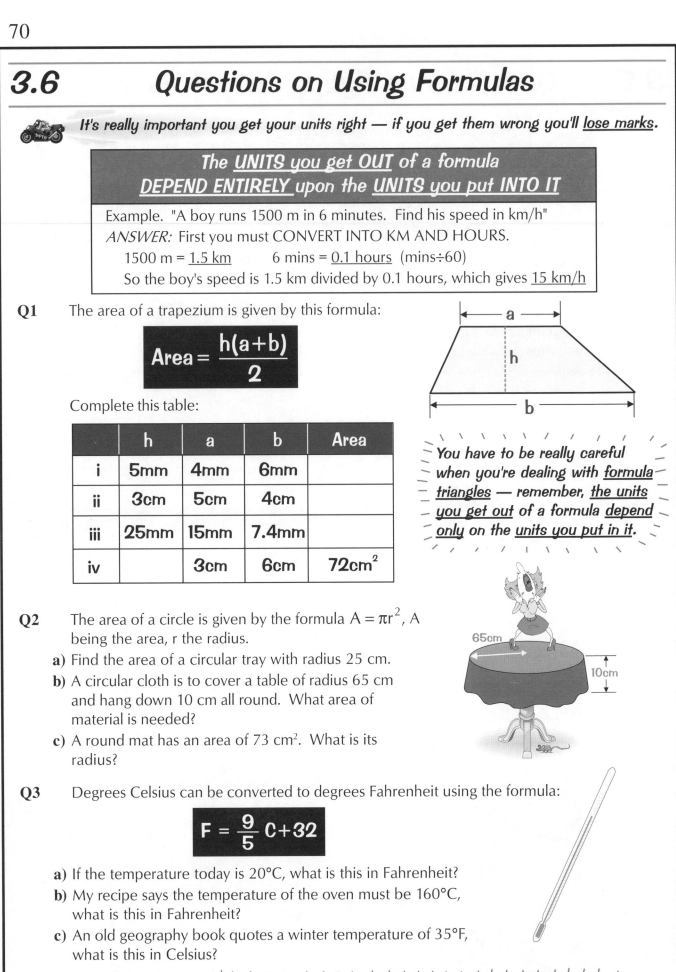

Q1   The area of a trapezium is given by this formula:

$$\text{Area} = \frac{h(a+b)}{2}$$

Complete this table:

	h	a	b	Area
i	5mm	4mm	6mm	
ii	3cm	5cm	4cm	
iii	25mm	15mm	7.4mm	
iv		3cm	6cm	72cm^2

You have to be really careful when you're dealing with <u>formula triangles</u> — remember, <u>the units you get out</u> of a formula <u>depend only</u> on the <u>units you put in it</u>.

Q2   The area of a circle is given by the formula $A = \pi r^2$, A being the area, r the radius.

a) Find the area of a circular tray with radius 25 cm.

b) A circular cloth is to cover a table of radius 65 cm and hang down 10 cm all round. What area of material is needed?

c) A round mat has an area of 73 cm². What is its radius?

Q3   Degrees Celsius can be converted to degrees Fahrenheit using the formula:

$$F = \frac{9}{5}C + 32$$

a) If the temperature today is 20°C, what is this in Fahrenheit?

b) My recipe says the temperature of the oven must be 160°C, what is this in Fahrenheit?

c) An old geography book quotes a winter temperature of 35°F, what is this in Celsius?

If you need to give the answer in a particular unit, you'll save yourself a lot of hassle if you convert the measurements into the right units before you do the calculation.

3.7   *Questions on Speed*

This is an easy enough formula — and of course you can put it in that good old formula triangle as well.

$$\text{Average speed} = \frac{\text{Total distance}}{\text{Total time}}$$

Q1   A train travels 240 km in 4 hours. What is its <u>average speed</u>?

Q2   A car travels for 3 hours at an average speed of 55 m.p.h. How far has it travelled?

Q3   A boy rides a bike at an average speed of 15 km/hr. How long will it take him to ride 40 km?

Q4   <u>Complete</u> this table.

Distance Travelled	Time taken	Average Speed
210 km	3 hrs	
135 miles		30 mph
	2 hrs 30 mins	42 km/h
9 miles	45 mins	
640 km		800 km/h
	1 hr 10 mins	60 mph

Q5   The distance from Kendal (Oxenholme) to London (Euston) is 280 miles. The train travels at an average speed of 63 m.p.h. If I catch the 07.05 from Kendal, can I be at a meeting in London by 10.30? <u>Show all your working</u>.

Q6   A plane flies over city A at 09.55 and over city B at 10.02. What is its <u>average</u> speed if these cities are 63 miles apart?

Q7   An athlete can run 100 m in 28 seconds.
Calculate the athlete's speed in:

     a) m/sec

     b) km/hr.

Q8   In a speed trial a sand yacht travelled a measured mile in 36.4 seconds.

     a) Calculate this speed in m.p.h.
On the return mile he took 36.16 seconds.

     b) Find his <u>total time</u> for the two runs.

     c) Calculate the average speed in m.p.h.

Remember, for the <u>average</u> speed, you use the <u>total</u> time and <u>total</u> distance.

Q9   A motorist drives from Manchester to London. 180 miles is on motorway where he averages 65 m.p.h. 55 miles is on city roads where he averages 28 m.p.h. 15 miles is on country roads where he averages 25 m.p.h.

     a) Calculate the total time taken for the journey.

     b) How far did he travel altogether?

     c) Calculate the average speed for the journey.

I reckon this is <u>pretty easy</u> — it's just a case of taking your time, putting the right numbers into the <u>speed formula triangle</u> and getting the answer out. And don't forget to check your answer is in the <u>right units</u>.

3.8 Questions on Density

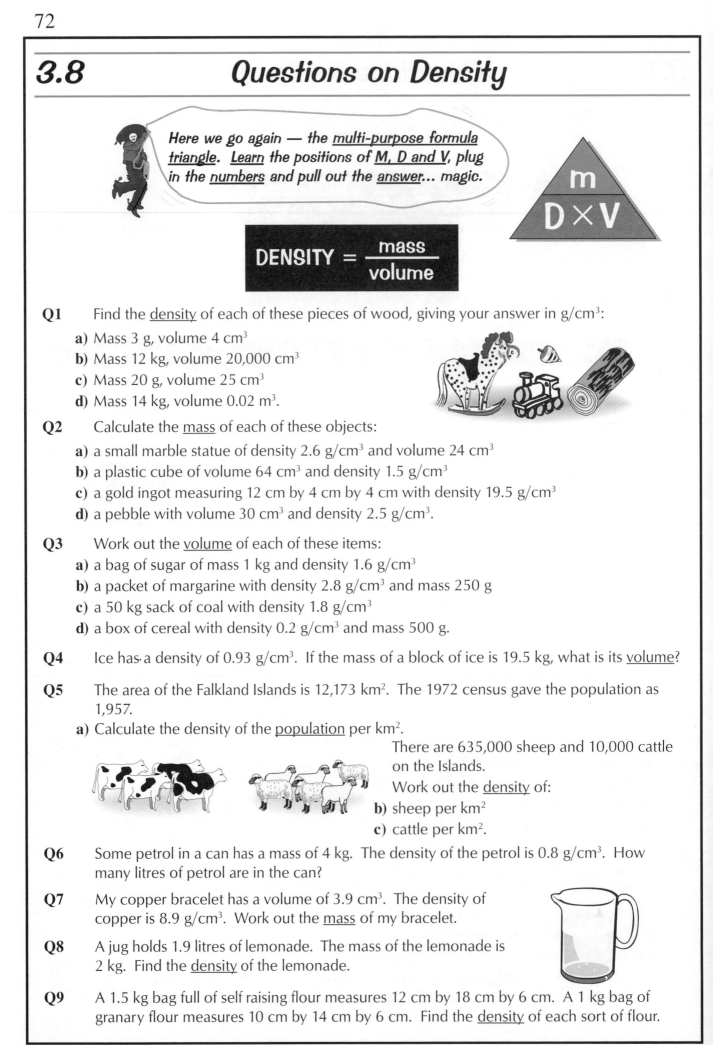

Here we go again — the <u>multi-purpose formula triangle</u>. <u>Learn</u> the positions of <u>M, D and V</u>, plug in the <u>numbers</u> and pull out the <u>answer</u>... magic.

$$\text{DENSITY} = \frac{\text{mass}}{\text{volume}}$$

Q1 Find the <u>density</u> of each of these pieces of wood, giving your answer in g/cm³:

a) Mass 3 g, volume 4 cm³

b) Mass 12 kg, volume 20,000 cm³

c) Mass 20 g, volume 25 cm³

d) Mass 14 kg, volume 0.02 m³.

Q2 Calculate the <u>mass</u> of each of these objects:

a) a small marble statue of density 2.6 g/cm³ and volume 24 cm³

b) a plastic cube of volume 64 cm³ and density 1.5 g/cm³

c) a gold ingot measuring 12 cm by 4 cm by 4 cm with density 19.5 g/cm³

d) a pebble with volume 30 cm³ and density 2.5 g/cm³.

Q3 Work out the <u>volume</u> of each of these items:

a) a bag of sugar of mass 1 kg and density 1.6 g/cm³

b) a packet of margarine with density 2.8 g/cm³ and mass 250 g

c) a 50 kg sack of coal with density 1.8 g/cm³

d) a box of cereal with density 0.2 g/cm³ and mass 500 g.

Q4 Ice has a density of 0.93 g/cm³. If the mass of a block of ice is 19.5 kg, what is its <u>volume</u>?

Q5 The area of the Falkland Islands is 12,173 km². The 1972 census gave the population as 1,957.

a) Calculate the density of the <u>population</u> per km².

There are 635,000 sheep and 10,000 cattle on the Islands.

Work out the <u>density</u> of:

b) sheep per km²

c) cattle per km².

Q6 Some petrol in a can has a mass of 4 kg. The density of the petrol is 0.8 g/cm³. How many litres of petrol are in the can?

Q7 My copper bracelet has a volume of 3.9 cm³. The density of copper is 8.9 g/cm³. Work out the <u>mass</u> of my bracelet.

Q8 A jug holds 1.9 litres of lemonade. The mass of the lemonade is 2 kg. Find the <u>density</u> of the lemonade.

Q9 A 1.5 kg bag full of self raising flour measures 12 cm by 18 cm by 6 cm. A 1 kg bag of granary flour measures 10 cm by 14 cm by 6 cm. Find the <u>density</u> of each sort of flour.

3.9   *Questions on Tessellations*

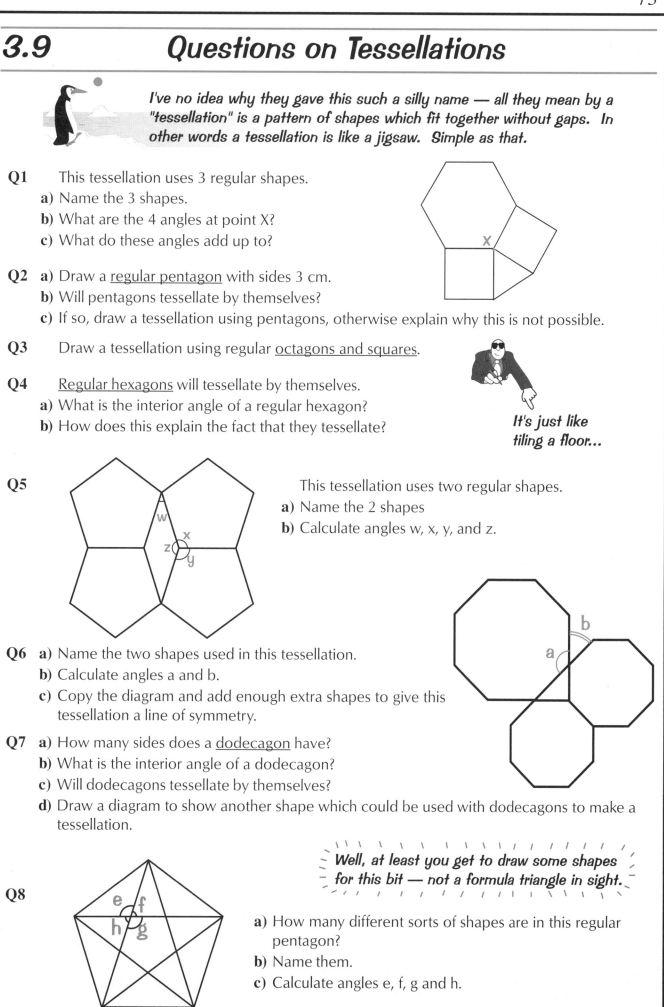

I've no idea why they gave this such a silly name — all they mean by a "tessellation" is a pattern of shapes which fit together without gaps. In other words a tessellation is like a jigsaw. Simple as that.

Q1   This tessellation uses 3 regular shapes.
- **a)** Name the 3 shapes.
- **b)** What are the 4 angles at point X?
- **c)** What do these angles add up to?

Q2 **a)** Draw a <u>regular pentagon</u> with sides 3 cm.
- **b)** Will pentagons tessellate by themselves?
- **c)** If so, draw a tessellation using pentagons, otherwise explain why this is not possible.

Q3   Draw a tessellation using regular <u>octagons and squares</u>.

Q4   <u>Regular hexagons</u> will tessellate by themselves.
- **a)** What is the interior angle of a regular hexagon?
- **b)** How does this explain the fact that they tessellate?

It's just like tiling a floor...

Q5

This tessellation uses two regular shapes.
- **a)** Name the 2 shapes
- **b)** Calculate angles w, x, y, and z.

Q6 **a)** Name the two shapes used in this tessellation.
- **b)** Calculate angles a and b.
- **c)** Copy the diagram and add enough extra shapes to give this tessellation a line of symmetry.

Q7 **a)** How many sides does a <u>dodecagon</u> have?
- **b)** What is the interior angle of a dodecagon?
- **c)** Will dodecagons tessellate by themselves?
- **d)** Draw a diagram to show another shape which could be used with dodecagons to make a tessellation.

Well, at least you get to draw some shapes for this bit — not a formula triangle in sight.

Q8

- **a)** How many different sorts of shapes are in this regular pentagon?
- **b)** Name them.
- **c)** Calculate angles e, f, g and h.

3.10   *Questions on Ratios*

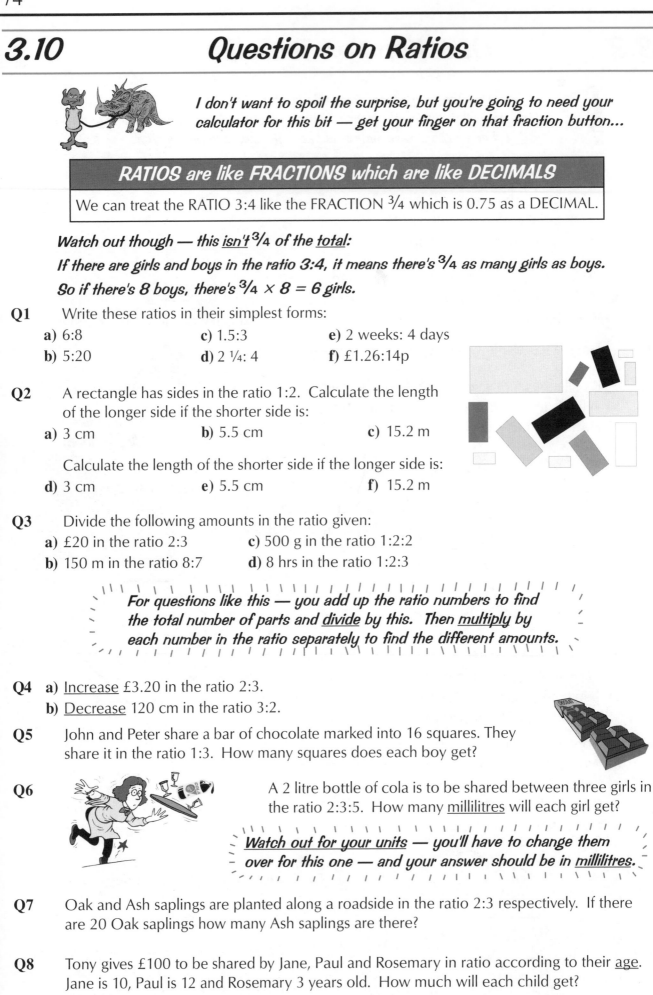

I don't want to spoil the surprise, but you're going to need your calculator for this bit — get your finger on that fraction button...

RATIOS are like FRACTIONS which are like DECIMALS

We can treat the RATIO 3:4 like the FRACTION ¾ which is 0.75 as a DECIMAL.

Watch out though — this isn't ¾ of the total:

If there are girls and boys in the ratio 3:4, it means there's ¾ as many girls as boys.

So if there's 8 boys, there's ¾ × 8 = 6 girls.

Q1   Write these ratios in their simplest forms:

     a) 6:8   **c)** 1.5:3   **e)** 2 weeks: 4 days

     b) 5:20   **d)** 2 ¼: 4   **f)** £1.26:14p

Q2   A rectangle has sides in the ratio 1:2. Calculate the length of the longer side if the shorter side is:

     a) 3 cm   **b)** 5.5 cm   **c)** 15.2 m

     Calculate the length of the shorter side if the longer side is:

     d) 3 cm   **e)** 5.5 cm   **f)** 15.2 m

Q3   Divide the following amounts in the ratio given:

     a) £20 in the ratio 2:3   **c)** 500 g in the ratio 1:2:2

     b) 150 m in the ratio 8:7   **d)** 8 hrs in the ratio 1:2:3

For questions like this — you add up the ratio numbers to find the total number of parts and <u>divide</u> by this. Then <u>multiply</u> by each number in the ratio separately to find the different amounts.

Q4   **a)** <u>Increase</u> £3.20 in the ratio 2:3.

     b) <u>Decrease</u> 120 cm in the ratio 3:2.

Q5   John and Peter share a bar of chocolate marked into 16 squares. They share it in the ratio 1:3. How many squares does each boy get?

Q6   A 2 litre bottle of cola is to be shared between three girls in the ratio 2:3:5. How many <u>millilitres</u> will each girl get?

<u>Watch out for your units</u> — you'll have to change them over for this one — and your answer should be in <u>millilitres</u>.

Q7   Oak and Ash saplings are planted along a roadside in the ratio 2:3 respectively. If there are 20 Oak saplings how many Ash saplings are there?

Q8   Tony gives £100 to be shared by Jane, Paul and Rosemary in ratio according to their <u>age</u>. Jane is 10, Paul is 12 and Rosemary 3 years old. How much will each child get?

3.10   *Questions on Ratios*

Q9   The recipe for flapjacks is 250 g of oats, 150 g of brown sugar and
100 g of margarine. What <u>fraction of the mixture</u> is:

    a) oats?

    b) sugar?

Don't forget to check your units. (I reckon if I say it enough times, you'll eventually cave in and start doing it — betcha)

Q10   The plan of a house is drawn to a scale of 1 cm to 3 m.

    a) Write this ratio in its simplest form.

    b) How wide is a room that shows as 2 cm on the drawing?

    c) How long will a 10 m hall look on the drawing?

Q11   The ratio of girls to boys in a school is 7:6. If there are 455 pupils in total, how many are

    a) girls?

    b) boys?

Q12   Concrete is mixed using cement, sand and gravel in the
ratio 1:3:6. If a 5 kg bag of cement is used how much:

    a) sand is needed?

    b) gravel is needed?

    If the builder needs 80 kg of concrete,

    c) how much of each substance does he need?

Q13

I picked some strawberries after a few wet days.
Some were eaten by slugs, some were mouldy and
some fine. The ratio was 2:3:10 respectively. If <u>9
strawberries were mouldy</u> how many:

    a) were good?

    b) did I lose altogether?

    c) What fraction of the total amount were good?

Q14   Salt & Vinegar, Cheese & Onion and
Prawn Cocktail flavour crisps were sold
in the school tuck shop in <u>the ratio
5:3:2</u>. If 18 Bags of Prawn Cocktail
were sold, how many bags:

    a) of Salt & Vinegar were sold?

    b) were sold altogether?

*Yeah, OK, this ratio stuff isn't nice, but it's loads <u>easier</u> if you
<u>learn "A Ratio is a Fraction is a Decimal"</u>. It won't impress
anyone, but you'll have a better time of it in the Exam.*

4.1 Questions on Averages and Range

If you don't learn these 4 basic definitions, you'll miss out on some of the easiest marks. Have a go at the questions on the next few pages and you'll see what I mean.

The 4 basic definitions:

1) <u>Mode</u>	Most <u>Common</u>
2) <u>Median</u>	<u>Middle</u> Value
3) <u>Mean</u>	<u>Average</u> (Total of Items ÷ Number of Items)
4) <u>Range</u>	<u>Difference</u> between the <u>Smallest</u> and the <u>Biggest</u>

Q1 Metre rulers are made by a machine. Accurate measurements with a micrometer show that they lie between 99 cm and 101 cm. A <u>sample of 20</u> gave the following readings:

101.0	100.5	99.4	100.2	100.6	100.0	100.6	100.7	100.9	99.8
99.7	99.3	99.7	100.1	100.0	99.7	99.5	99.6	100.7	100.9

a) What is the <u>mean</u> length?

b) What is the <u>modal</u> length?

The mean involves a bit more calculation, but hey, you are doing maths.

c) What is the <u>median</u> length?

Q2 Find the mode and median <u>shoe size</u> of the 30 school children whose shoe sizes are:

4	2	3	4	4	5	4	2	4	3
2	1	3	1	3	2	5	3	2	3
3	2	3	2	4	6	7	2	3	1

Q3 Find the <u>mean age</u> of eight children whose ages are:

13 years 6 months	13 years 8 months	13 years 4 months	13 years
13 years 1 month	12 years 10 months	12 years 9 months	12 years 6 months

Q4 Find the median of 8, 6, 6, 3, 2 and 1.

Just identify the most frequent value and the middle value — easy.

Q5 Find the mode of 10, 9, 8, 8, 8, 8, 7, 7, 4 and 3.

Q6 A firm sending out catalogues throughout the country posted <u>88 catalogues</u> first class on <u>Monday</u>. The clients received them over the week: <u>40 on Tuesday</u>, <u>28 on Wednesday</u>, <u>9</u> on <u>Thursday</u>, <u>6</u> on <u>Friday</u> and the <u>remainder</u> on <u>Saturday</u>.

a) Find the modal number of days necessary for the catalogues to arrive.

b) Find the median number of days necessary for the catalogues to arrive.

c) "The <u>majority</u> of first class post arrives <u>within 2 days</u>."
Is the above statement <u>true</u> or <u>false</u> in the the light of the data?

Q7 Find the median, mode, mean and range of the following data:

a) 20, 18, 16, 14, 12, 16, 0, 4, 6, 8

b) 5, 1, 2, 2, 4, 3, 3, 4, 3

Q8 **a)** Give two advantages and one disadvantage of using the mean.

b) Give two advantages and one disadvantage of using the mode.

c) Give three advantages and disadvantages of using the median.

4.1   Questions on Averages and Range

In these questions, you only need to look at the numbers and work out the averages. There's loads of stuff in here that you really don't need, so ignore it.

Q9   The National Tree Service has collected data on <u>two woods</u> it manages. One in the North is Crookthwaite, and one in the South is Acornwood. The <u>diameters of trees</u> are calculated from their circumferences to the nearest centimetre.

diameter of trees	1 - 5	6 - 10	11 - 15	16 - 20	21 - 25	26 - 30	31 - 35	Total
Acornwood	1	5	8	20	4	1	1	40
Crookthwaite	6	4	5	4	7	3	1	30

a) Draw <u>two frequency polygons</u> to show this information.

b) What is the <u>modal class interval</u> for <u>Acornwood</u>?

c) What is the modal class interval for <u>Crookthwaite</u>?

d) Using your answers to the previous parts of the question, comment upon the populations found in each of the woods, and compare the two.

Thin tree   Fat tree

Don't forget, put the data into ascending order before looking for the averages.

Q10   The population of a small hamlet reported the following household incomes:

a) Calculate the mean income of the population.

b) Calculate the mode and the median.

c) The mode and the median appear to agree very closely. Why is the mean so different?

d) Which measure would you quote as the "average" income for this small hamlet?

£30,000	£22,000
£37,500	£27,500
£32,500	£25,000
£30,000	£40,000
£200,000	£35,000

Q11   The Borders Orchid Growers Society has measured the height of all the Lesser Plumed Bog Orchids in the 5 miles wide strip each side of the border, to the nearest cm.

5 miles on Scottish side	5 miles on English side
Heights 14, 15, 17, 14, 17, 16, 14, 13 15, 17, 16, 14, 15, 17, 14, 13	Heights 14, 12, 16, 18, 19, 17, 16, 15 13, 14, 15, 16, 17, 18, 19, 13

a) Draw a tally chart for each set of data the Borders Orchid Growers Society has collected.

b) Draw a bar chart for each set of data.

c) State the mode and median for each set of data.

d) Find the range for each set of data.

e) Compare and contrast the two sides of the border using the data you have compiled.

If you've learnt anything about fat trees or bog orchids you've missed my point.

4.1 Questions on Averages and Range

Plenty of practice — that's what you need and that's what you're gonna get.

Q12 From the frequency charts calculate the <u>mean of the distributions</u>.

x	frequency
100	5
101	6
102	4
103	5

x	frequency
10	5
10.1	6
10.2	4
10.3	5

x	frequency
1000	5
1010	6
1020	4
1030	5

Q13 There are three 1 inch inchworms, five 1.5 inch inchworms, seven 2 inch inchworms and three 3 inch inchworms. These inchworms now have to be measured in mm. Assuming there are <u>2.5 cm to the inch</u>, convert each of the measurements to mm. Find the mean, mode and median length.

Q14 School inspectors who visit classes need to know <u>which students</u> are at the <u>most common National Curriculum Level</u>. They need to talk with students who are of <u>average age and ability</u>, and they need to see the exercise books of a student who is in the <u>middle of the whole class</u> in terms of ability. Which of the 3 usual averages cover these criteria?

Q15 <u>Mobile phone</u> users can buy calls in <u>prepaid</u> amounts ranging from £5, £20, £50 up to £100. Darcy logs <u>all his payments</u> for his phone for a <u>year</u>. He needs to show head office his accounts using a <u>stick frequency chart</u> and the <u>mean amount</u> he pays. Draw such a chart and calculate the mean, from the data below.

Darcy's Accounts	£5 credit	£20 credit	£50 credit	£100 credit
frequency	14	22	9	7

One thing I hate more than questions on averages is going to the dentist. Oh my...

Q16 A dentist is about to employ a <u>dental hygienist</u>. She wishes to know if having a dental hygienist has an <u>effect on the number of fillings</u> she has to perform each year. So, prior to appointing him, the dentist takes some data from the record cards. Here it is:

No. of fillings	0	1	2	3	4	5
No. of children	1	2	8	30	60	12

<u>Three years after</u> appointing the dental hygienist, the dentist takes another set of data from the record cards. Here it is:

No. of fillings	0	1	2	3	4	5
No. of children	11	16	40	32	4	2

Using any statistical average you need, state what you see from the data, assuming that these records are for <u>new patients</u>.

4.1 Questions on Averages and Range

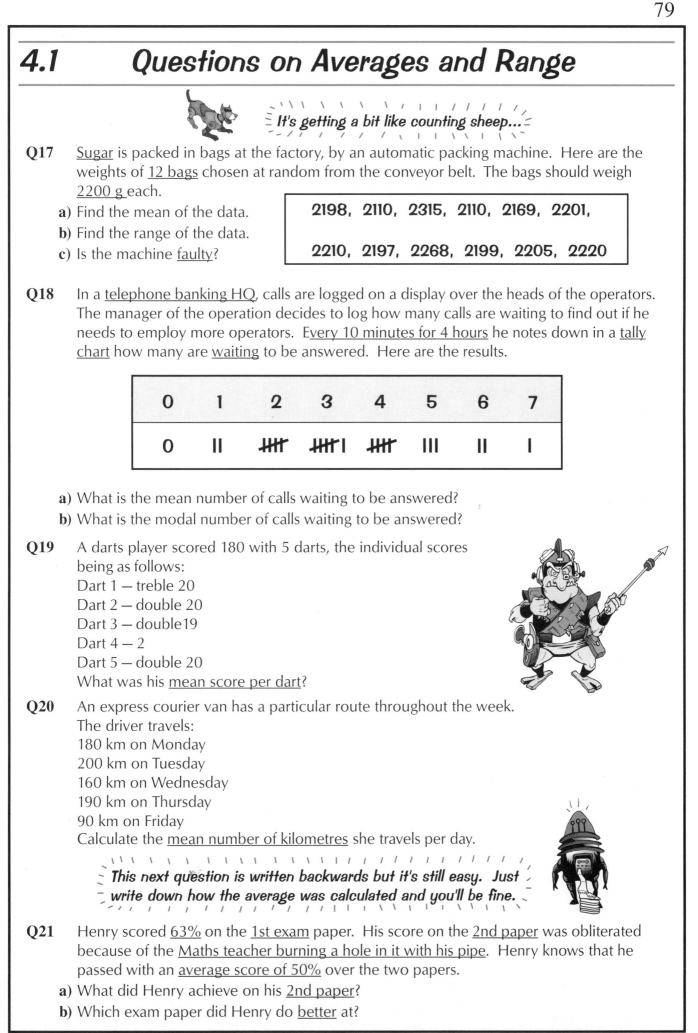

It's getting a bit like counting sheep...

Q17 <u>Sugar</u> is packed in bags at the factory, by an automatic packing machine. Here are the weights of <u>12 bags</u> chosen at random from the conveyor belt. The bags should weigh <u>2200 g</u> each.

    a) Find the mean of the data.

    b) Find the range of the data.

    c) Is the machine <u>faulty</u>?

> 2198, 2110, 2315, 2110, 2169, 2201,
>
> 2210, 2197, 2268, 2199, 2205, 2220

Q18 In a <u>telephone banking HQ</u>, calls are logged on a display over the heads of the operators. The manager of the operation decides to log how many calls are waiting to find out if he needs to employ more operators. <u>Every 10 minutes for 4 hours</u> he notes down in a <u>tally chart</u> how many are <u>waiting</u> to be answered. Here are the results.

0	1	2	3	4	5	6	7
0	II	IIII	IIIII	IIIII	III	II	I

    a) What is the mean number of calls waiting to be answered?

    b) What is the modal number of calls waiting to be answered?

Q19 A darts player scored 180 with 5 darts, the individual scores being as follows:

Dart 1 — treble 20

Dart 2 — double 20

Dart 3 — double 19

Dart 4 — 2

Dart 5 — double 20

What was his <u>mean score per dart</u>?

Q20 An express courier van has a particular route throughout the week. The driver travels:

180 km on Monday

200 km on Tuesday

160 km on Wednesday

190 km on Thursday

90 km on Friday

Calculate the <u>mean number of kilometres</u> she travels per day.

This next question is written backwards but it's still easy. Just write down how the average was calculated and you'll be fine.

Q21 Henry scored <u>63%</u> on the <u>1st exam</u> paper. His score on the <u>2nd paper</u> was obliterated because of the <u>Maths teacher burning a hole in it with his pipe</u>. Henry knows that he passed with an <u>average score of 50%</u> over the two papers.

    a) What did Henry achieve on his <u>2nd paper</u>?

    b) Which exam paper did Henry do <u>better</u> at?

4.2   *Questions on Simple Probability*

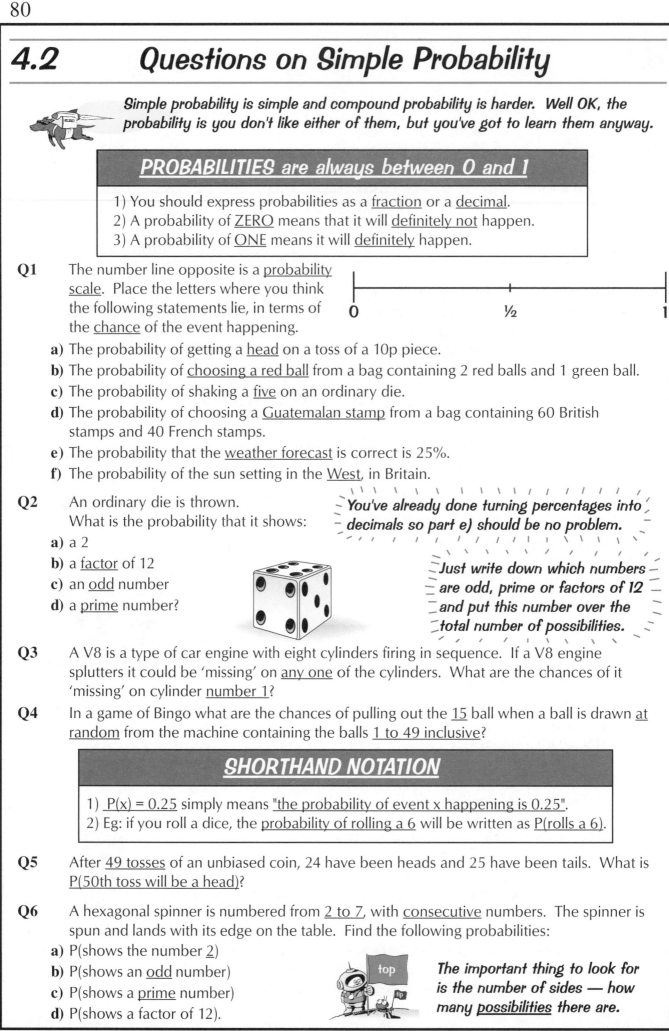

Simple probability is simple and compound probability is harder. Well OK, the probability is you don't like either of them, but you've got to learn them anyway.

PROBABILITIES are always between 0 and 1

1) You should express probabilities as a <u>fraction</u> or a <u>decimal</u>.
2) A probability of <u>ZERO</u> means that it will <u>definitely not</u> happen.
3) A probability of <u>ONE</u> means it will <u>definitely</u> happen.

Q1   The number line opposite is a <u>probability scale</u>. Place the letters where you think the following statements lie, in terms of the <u>chance</u> of the event happening.

0   ½   1

a) The probability of getting a <u>head</u> on a toss of a 10p piece.

b) The probability of <u>choosing a red ball</u> from a bag containing 2 red balls and 1 green ball.

c) The probability of shaking a <u>five</u> on an ordinary die.

d) The probability of choosing a <u>Guatemalan stamp</u> from a bag containing 60 British stamps and 40 French stamps.

e) The probability that the <u>weather forecast</u> is correct is 25%.

f) The probability of the sun setting in the <u>West</u>, in Britain.

Q2   An ordinary die is thrown.
What is the probability that it shows:

a) a 2

b) a <u>factor</u> of 12

c) an <u>odd</u> number

d) a <u>prime</u> number?

You've already done turning percentages into decimals so part e) should be no problem.

Just write down which numbers are odd, prime or factors of 12 and put this number over the total number of possibilities.

Q3   A V8 is a type of car engine with eight cylinders firing in sequence. If a V8 engine splutters it could be 'missing' on <u>any one</u> of the cylinders. What are the chances of it 'missing' on cylinder <u>number 1</u>?

Q4   In a game of Bingo what are the chances of pulling out the <u>15</u> ball when a ball is drawn <u>at random</u> from the machine containing the balls <u>1 to 49 inclusive</u>?

SHORTHAND NOTATION

1) <u>P(x) = 0.25</u> simply means "<u>the probability of event x happening is 0.25</u>".
2) Eg: if you roll a dice, the <u>probability of rolling a 6</u> will be written as <u>P(rolls a 6)</u>.

Q5   After <u>49 tosses</u> of an unbiased coin, 24 have been heads and 25 have been tails. What is <u>P(50th toss will be a head)</u>?

Q6   A hexagonal spinner is numbered from <u>2 to 7</u>, with <u>consecutive</u> numbers. The spinner is spun and lands with its edge on the table. Find the following probabilities:

a) P(shows the number <u>2</u>)

b) P(shows an <u>odd</u> number)

c) P(shows a <u>prime</u> number)

d) P(shows a factor of 12).

The important thing to look for is the number of sides — how many possibilities there are.

4.2   Questions on Simple Probability

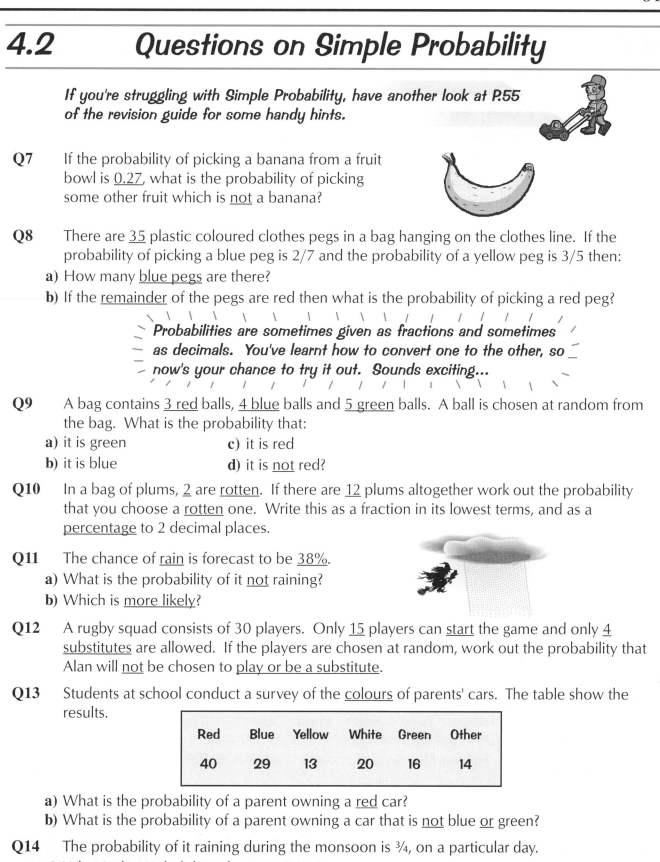

If you're struggling with Simple Probability, have another look at P.55 of the revision guide for some handy hints.

Q7   If the probability of picking a banana from a fruit bowl is <u>0.27</u>, what is the probability of picking some other fruit which is <u>not</u> a banana?

Q8   There are <u>35</u> plastic coloured clothes pegs in a bag hanging on the clothes line. If the probability of picking a blue peg is 2/7 and the probability of a yellow peg is 3/5 then:
   a) How many <u>blue pegs</u> are there?
   b) If the <u>remainder</u> of the pegs are red then what is the probability of picking a red peg?

Probabilities are sometimes given as fractions and sometimes as decimals. You've learnt how to convert one to the other, so now's your chance to try it out. Sounds exciting...

Q9   A bag contains <u>3 red</u> balls, <u>4 blue</u> balls and <u>5 green</u> balls. A ball is chosen at random from the bag. What is the probability that:
   a) it is green   **c)** it is red
   b) it is blue   **d)** it is <u>not</u> red?

Q10   In a bag of plums, <u>2</u> are <u>rotten</u>. If there are <u>12</u> plums altogether work out the probability that you choose a <u>rotten</u> one. Write this as a fraction in its lowest terms, and as a <u>percentage</u> to 2 decimal places.

Q11   The chance of <u>rain</u> is forecast to be <u>38%</u>.
   a) What is the probability of it <u>not</u> raining?
   b) Which is <u>more likely</u>?

Q12   A rugby squad consists of 30 players. Only <u>15</u> players can <u>start</u> the game and only <u>4</u> <u>substitutes</u> are allowed. If the players are chosen at random, work out the probability that Alan will <u>not</u> be chosen to <u>play or be a substitute</u>.

Q13   Students at school conduct a survey of the <u>colours</u> of parents' cars. The table show the results.

Red	Blue	Yellow	White	Green	Other
40	29	13	20	16	14

   a) What is the probability of a parent owning a <u>red</u> car?
   b) What is the probability of a parent owning a car that is <u>not</u> blue <u>or</u> green?

Q14   The probability of it raining during the monsoon is ¾, on a particular day.
   a) What is the probability of it <u>not raining</u>?
   b) If a monsoon 'season' lasts approximately <u>100 days</u>, how many days are likely to be <u>dry</u>?

Q15   In a lottery <u>2000</u> tickets are sold. If Mr Winter buys <u>2 tickets</u> what are the chances of him winning the single prize? If Mrs Winter buys <u>10 tickets</u> what are her chances of winning? If Mr and Mrs Winter decide to 'pool' their tickets they have <u>12 chances of winning</u> the single fist prize. Work out the probability that the Winter household will <u>not</u> win the first prize.

4.3 Questions on Compound Probability

"Compound" or "Combined" Probability is when there are two or more events. The best way to get to grips with it is by learning the 3 simple rules.

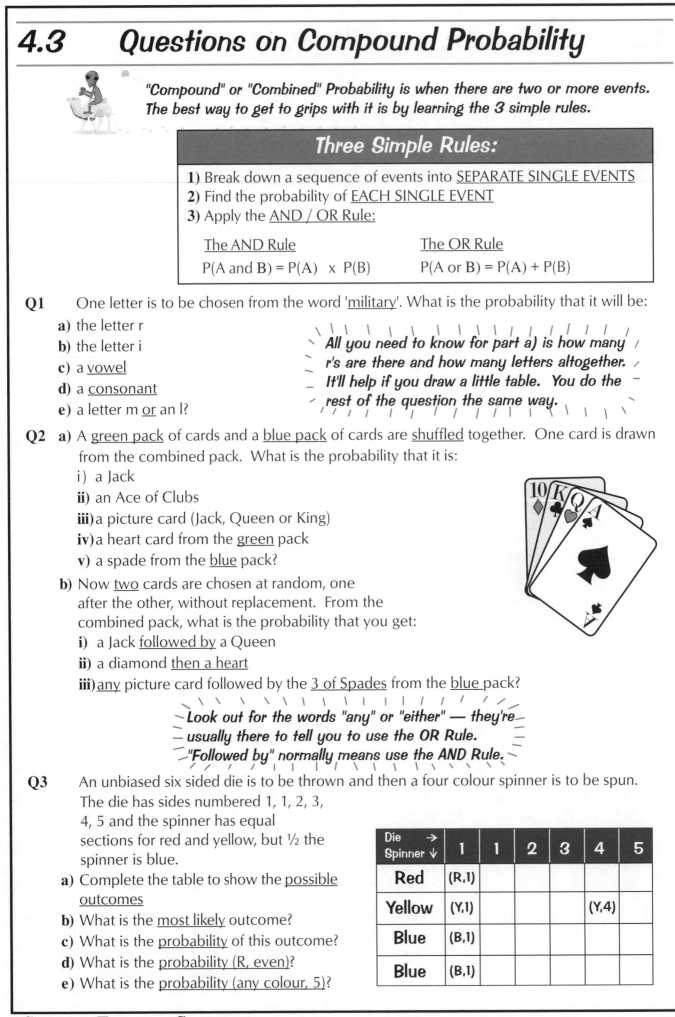

Three Simple Rules:

1) Break down a sequence of events into <u>SEPARATE SINGLE EVENTS</u>
2) Find the probability of <u>EACH SINGLE EVENT</u>
3) Apply the <u>AND / OR Rule</u>:

| <u>The AND Rule</u> | <u>The OR Rule</u> |
| P(A and B) = P(A) x P(B) | P(A or B) = P(A) + P(B) |

Q1 One letter is to be chosen from the word '<u>military</u>'. What is the probability that it will be:

a) the letter r
b) the letter i
c) a <u>vowel</u>
d) a <u>consonant</u>
e) a letter m <u>or</u> an l?

All you need to know for part a) is how many r's are there and how many letters altogether. It'll help if you draw a little table. You do the rest of the question the same way.

Q2 **a)** A <u>green pack</u> of cards and a <u>blue pack</u> of cards are <u>shuffled</u> together. One card is drawn from the combined pack. What is the probability that it is:

i) a Jack
ii) an Ace of Clubs
iii) a picture card (Jack, Queen or King)
iv) a heart card from the <u>green</u> pack
v) a spade from the <u>blue</u> pack?

b) Now <u>two</u> cards are chosen at random, one after the other, without replacement. From the combined pack, what is the probability that you get:

i) a Jack <u>followed by</u> a Queen
ii) a diamond <u>then a heart</u>
iii) <u>any</u> picture card followed by the <u>3 of Spades</u> from the <u>blue</u> pack?

Look out for the words "any" or "either" — they're usually there to tell you to use the OR Rule.
"Followed by" normally means use the AND Rule.

Q3 An unbiased six sided die is to be thrown and then a four colour spinner is to be spun. The die has sides numbered 1, 1, 2, 3, 4, 5 and the spinner has equal sections for red and yellow, but ½ the spinner is blue.

a) Complete the table to show the <u>possible outcomes</u>
b) What is the <u>most likely</u> outcome?
c) What is the <u>probability</u> of this outcome?
d) What is the <u>probability (R, even)</u>?
e) What is the <u>probability (any colour, 5)</u>?

Die → Spinner ↓	1	1	2	3	4	5
Red	(R,1)					
Yellow	(Y,1)				(Y,4)	
Blue	(B,1)					
Blue	(B,1)					

4.3   Questions on Compound Probability

When you see these phrases like "with replacement", "without replacement" and "followed by" think COMPOUND PROBABILITY, Yuk.

Q4 There are 30 balls in a bag. 6 are red, 14 are blue, 3 are green and the remainder are yellow. <u>Two balls</u> are to be picked out of the bag, without replacement. What is the probability of picking

a) 2 red balls

b) a red and a yellow ball in any order

c) 2 greens or 2 blues

d) a red or blue followed by a green?

Q5 A four edged spinner has numbers 6, 7, 8 and 9.
A three edged spinner has numbers 3, 4 and 5 on it.

a) Complete the table to show all the possible scores when both spinners are spun together and their scores <u>multiplied</u>.

b) What is the probability of achieving the <u>maximum</u> score?

c) What is the probability of achieving an <u>odd score</u>?

d) What is the probability of scoring a <u>multiple of 3</u>?

e) What is the probability of scoring a <u>multiple of 10</u>?

f) What is the probability of scoring a <u>factor of 60</u>?

X	6	7	8	9
3				
4				
5				

Q6 In a game a child is to pick twice out of a bucket containing various foam shapes. The bucket contains a square, a rectangle, a regular pentagon, a parallelogram, an equilateral triangle and an isoceles triangle.

After being chosen, the foam shape is replaced and the bucket is shaken to mix up the shapes.

Find the probability of the infant choosing

a) a square followed by a pentagon

b) a shape with 90° corners followed by the isosceles triangle

c) the pentagon, followed by any four-sided shape.

The game is now repeated, but without the replacement of the chosen foam shape.
Work out the probabilities that the infant chooses

d) the equilateral triangle and a shape with no lines of symmetry in any order

e) the two triangles in any order

f) any quadrilateral and any triangle in any order.

One thing that'll catch you out here, is that business about replacement. If the question says 'with replacement', the thing gets put back so there are the same number of things to pick from next time. If it says 'without replacement' then it stays out and there's one less to pick from. So the number on the bottom of the probability fraction is one less.

4.3   Questions on Compound Probability

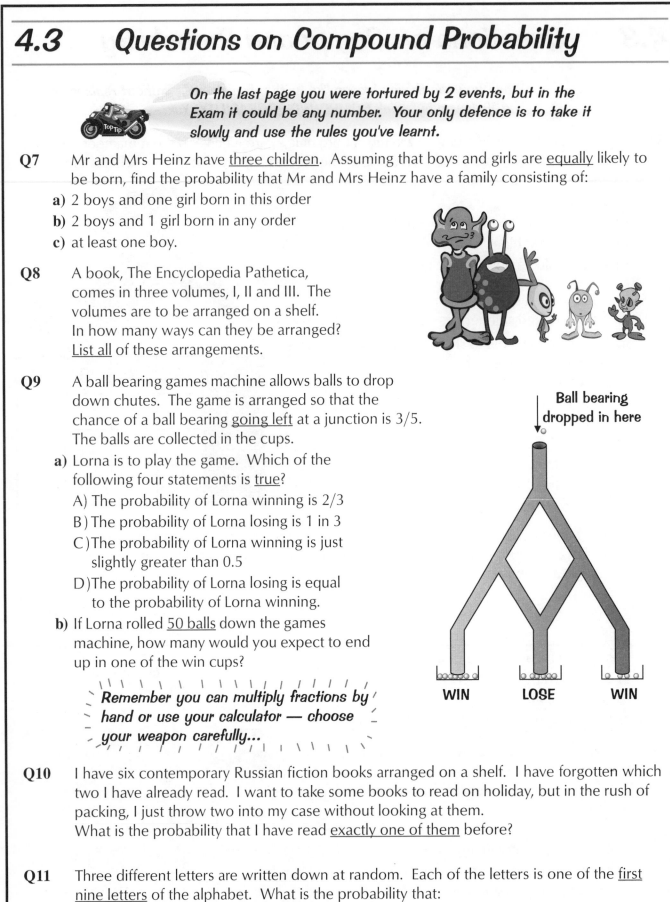

On the last page you were tortured by 2 events, but in the Exam it could be any number. Your only defence is to take it slowly and use the rules you've learnt.

Q7   Mr and Mrs Heinz have <u>three children</u>. Assuming that boys and girls are <u>equally</u> likely to be born, find the probability that Mr and Mrs Heinz have a family consisting of:

a) 2 boys and one girl born in this order

b) 2 boys and 1 girl born in any order

c) at least one boy.

Q8   A book, The Encyclopedia Pathetica, comes in three volumes, I, II and III. The volumes are to be arranged on a shelf. In how many ways can they be arranged? <u>List all</u> of these arrangements.

Q9   A ball bearing games machine allows balls to drop down chutes. The game is arranged so that the chance of a ball bearing <u>going left</u> at a junction is 3/5. The balls are collected in the cups.

Ball bearing dropped in here

a) Lorna is to play the game. Which of the following four statements is <u>true</u>?

A) The probability of Lorna winning is 2/3

B) The probability of Lorna losing is 1 in 3

C) The probability of Lorna winning is just slightly greater than 0.5

D) The probability of Lorna losing is equal to the probability of Lorna winning.

b) If Lorna rolled <u>50 balls</u> down the games machine, how many would you expect to end up in one of the win cups?

Remember you can multiply fractions by hand or use your calculator — choose your weapon carefully...

WIN   LOSE   WIN

Q10   I have six contemporary Russian fiction books arranged on a shelf. I have forgotten which two I have already read. I want to take some books to read on holiday, but in the rush of packing, I just throw two into my case without looking at them. What is the probability that I have read <u>exactly one of them</u> before?

Q11   Three different letters are written down at random. Each of the letters is one of the <u>first nine letters</u> of the alphabet. What is the probability that:

a) all three letters are <u>different vowels</u>?

b) all three letters are <u>different consonants</u>?

c) at least one of the three letters is a <u>vowel</u>?

4.3 Questions on Compound Probability

The end is in sight...

Q12 A computer randomly chooses <u>Zero or One</u>, a magician cuts an ordinary pack of <u>playing cards</u> and a nurse throws an unbiased <u>six sided die</u>.

In the following possible sets of results, find the probability that <u>all three events</u> will happen.

a) A Zero, King of Hearts and a 6.
b) A One, any heart and any even number.
c) A One, any ace and an odd number.
d) A Zero, Ace of Clubs and a 1.

Q13 James is building a bedside cabinet.
The chance of him <u>hitting his thumb</u> with a hammer is 1/25.
The chance of James <u>dropping</u> the hammer at any time is 1/30.
The chance of the hammer <u>hitting someone</u> walking by is 1/12.
Find the probability that <u>all three</u> events will happen.

If the word "all" is used, you need to use the AND Rule.

Q14 Are these sentences describing <u>independent</u> events? Write <u>true</u> or <u>false</u> for each one.

a) It is raining today and picking a diamond from a pack of cards.
b) Picking an ace of clubs from a pack of cards and missing the bus to work.
c) Picking an ace from a pack of cards and keeping it, then picking another ace from the pack.
d) Choosing a red ball from a bag, then a black ball, without replacement.

Q15 The supermarket Aswayco sells damaged tins at a greatly reduced price. In its basket of damaged tins this week it had 16 tins of the same shape and size, but all without labels. The store manager assures me that 6 tins are mushroom soup, 8 are tinned prunes and 2 are strawberries in syrup.

a) If I buy the 16 tins what is the probability that I open a can of <u>strawberries</u>?
b) If on my first choice I do get a can of strawberries, when I next choose a can to open, what is the probability of it being a tin of <u>mushroom soup</u>?

Q16 A fair coin is tossed and a tetrahedron die is rolled, with numbers 1, 2, 3 and 4 on its faces.

a) Compile a table showing all possible combinations.
b) Find the probability of getting
  i) a head and a 2
  ii) a tail and a prime number
  iii) either a head or a 3 or both.

Q17 What is the probability of choosing 1 red ball, and 2 green balls on three choices from a bag containing 3 red and 3 green balls? Each ball is replaced after being chosen.

Top Tips

Phew, I bet you're glad you've finished that little lot. Don't forget all those rules, though — you'll need them in the Exam.

4.4 Questions on Tree Diagrams

Tree Diagrams are still Compound Probability, so you haven't really escaped. You'll be using what you know as well as new stuff — look at the example to see how it works.

A Likely Tree Diagram Question

I have a tub of sweets containing 4 lemon sherbets and 3 toffees. I take two sweets out to eat. Using a tree diagram, find the probability of both sweets being toffees.

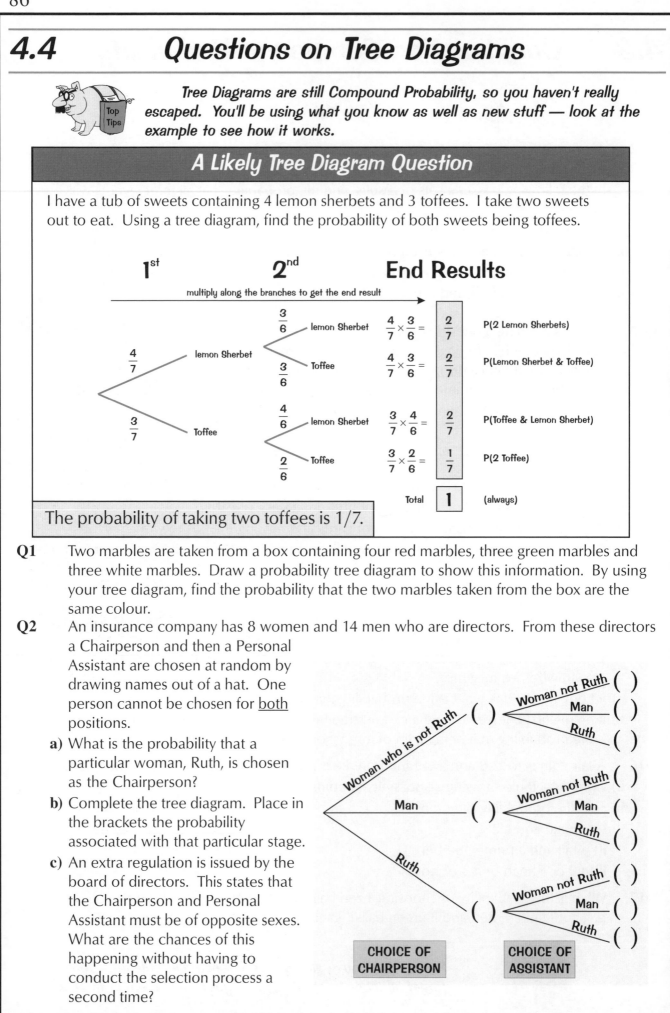

The probability of taking two toffees is 1/7.

Q1 Two marbles are taken from a box containing four red marbles, three green marbles and three white marbles. Draw a probability tree diagram to show this information. By using your tree diagram, find the probability that the two marbles taken from the box are the same colour.

Q2 An insurance company has 8 women and 14 men who are directors. From these directors a Chairperson and then a Personal Assistant are chosen at random by drawing names out of a hat. One person cannot be chosen for <u>both</u> positions.

a) What is the probability that a particular woman, Ruth, is chosen as the Chairperson?

b) Complete the tree diagram. Place in the brackets the probability associated with that particular stage.

c) An extra regulation is issued by the board of directors. This states that the Chairperson and Personal Assistant must be of opposite sexes. What are the chances of this happening without having to conduct the selection process a second time?

4.4   Questions on Tree Diagrams

If you have to draw a tree diagram yourself, just make sure you allow yourself plenty of room for all the possibilities.

Q3 A student needs to catch a <u>bus and a train</u> to get to university. The events and probabilities associated with each are shown on the tree diagram. For each event he can be <u>late</u> or <u>on time</u>. If he is <u>late</u> then he can catch the <u>next bus or train</u>. Work out the probability that:

a) the student <u>catches the bus</u> but <u>misses the train</u>

b) the student <u>misses the bus</u> but still manages to <u>catch the train</u>.

c) the student <u>misses</u> at least <u>one mode of transport</u> on his way to university.

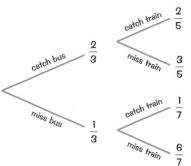

Q4 The probability that a football team will <u>win</u> a match is <u>50%</u>. By drawing a tree diagram, work out the chances of the team winning <u>four games in a row</u>.

Q5 The manager of the "Meat-Bar", a well-frequented burger franchise, has the sales figures in front of him for the last quarter. He sees in his sales column that they sold:

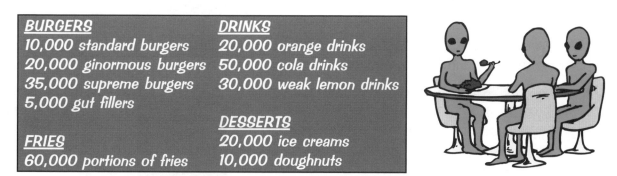

BURGERS	DRINKS
10,000 standard burgers	20,000 orange drinks
20,000 ginormous burgers	50,000 cola drinks
35,000 supreme burgers	30,000 weak lemon drinks
5,000 gut fillers	
	DESSERTS
FRIES	20,000 ice creams
60,000 portions of fries	10,000 doughnuts

a) The manager thinks that he can use the last quarter's sales figures to predict the probability of a customer buying a "<u>gut filler burger and a weak lemon drink, followed by a doughnut</u>". <u>How</u> do you think he does this? Write down your estimated probabilities in their <u>lowest terms</u>.

Ignoring the sales of fries, and by drawing a tree diagram or otherwise:

b) Discover the "meal" (<u>burger, drink and dessert</u>) that is <u>most likely</u> to be ordered, based on last quarter's figures.

c) What is the <u>probability</u> of that meal being sold?

d) How could the answer to **c)** help the manager operate the restaurant more

It's dead easy to see what's going on in a tree diagram, so if it suggests doing one, do it.

Q6 Two pool players, Sarah and Tina, play <u>3 games of pool</u> in a match. Sarah is not as good as Tina. <u>Sarah's chance of winning</u> a game is <u>45%</u>.

a) Draw a <u>tree diagram</u> to show the possible results of the 3 games.

b) What are the chances that <u>Tina</u> will win <u>all 3</u> games?

c) As long as 1 player <u>wins 2 or more</u> games then they will win the actual <u>match</u>. What are the chances that <u>Sarah will beat Tina</u> over the <u>3 game match</u>?

4.5 Questions on Frequency Tables

Frequency Tables look quite tricky, so you'd better make sure you know how they work.

Frequency Tables contain three rows:

1) The 1st row (or column) gives us the Group Labels, eg weights of 50 kg, 55 kg, etc.
2) The 2nd row (or column) is the actual frequency data, eg 10 people weigh 50 kg, etc.
3) The 3rd row (or column) is just the other two multiplied together and is left for you to fill in.

Q1 120 male pupils were weighed to the nearest kg. Calculate:

a) the median weight

b) the modal weight

c) the mean weight, by first completing the table.

Mass (kg)	Frequency	Mass x Freq.
61	22	
62	44	
63	35	
64	19	

Q2 100 female pupils were weighed to the nearest kg. Calculate:

a) the median weight

b) the mode

c) the mean by completing the table

Mass	49	50	51	52
Frequency	20	35	25	20

Q3 The pages of my text book are <u>numbered</u> from <u>1 to 300</u>. Complete the table showing the frequencies of pages whose numbers have <u>1, 2 and 3 digits</u>.

a) State <u>directly</u> the mode.

b) Find the median

No. of digits	1	2	3
Frequency			

c) Find the mean. Does it <u>make sense</u> to have this value? Why / why not?

Q4 The Samaritans log all calls to their helpline. The number of <u>calls per day</u> received by their helpline over a given <u>year</u> are shown below. Find the median and mode.

No. of calls	10	11	12	13	14	15	16 and over
No. of days	137	104	56	31	18	13	6

Q5 20 pupils are asked to estimate the length, to the nearest cm, of their teacher's table. Put the estimates in the <u>frequency table</u> below:

148 142 140 138 136 136 132 128 126 128
146 144 138 140 138 134 138 128 124 124

Estimate	124	126	128	132	134	136	138	140	142	144	146	148
Frequency												

a) Find the mode. **b)** Find the median. **c)** State the <u>range</u>.

4.5 Questions on Frequency Tables

Q6 Using the computerised till in a shoe shop, the manager can predict what stock to order from the previous week's sales. Below is the tabularised print out for <u>last week</u> for <u>men's shoes</u>.

Shoe size	5	6	7	8	9	10	11
frequency	9	28	56	70	56	28	9

a) The mean, mode and median for this data can be compared. For each of the following statements decide whether it <u>could be true</u> or is <u>definitely false</u>?

i) The <u>mode</u> for this data is <u>70</u>.

ii) The <u>mean</u> is <u>greater than</u> the <u>median</u> for this distribution.

iii) The mean, median and mode are <u>all equal</u> in this distribution.

b) What <u>percentage</u> of customers bought shoes of the <u>mean size</u> from last weeks sales data?

i) 30%   **ii)** 70%   **iii)** 0.273% or   **iv)** 27.3% ?

Q7 'White Ridge Back' sows can give birth to a mumber of piglets between 5 and 10 inclusive.

From the table:
a) state the mode
b) state the median
c) find the mean.

Number of piglets born	5	6	7	8	9	10
frequency	3	4	5	4	7	2

If a farmer wishes to promote the 'White Ridge Back' sow as the <u>most prolific breeder</u>, then which of the three 'averages' would he <u>not include</u> in his advert in 'Bacon & Ham' weekly?

Q8 Blackshire County Libraries store data on borrowers who they lend books to. The figures in the table show books

Number of books lent to a person over six months	<10	11	12	13	14	15	16	17
Frequency	20	32	38	40	70	28	14	6

lent over a six month period. Find the <u>mean number of books</u> lent <u>per person</u> for the six month period. Give an approximate, <u>sensible</u> value for this.

Q9 The <u>total</u> weight of 15 rugby players is 1350 kg.
The <u>total</u> weight of 9 ballet dancers is 360 kg.
What is the <u>mean</u> weight of the <u>group</u> of 24 people when put together?

Q10 A survey of the number of <u>occupants</u> in cars arriving at Blugdon High, shows that the mean number of occupants is 2.
Unfortunately whilst carrying out the survey a raindrop obliterated the number of cars with <u>3</u>

Number of occupants	0	1	2	3	4
Number of cars	0	27	15		0

occupants. Find out how many cars had <u>exactly 3 occupants</u> by using the legible data.

4.6 Questions on Grouped Frequency Tables

As a rule these are trickier than standard frequency tables — you'll certainly have to tread carefully here. Have a good look at the box below and make sure you remember it.

Class Boundaries and Mid-Interval Values

1) The CLASS BOUNDARIES are the precise values where you go from one group to the next.
2) The MID-INTERVAL VALUES are just what they sound like — the middle of the group.

shoe size	1 - 2	3 - 4	5 - 6	7 - 8
frequency	15	10	3	1

The Mid-Interval Values are 1.5, 3.5, 5.5, etc.
The Class Boundaries are 2.5, 4.5, 6.5, etc.

Q1 In a survey of test results in a French class at Blugdon High, these grades were achieved by the 23 pupils.

Identify:
a) the Class Boundaries between the groups
b) the Mid-Interval Values for each of the groups.

(grade) score	(E) 31-40	(D) 41-50	(C) 51-60	(B) 61-70
frequency	4	7	8	4

$$\text{Mean} = \frac{\text{Overall Total (Frequency} \times \text{Mid-Interval Value)}}{\text{Frequency Total}}$$

Q2 This table shows times for each team of swimmers, the Dolphins and the Sharks. Complete the table then use the mid-interval technique to estimate the mean time for each team.

Dolphins			Sharks		
Time interval (seconds)	Frequency	Mid-interval value	Time interval (seconds)	Frequency	Mid-interval value
14-19	3	16.5	14-19	6	16.5
20-25	7	22.5	20-25	15	22.5
26-31	15		26-31	33	
32-37	32		32-37	59	
38-43	45		38-43	20	
44-49	30		44-49	8	
50-55	5		50-55	2	

Q3 Complete the table below by filling in the cumulative frequency.

Sponsored Walk Donations	1p - 10p	11p - 20p	21p - 30p	31p - 40p	41p - 50p
Frequency	10	13	16	15	12
Cumulative Frequency	10	23			

Cumulative frequency just means a running total of the frequency data.

4.6 Questions on Grouped Frequency Tables

Ah, curves, that's more like it. From cumulative frequency curves you can find three lovely things with three lovely names. Look at this box and make sure you know what to do.

From the Cumulative Frequency Curve you can get 3 vital statistics:

1) <u>MEDIAN</u>
2) <u>LOWER / UPPER QUARTILES</u>
3) <u>INTERQUARTILE RANGE</u>

From the graph:
MEDIAN = 40 kg
LOWER QUARTILE = 30 kg
UPPER QUARTILE = 60 kg
INTER-QUARTILE RANGE = 60 kg–30 kg
= 30 kg

Total Cumulative Frequency = 160

¾ of the way up
½ the way up
¼ the way up

lower quartile   median   upper quartile

(Cumulative Frequency vs weight in Kg graph)

Q4 This table shows the number of bowlers, out of a total of 80, who took the wickets in cricket matches over the course of a season.

a) Draw a cumulative frequency diagram from this data.

No. of Wickets	1 - 10	11 - 20	21 - 30	31 - 40	41 - 50	51 - 60	61 - 70	71 - 80	81 - 90	91 - 100
No. of Bowlers	2	3	5	7	19	16	14	10	3	1
Cumulative Freq.										

b) Use it to estimate the median.

c) What is the interquartile range of the data?

Q5 The lengths of 25 snakes are measured to the nearest cm, and then grouped in a frequency table. Which of the following sentences may be true and which have to be false?

a) The median length is 161cm.

b) The range is 20 cm.

c) The modal class has 7 snakes.

d) The median length is 158cm.

Length	151 - 155	156 - 160	161 -165	166 - 170	171 - 175	Total
frequency	4	8	7	5	1	25

Q6 This table shows the frequency distribution for 70 candidates taking a Christmas Mock Exam.
Draw a cumulative frequency curve and use it to estimate:

a) the median

b) the Upper and Lower quartiles

c) the Interquartile Range.

Class interval	Frequency	Cumulative Frequency
45-49	1	
50-54	0	
55-59	3	
60-64	6	
65-69	11	
70-74	18	
75-79	16	
80-84	9	
85-89	5	
90-94	1	
95-99	0	

I know that "interquartile range" sounds a bit of a ridiculous name, but it's actually not a bad description — it's the difference between the quartiles. Remember to take your reading from the bottom scale — take it from anywhere else and you've blown it.

4.7 *Questions on Scatter Graphs*

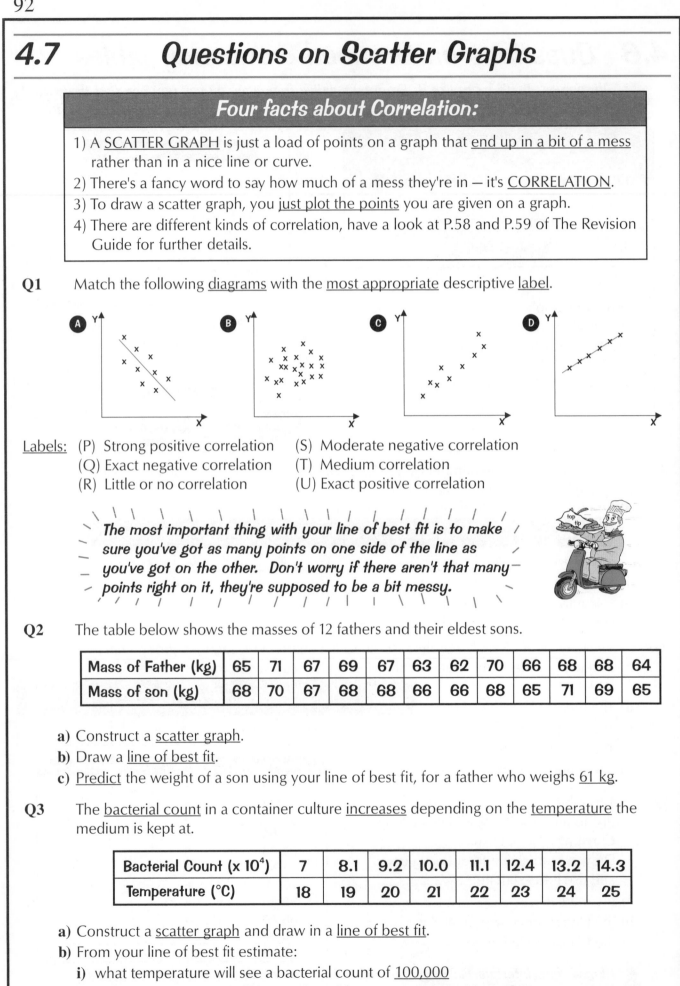

Four facts about Correlation:

1) A SCATTER GRAPH is just a load of points on a graph that end up in a bit of a mess rather than in a nice line or curve.

2) There's a fancy word to say how much of a mess they're in — it's CORRELATION.

3) To draw a scatter graph, you just plot the points you are given on a graph.

4) There are different kinds of correlation, have a look at P.58 and P.59 of The Revision Guide for further details.

Q1 Match the following diagrams with the most appropriate descriptive label.

Labels: (P) Strong positive correlation (S) Moderate negative correlation
(Q) Exact negative correlation (T) Medium correlation
(R) Little or no correlation (U) Exact positive correlation

The most important thing with your line of best fit is to make sure you've got as many points on one side of the line as you've got on the other. Don't worry if there aren't that many points right on it, they're supposed to be a bit messy.

Q2 The table below shows the masses of 12 fathers and their eldest sons.

Mass of Father (kg)	65	71	67	69	67	63	62	70	66	68	68	64
Mass of son (kg)	68	70	67	68	68	66	66	68	65	71	69	65

a) Construct a scatter graph.

b) Draw a line of best fit.

c) Predict the weight of a son using your line of best fit, for a father who weighs 61 kg.

Q3 The bacterial count in a container culture increases depending on the temperature the medium is kept at.

Bacterial Count (x 10^4)	7	8.1	9.2	10.0	11.1	12.4	13.2	14.3
Temperature (°C)	18	19	20	21	22	23	24	25

a) Construct a scatter graph and draw in a line of best fit.

b) From your line of best fit estimate:

  i) what temperature will see a bacterial count of 100,000

  ii) what bacterial count will be predicted for a temperature of 23.5°C?

4.8 Questions on Bar Charts

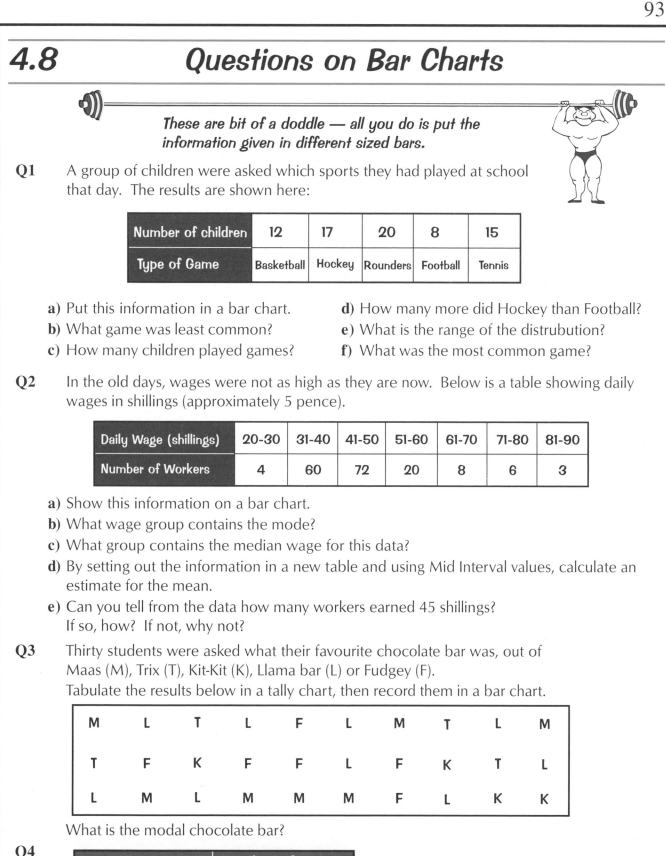

These are bit of a doddle — all you do is put the information given in different sized bars.

Q1 A group of children were asked which sports they had played at school that day. The results are shown here:

Number of children	12	17	20	8	15
Type of Game	Basketball	Hockey	Rounders	Football	Tennis

a) Put this information in a bar chart.
b) What game was least common?
c) How many children played games?
d) How many more did Hockey than Football?
e) What is the range of the distrubution?
f) What was the most common game?

Q2 In the old days, wages were not as high as they are now. Below is a table showing daily wages in shillings (approximately 5 pence).

Daily Wage (shillings)	20-30	31-40	41-50	51-60	61-70	71-80	81-90
Number of Workers	4	60	72	20	8	6	3

a) Show this information on a bar chart.
b) What wage group contains the mode?
c) What group contains the median wage for this data?
d) By setting out the information in a new table and using Mid Interval values, calculate an estimate for the mean.
e) Can you tell from the data how many workers earned 45 shillings? If so, how? If not, why not?

Q3 Thirty students were asked what their favourite chocolate bar was, out of Maas (M), Trix (T), Kit-Kit (K), Llama bar (L) or Fudgey (F).
Tabulate the results below in a tally chart, then record them in a bar chart.

M	L	T	L	F	L	M	T	L	M
T	F	K	F	F	L	F	K	T	L
L	M	L	M	M	M	F	L	K	K

What is the modal chocolate bar?

Q4

Number of Heads	Number of Tosses (frequency)
0	5
1	11
2	17
3	32
4	20
5	9
6	6
Total	

The results of tossing six coins 100 times were recorded by saying how many heads were showing, after the coins had landed. Represent this information in a bar chart and state or calculate the mean, range, mode and median. With reference to any or all of this information are the coins unbiased?

4.9   *Questions on Pie Charts*

Everyone loves a pie chart. Oh, no, sorry, that's pies.

When constructing a pie chart, follow the three steps:

1) Add up the numbers in each sector to get the <u>TOTAL</u>.
2) Divide 360° by the <u>TOTAL</u> to get the <u>MULIPLIER</u>.
3) Multiply <u>EVERY</u> number by the <u>MULTIPLIER</u> to get the <u>ANGLE</u> of each <u>SEGMENT</u>.

Q1   <u>Construct a pie chart</u>, using the template on the right, to show the following data:

Type of washing powder	Households on one estate using it
Swash	22
Sudso	17
Bubblefoam	18
Cleanyo	21
Wundersuds	12

Q2   A computerised attendance package is operated at a chicken plucking factory, to monitor <u>absence</u> and <u>lateness</u>. The list of absence or lateness is printed below for a particular week in January.

CHICKEN POX 4%   COLD 39%
BROKEN FINGERS 5%   OVERSLEPT 20%
DOCTORS APPOINTMENT 9%   FLU 23%

a) If these figures represent <u>200</u> absences or latenesses at the factory, how many people <u>overslept</u>?

b) Show this data on a <u>pie chart</u>, using the template on the left.

Q3   In the year 1998/99, 380,000 students studied IT in Scotland. The <u>distribution</u> of students for the <u>whole of Britain</u> is shown in the pie chart.
Use a <u>protractor</u> on the diagram to find the number of students studying IT in each of the <u>other countries</u> (rounded to the nearest 10,000).

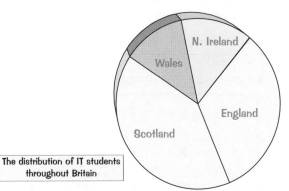

The distribution of IT students throughout Britain

Q4   The pie chart shows the results of a survey of forty 11 year olds when asked what their <u>favourite vegetable</u> is with Sunday lunch. Which one of the following may be <u>deduced</u> from the information in the <u>pie chart</u>?

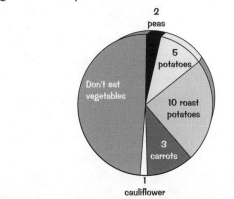

a) Potatoes are the <u>least popular</u> vegetable.
b) 3/4 of the children <u>like potatoes</u> of some type.
c) 1/10 of the children like <u>carrots or cauliflower</u>.
d) 11/40 of the children asked what their favourite vegetable is, replied "<u>Don't eat vegetables</u>."

4.9 Questions on Pie Charts

The maths in these long wordy questions is usually fairly easy, but you can still get caught out. For each bit you need to be sure you're using the right piece of information. Read the question properly — you don't get any marks for answering the wrong thing.

Q5 A <u>chocolate cake</u> is to be made up to a recipe containing 1/8 <u>cocoa</u>, 1/3 <u>butter</u>, 1/4 <u>flour</u>, 1/6 <u>sugar</u> and 1/8 <u>melted chocolate</u>. The cake is to weigh <u>270</u> grammes.

  a) What <u>percentage</u> of the weight of the cake is <u>flour</u>?

  b) Which ingredient has the <u>largest weight</u>?

  c) What <u>percentage</u> of the weight of the whole cake is the <u>sugar</u> and the <u>cocoa</u> (to the nearest whole number)

  d) If a pie chart were to be drawn representing the information, how many <u>degrees</u> would represent the <u>melted chocolate</u>?

  e) If a 'special order' cake was made to the same recipe, weighing 800 g, what <u>fraction</u> of it would be <u>butter</u>?

  f) If this 'special order' cake was sliced into <u>12 equal sized pieces</u>:

    i) How much would <u>each piece</u> weigh? (to the nearest gramme)

    ii) How many <u>degrees</u> would each piece measure at the centre?

Q6 Mr Smith decides to sell his car and buy a <u>motorbike</u>. The pie chart illustrates his estimates for annual running costs.

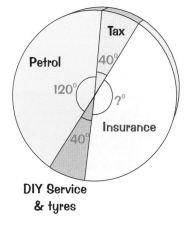

  a) What is the <u>missing angle</u>?

  b) If motorbike road tax is £50, calculate Mr Smith's estimates for:

    i) DIY, service and tyres

    ii) Insurance

    iii) Petrol

    iv) Total annual running costs

  c) If <u>all</u> the costs were increased by <u>5%</u> due to inflation, what angle should the <u>insurance</u> be?

Q7 Mr and Mrs Tight think they have the family <u>budget</u> under control. Mr and Mrs Spendthrift try to argue with Mr and Mrs Tight that they too can control their spending.
They produce <u>two pie charts</u> to represent their spending habits. Give <u>2 reasons</u> why these pie charts are <u>unhelpful</u>.

Q8 Year Nine Maths watch an awful lot of '<u>soaps</u>' on TV. Here is their tally chart. Represent this raw data by means of a <u>bar chart</u> and a <u>pie chart</u>.

CORNY ST.	FAR & AWAY	DEADENDERS
‖‖ |||	‖‖ ‖‖ ||	‖‖ ‖‖

4.10 Questions on Graphs and Charts

It seems we're finishing with a compilation of "The Best Statistics Questions in the World...Ever" It'll never make the charts.

Q1 Draw a typical <u>scatter graph</u> that you think would be associated with each of the pair of variables below. Say in each case what type of correlation you are intending to show, and label the axes with the variable.
a) Ice cream sales and temperature.
b) Umbrellas sold and rainfall.
c) Caravan prices and age of caravans.
d) Number of motorcyclists on the road and the number of PC's sold.

Q2 Shown below are tyre sales figures collected over a 3 month period.

Tombo: 4500	Multiroyal: 1000
Polnud: 2250	Bechstein: 3000

Represent these sales figures by drawing:
a) A <u>pictogram</u>
b) A <u>bar-line</u> graph.

Q3 The table contains the mean monthly temperatures for Leaningdale, a hamlet in Cumbria, and the rainfall/snowfall for each month.

Month	J	F	M	A	M	J	J	A	S	O	N	D
Temperature (°C)	2	1	3	6	8	12	16	18	19	11	9	2
Rainfall/snowfall (mm)	30	34	20	24	15	10	13	15	11	11	26	32

a) Draw a <u>scatter diagram</u> to see if a correlation exists between <u>temperature</u> and <u>rainfall/snowfall</u> in the hamlet of Leaningdale.
b) Put on your diagram a <u>line of best fit</u>. Give a sentence describing the type of correlation you see.

Q4 The <u>grading for skiers</u> to be awarded certificates is as follows:
B - beginner, I - intermediate, G - good, VG - very good, R - racer.

To clarify the situation for a school group travelling to the Alps, the ski company would like a <u>table and a chart</u> to show the information as clearly as possible.

B	I	B	I	R	VG	I
I	R	G	VG	VG	B	B
I	I	B	B	R	B	G
I	B	G	G	I	I	I

a) What sort of <u>table</u> can you suggest? Draw it accurately.
b) What sort of <u>chart</u> can you show? Draw it accurately.
c) What is the <u>most common</u> type of skier?

There are lies, damn lies and statistics...

4.10   Questions on Graphs and Charts

If you're not sure what to do for any of these questions, have a look back over the ones you've already done. There's nothing actually new on any of these pages.

Q5   Stagerunner, an independent <u>bus company</u>, runs a coach from London to Bristol each day except Sunday. Shown below are the times for the journey each day, recorded over a two week period. Show this information in a <u>tally chart</u> and determine the <u>modal group</u> for the journey times.

3hr 44 min	3 hr 47 min
2 hr 46 min	2 hr 32 min
2 hr 19 min	2 hr 36 min
3 hr 25 min	3 hr 29 min
3 hr 45 min	2 hr 27 min
4 hr 5 min	3 hr 20 min

Times	Tally
2-2½ hrs	
2½-3 hrs	
3-3½ hrs	
3½-4 hrs	
4-4½ hrs	

Q6   Having seen the <u>line graph</u> opposite, a Quality Control Manager said "Admittedly we do have some complaints about our products, but from July complaints have tailed off, so our products must be of a better quality."
From the graph, do you think this statement is <u>correct</u>? Why/Why not?

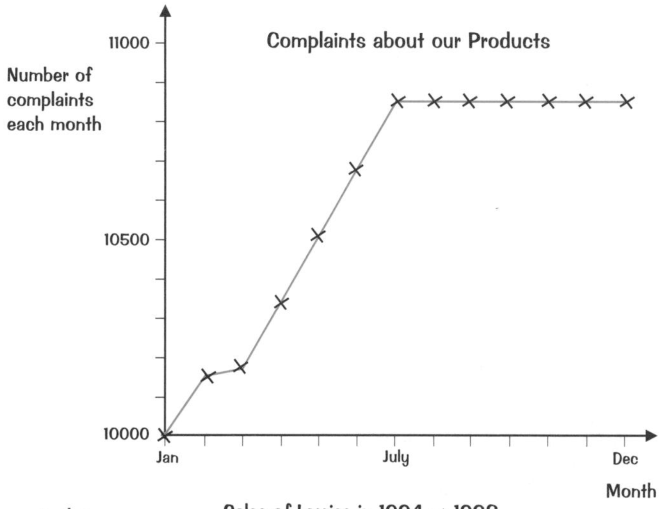

Complaints about our Products

Number of complaints each month

Q7   Answer the following questions about this <u>pictogram</u>.
a) How many lorries were sold in <u>1998</u>?
b) In which year were the <u>most</u> lorries sold?
c) How many lorries were sold in <u>1997</u>?
d) Estimate how many lorries were sold over <u>all 5 years</u>.

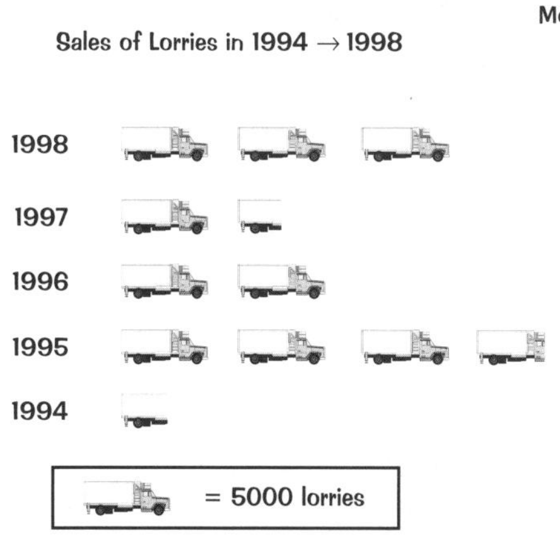

Sales of Lorries in 1994 → 1998

= 5000 lorries

Q8   The statement "<u>cheese sales</u> are <u>increasing year on year</u>, at a <u>phenomenal rate</u>" was recently released by a cheese manufacturer, along with the graph shown on the left.
Which <u>features</u> would you <u>change</u> about this graph, so that it shows <u>more obviously</u> the <u>huge increase</u> in cheese sales over the past few years?

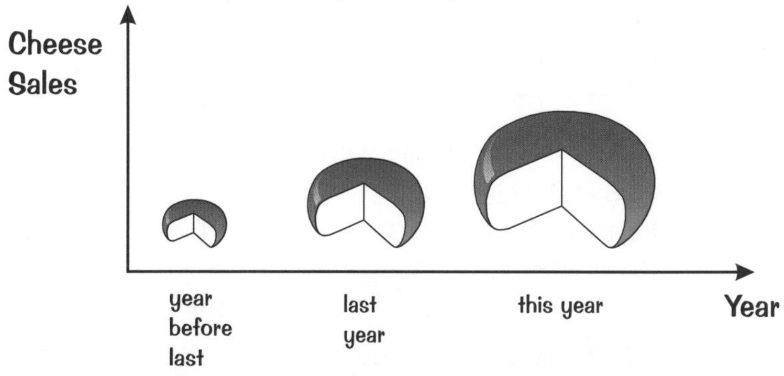

Cheese Sales

year before last   last year   this year   **Year**

5.1 Questions on Gradients of Lines

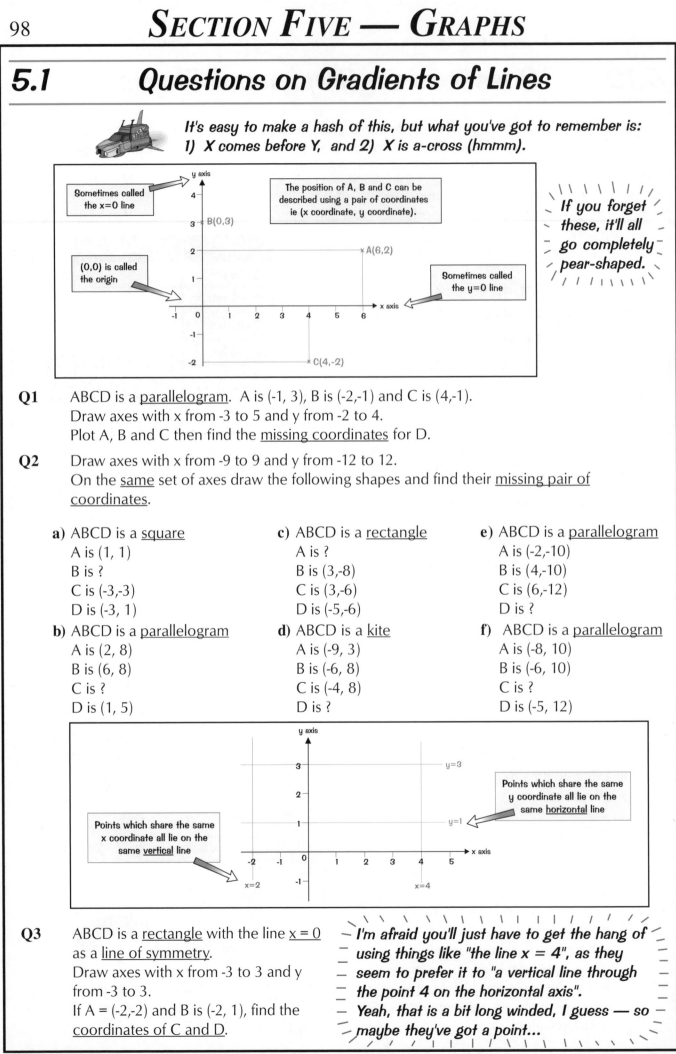

It's easy to make a hash of this, but what you've got to remember is:
1) *X* comes before *Y*, and 2) *X* is a-cross (hmmm).

Sometimes called the x=0 line

The position of A, B and C can be described using a pair of coordinates ie (x coordinate, y coordinate).

If you forget these, it'll all go completely pear-shaped.

(0,0) is called the origin

Sometimes called the y=0 line

Q1 ABCD is a <u>parallelogram</u>. A is (-1, 3), B is (-2,-1) and C is (4,-1).
Draw axes with x from -3 to 5 and y from -2 to 4.
Plot A, B and C then find the <u>missing coordinates</u> for D.

Q2 Draw axes with x from -9 to 9 and y from -12 to 12.
On the <u>same</u> set of axes draw the following shapes and find their <u>missing pair of coordinates</u>.

a) ABCD is a <u>square</u>
A is (1, 1)
B is ?
C is (-3,-3)
D is (-3, 1)

b) ABCD is a <u>parallelogram</u>
A is (2, 8)
B is (6, 8)
C is ?
D is (1, 5)

c) ABCD is a <u>rectangle</u>
A is ?
B is (3,-8)
C is (3,-6)
D is (-5,-6)

d) ABCD is a <u>kite</u>
A is (-9, 3)
B is (-6, 8)
C is (-4, 8)
D is ?

e) ABCD is a <u>parallelogram</u>
A is (-2,-10)
B is (4,-10)
C is (6,-12)
D is ?

f) ABCD is a <u>parallelogram</u>
A is (-8, 10)
B is (-6, 10)
C is ?
D is (-5, 12)

Points which share the same x coordinate all lie on the same <u>vertical</u> line

Points which share the same y coordinate all lie on the same <u>horizontal</u> line

Q3 ABCD is a <u>rectangle</u> with the line <u>x = 0</u> as a <u>line of symmetry</u>.
Draw axes with x from -3 to 3 and y from -3 to 3.
If A = (-2,-2) and B is (-2, 1), find the <u>coordinates of C and D</u>.

I'm afraid you'll just have to get the hang of using things like "the line x = 4", as they seem to prefer it to "a vertical line through the point 4 on the horizontal axis". Yeah, that is a bit long winded, I guess — so maybe they've got a point...

5.1   *Questions on Gradients of Lines*

Oooh — just one more, then we're on to gradients...I can't wait.

Q4   Draw a set of axes with x from –5 to 5 and y from –5 to 5.
Using these <u>axes</u> and the two <u>tables of values</u>, draw and label the <u>two lines</u>.

a)

x	-4	-1	0	2
y	-4	-1	0	2

b)

x	-4	-2	0	3	5
y	4	2	0	-3	-5

Now you've figured out coordinates, have a look at this.

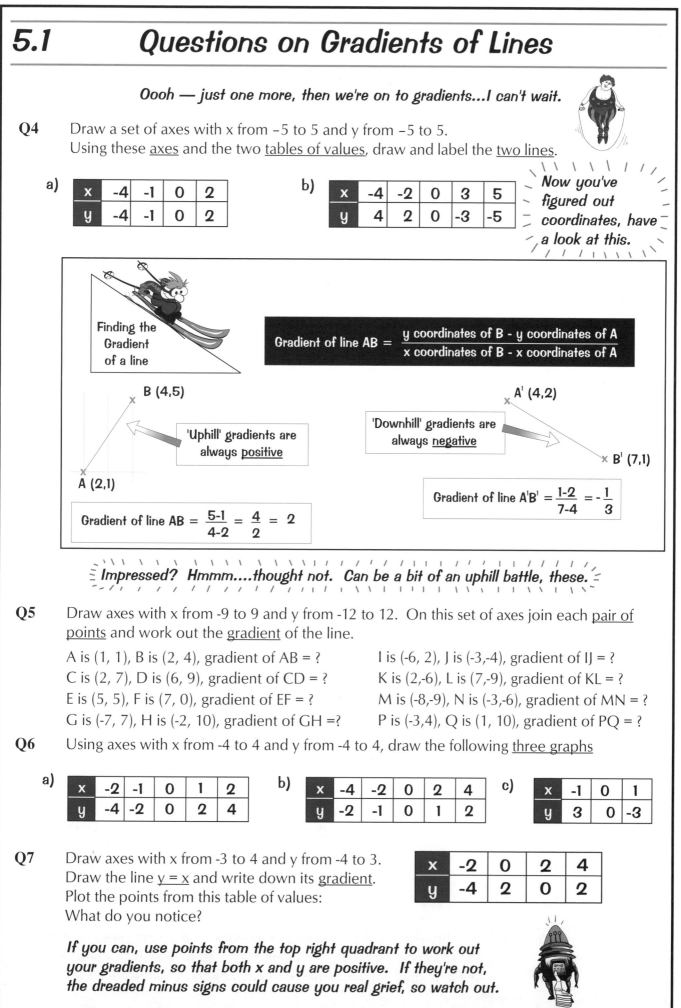

Finding the Gradient of a line

$$\text{Gradient of line AB} = \frac{\text{y coordinates of B - y coordinates of A}}{\text{x coordinates of B - x coordinates of A}}$$

B (4,5)

'Uphill' gradients are always <u>positive</u>

'Downhill' gradients are always <u>negative</u>

A' (4,2)

B' (7,1)

A (2,1)

$$\text{Gradient of line AB} = \frac{5\text{-}1}{4\text{-}2} = \frac{4}{2} = 2$$

$$\text{Gradient of line A'B'} = \frac{1\text{-}2}{7\text{-}4} = -\frac{1}{3}$$

Impressed? Hmmm....thought not. Can be a bit of an uphill battle, these.

Q5   Draw axes with x from -9 to 9 and y from -12 to 12. On this set of axes join each <u>pair of points</u> and work out the <u>gradient</u> of the line.

A is (1, 1), B is (2, 4), gradient of AB = ?   I is (-6, 2), J is (-3,-4), gradient of IJ = ?
C is (2, 7), D is (6, 9), gradient of CD = ?   K is (2,-6), L is (7,-9), gradient of KL = ?
E is (5, 5), F is (7, 0), gradient of EF = ?   M is (-8,-9), N is (-3,-6), gradient of MN = ?
G is (-7, 7), H is (-2, 10), gradient of GH =?   P is (-3,4), Q is (1, 10), gradient of PQ = ?

Q6   Using axes with x from -4 to 4 and y from -4 to 4, draw the following <u>three graphs</u>

a)

x	-2	-1	0	1	2
y	-4	-2	0	2	4

b)

x	-4	-2	0	2	4
y	-2	-1	0	1	2

c)

x	-1	0	1
y	3	0	-3

Q7   Draw axes with x from -3 to 4 and y from -4 to 3.
Draw the line <u>y = x</u> and write down its <u>gradient</u>.
Plot the points from this table of values:
What do you notice?

x	-2	0	2	4
y	-4	2	0	2

If you can, use points from the top right quadrant to work out your gradients, so that both x and y are positive. If they're not, the dreaded minus signs could cause you real grief, so watch out.

5.2   Questions on Straight Line Graphs

The _very first thing_ you've got to do is work out a _table of values_.

Example: Draw the graph of y = 3x – 1 for values of x
between 0 and 4.

1) First complete a table of values:

x	0	1	2	3	4
y	-1	2	5	8	11

← decided by the question

← worked out using y = 3x - 1

2) Draw the axes.
3) Plot the points.
4) Label the line y = 3x – 1.
    (step 4 has been left for you to complete)

Once you know they're in a straight line, just get your ruler out and you're away.

Q1   **a)** Complete the table below, for y = x + 2.

x	0	1	2	3	4	5	6
y	2			5			

   b) Use your _table of values_ to draw the graph
       y = x + 2.
   c) Where does your graph cross the _Y-axis_?
   d) What is the _gradient_ of your graph?

Q2   **a)** Complete the table below for y = 2x + 1.

x	0	1	2	3	4	5	6
y	1				9		

   b) Use your table of values to draw the
       graph y = 2x + 1.

   c) Where does your graph cross the Y-axis?
   d) What is the _gradient_ of your graph?

The x-intercept sounds pretty fancy but all it means is the place where the line crosses the X-axis. (Same with the y-intercept.) Easy lemons.

Q3   **a)** Draw the graph of y = 5 – x, for values of x _between 0 and 6_.
   b) Where does the graph cross the _Y-axis_?
   c) What is the gradient of the graph?

These questions give you a bit more practice with your gradients as well. Thought you'd like that.

Q4   By _drawing the graph_ of y = 3x – 3, find where it crosses the Y-axis and the gradient.

Q5   Find the _y-intercept_ (where it crosses the Y-axis) and the _gradient_ of the graph y = ½x + 3.

Once you've got the hang of this bit, look at the next page. You'll
need to know both ways of doing these, so be warned — you can't
just pick your favourite method and stick to it. More's the pity.

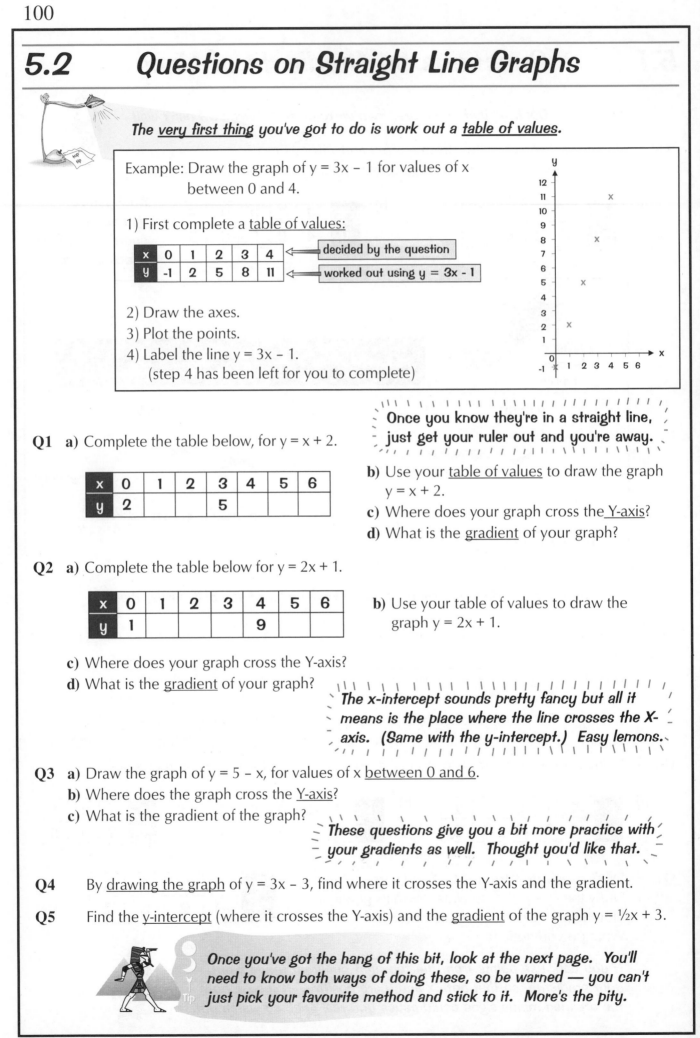

5.2 Questions on Straight Line Graphs

<u>Every</u> straight line graph can be written in the form:—

$$y = mx + c$$

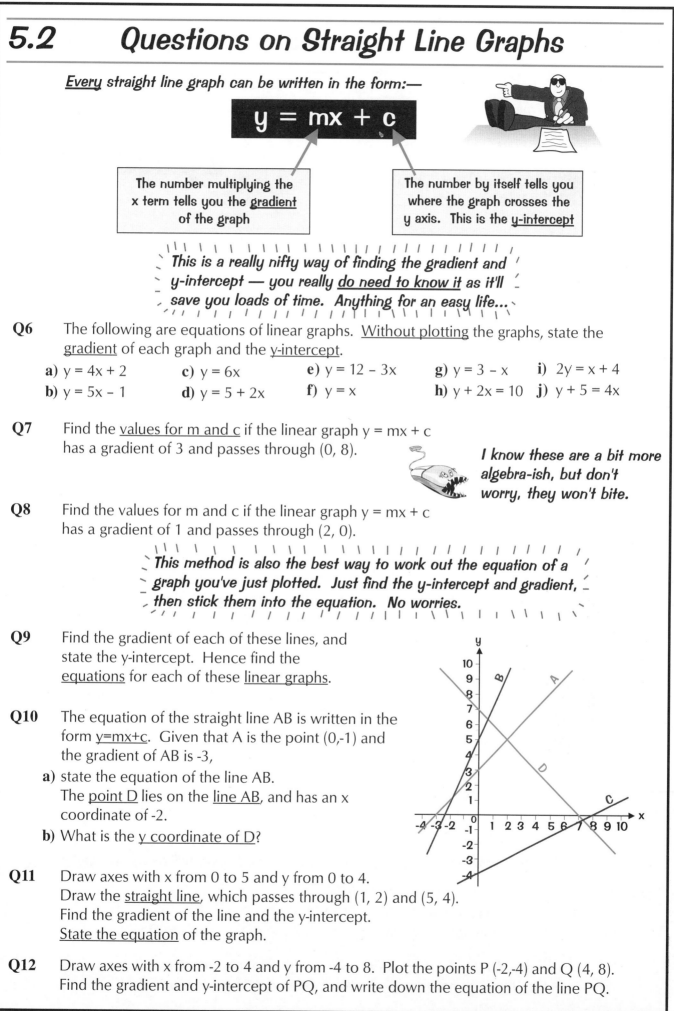

The number multiplying the x term tells you the <u>gradient</u> of the graph

The number by itself tells you where the graph crosses the y axis. This is the <u>y-intercept</u>

This is a really nifty way of finding the gradient and y-intercept — you really <u>do need to know it</u> as it'll save you loads of time. Anything for an easy life...

Q6 The following are equations of linear graphs. <u>Without plotting</u> the graphs, state the <u>gradient</u> of each graph and the <u>y-intercept</u>.

a) $y = 4x + 2$ **c)** $y = 6x$ **e)** $y = 12 - 3x$ **g)** $y = 3 - x$ **i)** $2y = x + 4$

b) $y = 5x - 1$ **d)** $y = 5 + 2x$ **f)** $y = x$ **h)** $y + 2x = 10$ **j)** $y + 5 = 4x$

Q7 Find the <u>values for m and c</u> if the linear graph $y = mx + c$ has a gradient of 3 and passes through (0, 8).

I know these are a bit more algebra-ish, but don't worry, they won't bite.

Q8 Find the values for m and c if the linear graph $y = mx + c$ has a gradient of 1 and passes through (2, 0).

This method is also the best way to work out the equation of a graph you've just plotted. Just find the y-intercept and gradient, then stick them into the equation. No worries.

Q9 Find the gradient of each of these lines, and state the y-intercept. Hence find the <u>equations</u> for each of these <u>linear graphs</u>.

Q10 The equation of the straight line AB is written in the form <u>y=mx+c</u>. Given that A is the point (0,-1) and the gradient of AB is -3,

a) state the equation of the line AB.
The <u>point D</u> lies on the <u>line AB</u>, and has an x coordinate of -2.

b) What is the <u>y coordinate of D</u>?

Q11 Draw axes with x from 0 to 5 and y from 0 to 4.
Draw the <u>straight line</u>, which passes through (1, 2) and (5, 4).
Find the gradient of the line and the y-intercept.
<u>State the equation</u> of the graph.

Q12 Draw axes with x from -2 to 4 and y from -4 to 8. Plot the points P (-2,-4) and Q (4, 8).
Find the gradient and y-intercept of PQ, and write down the equation of the line PQ.

5.3 Questions on Quadratic Graphs

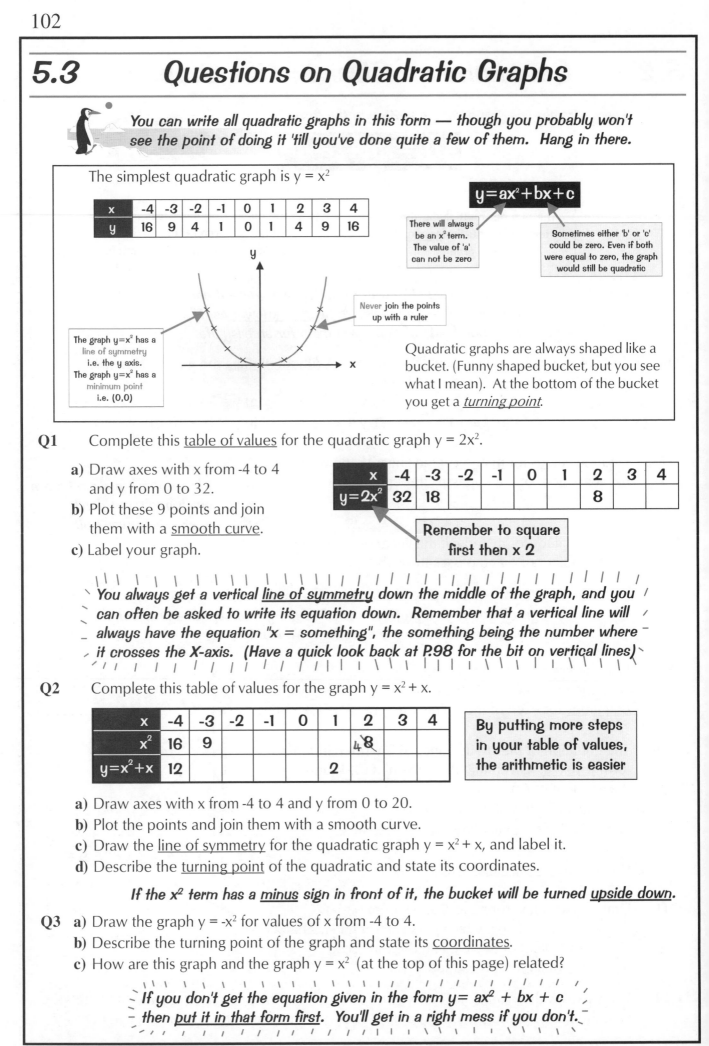

You can write all quadratic graphs in this form — though you probably won't see the point of doing it 'till you've done quite a few of them. Hang in there.

The simplest quadratic graph is $y = x^2$

x	-4	-3	-2	-1	0	1	2	3	4
y	16	9	4	1	0	1	4	9	16

$$y = ax^2 + bx + c$$

There will always be an x^2 term. The value of 'a' can not be zero

Sometimes either 'b' or 'c' could be zero. Even if both were equal to zero, the graph would still be quadratic

Never join the points up with a ruler

The graph $y = x^2$ has a line of symmetry i.e. the y axis.
The graph $y = x^2$ has a minimum point i.e. (0,0)

Quadratic graphs are always shaped like a bucket. (Funny shaped bucket, but you see what I mean). At the bottom of the bucket you get a *turning point*.

Q1 Complete this <u>table of values</u> for the quadratic graph $y = 2x^2$.

a) Draw axes with x from -4 to 4 and y from 0 to 32.

b) Plot these 9 points and join them with a <u>smooth curve</u>.

c) Label your graph.

x	-4	-3	-2	-1	0	1	2	3	4
$y = 2x^2$	32	18					8		

Remember to square first then x 2

You always get a vertical <u>line of symmetry</u> down the middle of the graph, and you can often be asked to write its equation down. Remember that a vertical line will always have the equation "x = something", the something being the number where it crosses the X-axis. (Have a quick look back at P.98 for the bit on vertical lines)

Q2 Complete this table of values for the graph $y = x^2 + x$.

x	-4	-3	-2	-1	0	1	2	3	4
x^2	16	9					4 8		
$y = x^2 + x$	12					2			

By putting more steps in your table of values, the arithmetic is easier

a) Draw axes with x from -4 to 4 and y from 0 to 20.

b) Plot the points and join them with a smooth curve.

c) Draw the <u>line of symmetry</u> for the quadratic graph $y = x^2 + x$, and label it.

d) Describe the <u>turning point</u> of the quadratic and state its coordinates.

If the x^2 term has a <u>minus</u> sign in front of it, the bucket will be turned <u>upside down</u>.

Q3 a) Draw the graph $y = -x^2$ for values of x from -4 to 4.

b) Describe the turning point of the graph and state its <u>coordinates</u>.

c) How are this graph and the graph $y = x^2$ (at the top of this page) related?

If you don't get the equation given in the form $y = ax^2 + bx + c$ then <u>put it in that form first</u>. You'll get in a right mess if you don't.

5.3   *Questions on Quadratic Graphs*

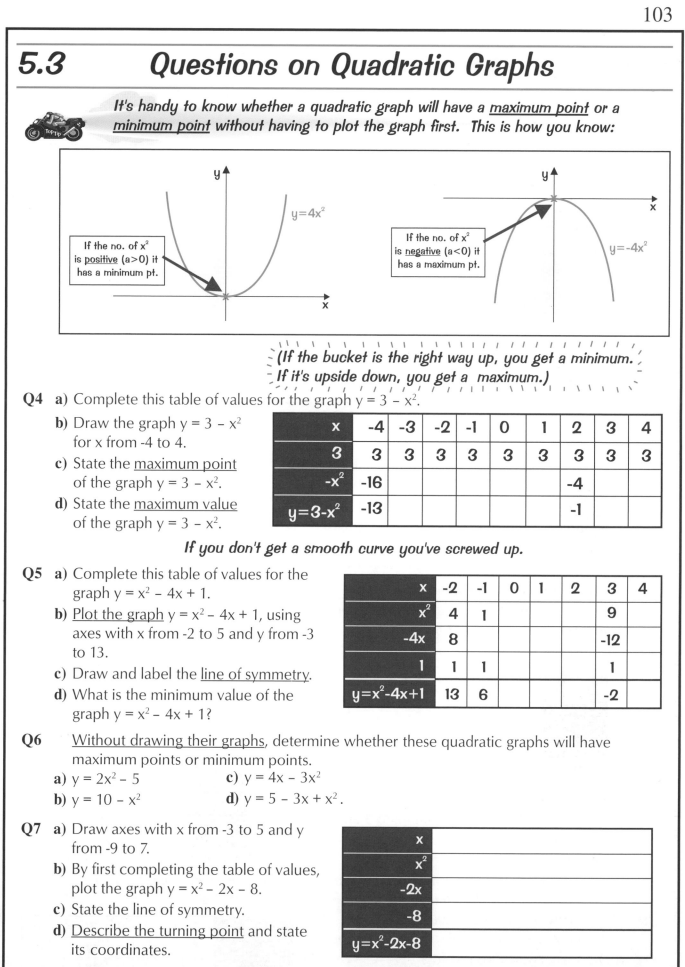

It's handy to know whether a quadratic graph will have a <u>maximum point</u> or a <u>minimum point</u> without having to plot the graph first. This is how you know:

If the no. of x^2 is <u>positive</u> (a>0) it has a minimum pt.

If the no. of x^2 is <u>negative</u> (a<0) it has a maximum pt.

$y=4x^2$

$y=-4x^2$

*(If the bucket is the right way up, you get a minimum.
If it's upside down, you get a maximum.)*

Q4 **a)** Complete this table of values for the graph $y = 3 - x^2$.

b) Draw the graph $y = 3 - x^2$ for x from -4 to 4.

c) State the <u>maximum point</u> of the graph $y = 3 - x^2$.

d) State the <u>maximum value</u> of the graph $y = 3 - x^2$.

x	-4	-3	-2	-1	0	1	2	3	4
3	3	3	3	3	3	3	3	3	3
$-x^2$	-16						-4		
$y=3-x^2$	-13						-1		

If you don't get a smooth curve you've screwed up.

Q5 **a)** Complete this table of values for the graph $y = x^2 - 4x + 1$.

b) <u>Plot the graph</u> $y = x^2 - 4x + 1$, using axes with x from -2 to 5 and y from -3 to 13.

c) Draw and label the <u>line of symmetry</u>.

d) What is the minimum value of the graph $y = x^2 - 4x + 1$?

x	-2	-1	0	1	2	3	4
x^2	4	1				9	
$-4x$	8					-12	
1	1	1				1	
$y=x^2-4x+1$	13	6				-2	

Q6 <u>Without drawing their graphs</u>, determine whether these quadratic graphs will have maximum points or minimum points.

a) $y = 2x^2 - 5$ **c)** $y = 4x - 3x^2$

b) $y = 10 - x^2$ **d)** $y = 5 - 3x + x^2$.

Q7 **a)** Draw axes with x from -3 to 5 and y from -9 to 7.

b) By first completing the table of values, plot the graph $y = x^2 - 2x - 8$.

c) State the line of symmetry.

d) <u>Describe the turning point</u> and state its coordinates.

x								
x^2								
$-2x$								
-8								
$y=x^2-2x-8$								

If any points look a bit strange, check you've got them right in the <u>table of values</u>. I know it's boring doing it all again, but it shouldn't be too hard if you've put all the steps in. And it'll mean you <u>don't get it wrong</u>. Which is always nice.

SECTION FIVE — GRAPHS

5.4   *Questions on Cubic Graphs*

The cubic graph now — it just gets worse, doesn't it.
It's got an extra term and it looks like this...

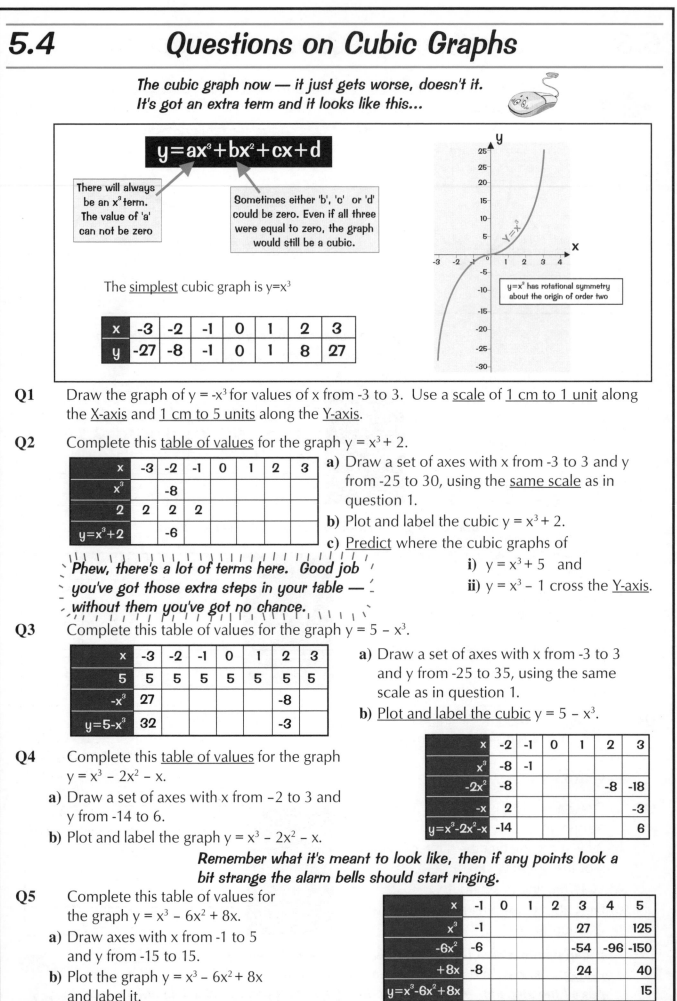

$$y=ax^3+bx^2+cx+d$$

There will always be an x^3 term. The value of 'a' can not be zero

Sometimes either 'b', 'c' or 'd' could be zero. Even if all three were equal to zero, the graph would still be a cubic.

The simplest cubic graph is $y=x^3$

x	-3	-2	-1	0	1	2	3
y	-27	-8	-1	0	1	8	27

$y=x^3$ has rotational symmetry about the origin of order two

Q1   Draw the graph of $y = -x^3$ for values of x from -3 to 3. Use a <u>scale</u> of <u>1 cm to 1 unit</u> along the <u>X-axis</u> and <u>1 cm to 5 units</u> along the <u>Y-axis</u>.

Q2   Complete this <u>table of values</u> for the graph $y = x^3 + 2$.

x	-3	-2	-1	0	1	2	3
x^3		-8					
2	2	2	2				
$y=x^3+2$		-6					

a) Draw a set of axes with x from -3 to 3 and y from -25 to 30, using the <u>same scale</u> as in question 1.

b) Plot and label the cubic $y = x^3 + 2$.

c) <u>Predict</u> where the cubic graphs of
    i) $y = x^3 + 5$ and
    ii) $y = x^3 - 1$ cross the <u>Y-axis</u>.

Phew, there's a lot of terms here. Good job you've got those extra steps in your table — without them you've got no chance.

Q3   Complete this table of values for the graph $y = 5 - x^3$.

x	-3	-2	-1	0	1	2	3
5	5	5	5	5	5	5	5
$-x^3$	27					-8	
$y=5-x^3$	32					-3	

a) Draw a set of axes with x from -3 to 3 and y from -25 to 35, using the same scale as in question 1.

b) <u>Plot and label the cubic</u> $y = 5 - x^3$.

Q4   Complete this <u>table of values</u> for the graph $y = x^3 - 2x^2 - x$.

a) Draw a set of axes with x from -2 to 3 and y from -14 to 6.

b) Plot and label the graph $y = x^3 - 2x^2 - x$.

x	-2	-1	0	1	2	3
x^3	-8	-1				
$-2x^2$	-8				-8	-18
$-x$	2					-3
$y=x^3-2x^2-x$	-14					6

Remember what it's meant to look like, then if any points look a bit strange the alarm bells should start ringing.

Q5   Complete this table of values for the graph $y = x^3 - 6x^2 + 8x$.

a) Draw axes with x from -1 to 5 and y from -15 to 15.

b) Plot the graph $y = x^3 - 6x^2 + 8x$ and label it.

x	-1	0	1	2	3	4	5
x^3	-1				27		125
$-6x^2$	-6				-54	-96	-150
$+8x$	-8				24		40
$y=x^3-6x^2+8x$							15

5.5   *Questions on Recognising Graphs*

Remember, you're going to need to be able to <u>sketch a graph</u> from <u>memory</u> — scary, huh. Don't worry — they don't expect you to remember them all (phew) but here are the ones you really need to know:

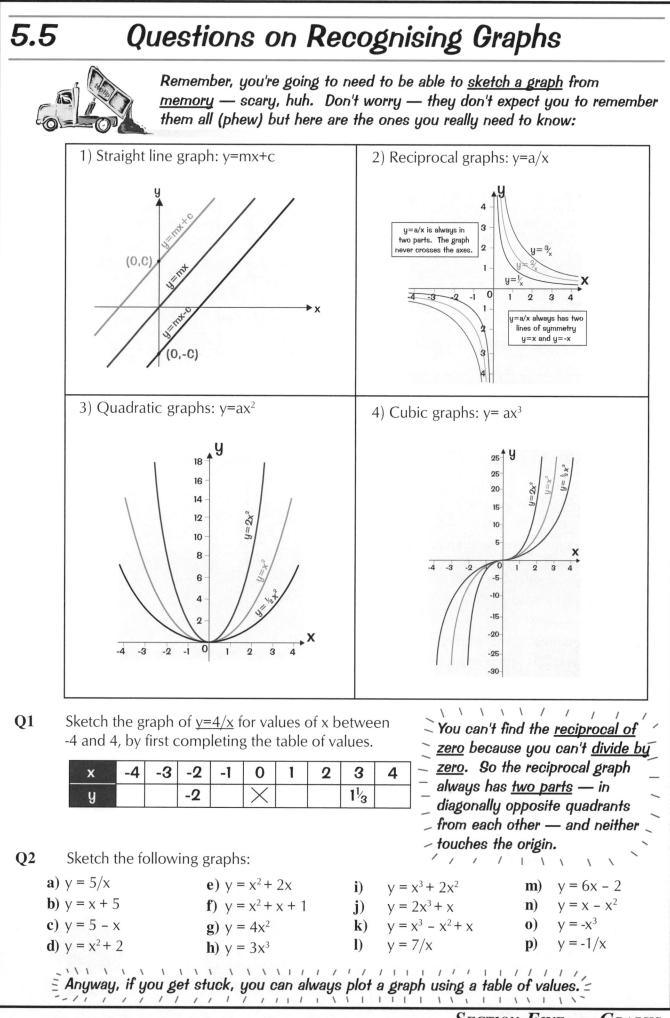

1) Straight line graph: y=mx+c

2) Reciprocal graphs: y=a/x

y=a/x is always in two parts. The graph never crosses the axes.

$y = {}^3/_x$

$y = {}^2/_x$

$y = {}^1/_x$

y=a/x always has two lines of symmetry y=x and y=-x

3) Quadratic graphs: $y = ax^2$

$y = 2x^2$

$y = x^2$

$y = \frac{1}{2}x^2$

4) Cubic graphs: $y = ax^3$

$y = 2x^3$

$y = x^3$

$y = \frac{1}{2}x^3$

Q1 Sketch the graph of <u>y=4/x</u> for values of x between -4 and 4, by first completing the table of values.

x	-4	-3	-2	-1	0	1	2	3	4
y			-2		✕			$1\frac{1}{3}$	

You can't find the <u>reciprocal of</u> <u>zero</u> because you can't <u>divide by</u> <u>zero</u>. So the reciprocal graph always has <u>two parts</u> — in diagonally opposite quadrants from each other — and neither touches the origin.

Q2 Sketch the following graphs:

a) y = 5/x   **e)** $y = x^2 + 2x$ **i)** $y = x^3 + 2x^2$ **m)** y = 6x – 2

b) y = x + 5   **f)** $y = x^2 + x + 1$ **j)** $y = 2x^3 + x$ **n)** $y = x – x^2$

c) y = 5 – x   **g)** $y = 4x^2$ **k)** $y = x^3 – x^2 + x$ **o)** $y = -x^3$

d) $y = x^2 + 2$ **h)** $y = 3x^3$ **l)** y = 7/x   **p)** y = -1/x

Anyway, if you get stuck, you can always plot a graph using a table of values.

5.6 Questions on Real Life Graphs

Conversion graphs let you swap from one unit to another, just by reading the graph — what fun.

Q1 Using the <u>conversion graph</u> convert the following to km, rounding your answers to the <u>nearest km</u>:

a) 5 miles   **c)** 11 miles

b) 20 miles   **d)** 23 miles.

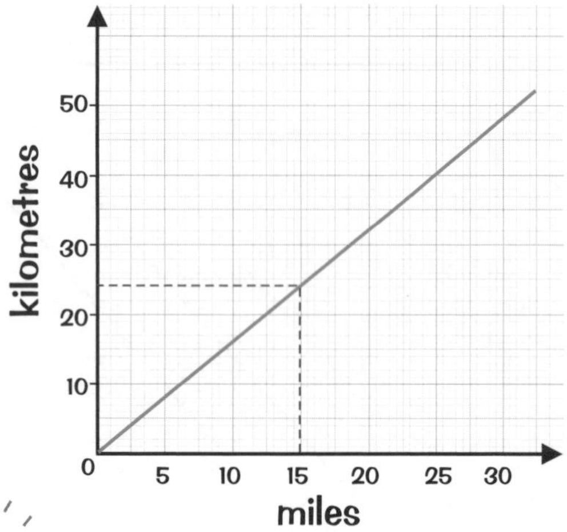

Q2 Change the following to <u>miles</u>, rounding your answers to the nearest mile:

a) 10 km   **c)** 27 km

b) 20 km   **d)** 35 km.

Q3 Find the <u>gradient</u> of the graph.

Careful — the axes have <u>different scales</u>. (One square is 5 miles, but 10 kilometres)

Q4 Using the conversion graph on the right change the following to <u>°C</u>:

a) 40°F   **c)** 75°F

b) 60°F   **d)** 120°F

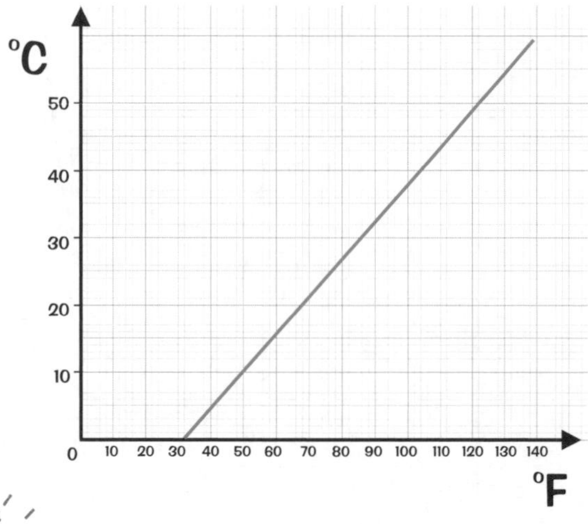

Q5 Using the conversion graph change the following to <u>°F</u>:

a) 10°C   **c)** 40°C

b) 28°C   **d)** 48°C

Q6 A person's normal body temperature is 98.4°F. What is this <u>approximately</u> in °C?

OK, this next question's a bit of a toughie, but at least there's some help on how to draw the graph.

Q7 To draw a conversion graph to change <u>£ into $</u>, you will need to:
-draw the £ axis horizontally and label it from 0 to 10 (1 cm for every pound).
-draw the $ axis vertically and label it from 0 to 16 (1 cm for every dollar).
-plot the point representing <u>£10 in dollars</u>, given that the <u>exchange rate</u> is 1.6 dollars to the pound, and join this to the origin with a straight line.

From your graph find:

a) how many dollars you would receive if you exchanged £7

b) how many pounds you would receive if you exchanged $6.
If the strength of the pound increased you would need to adjust this conversion graph.

c) Would the adjusted conversion graph's <u>gradient</u> be <u>greater or less</u> than the original graph's gradient?

For that last bit, remember that when the strength of the pound <u>increases</u>, you get <u>more dollars</u> for your pound.

5.6 Questions on Real Life Graphs

 Sometimes they'll only want the <u>shape</u> of a graph, so you can just <u>sketch</u> it. A sketch graph doesn't have any points plotted, but you still need to draw a pair of labelled axes (with a ruler, of course).

Q8 Show the general relationship between these quantities by <u>sketching</u> a graph for each case. Place the <u>first</u> quantity mentioned on the <u>Y-axis</u>.

a) The <u>level of water</u> in a rectangular tank when drained at a constant rate, <u>against time</u>.

b) The <u>volumes of cubes</u> with edges of different lengths.

c) The <u>amount</u> raised <u>per mile</u> on a sponsored walk.

d) The <u>area</u> of an <u>equilateral triangle</u> compared to the length of an edge.

When you're doing these questions, ask yourself these three main things:—

1) *is it a straight line or a curved one?*
2) *will the line be horizontal, vertical, uphill or downhill?*
3) *will it cross either of the axes and if it does, will it be left, right, above or below the origin?*

Q9 Match the following sketches with the statements below:

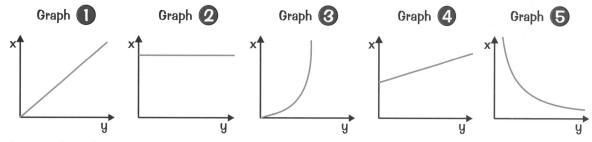

Graph ① Graph ② Graph ③ Graph ④ Graph ⑤

a) The graph is showing the cost of hiring a plumber <u>per hour</u> including a <u>fixed call-out fee</u>.

b) The graph is showing the connection between the <u>length and width</u> of a rectangle of a fixed area.

c) The graph is showing <u>speed against time</u> for a car travelling at constant speed.

d) The graph is showing the <u>area of a circle</u> as the radius increases.

<u>Keep asking yourself</u> the <u>three questions</u> about what you'd expect the graph to look like, then see if any of them are in there. If they aren't, you've gone wrong, so <u>try again</u>.

Q10 Water is poured into each of these containers at a <u>constant rate</u>.

Match the containers to the graphs showing the <u>depth</u> of water (d) against <u>time</u> (t) taken to fill the container.

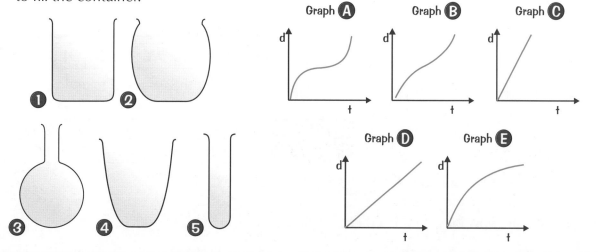

5.6 Questions on Real Life Graphs

This is the same sort of thing — drawing graphs from bits of real life information. How exciting.

Q12 A telephone company charges <u>£21 per quarter</u> to rent a line and <u>5p per unit</u> used.

Plot a graph showing the number of <u>units used</u> along the X-axis, with x from 0 to 800 units and the <u>cost in £</u> per quarter, of the corresponding telephone bill, along the Y-axis.

a) A household uses 600 units per quarter. Use your graph to <u>predict their bill</u>.
A household can opt to join a new scheme. The new billing system will only benefit the household if their quarterly bill is £50 or more.

b) How many <u>units</u> would this mean using per quarter before the new scheme would be of benefit to them?

c) A household receives a <u>quarterly bill</u> for £35.50. Estimate the number of units used that quarter.

Q13 For a cube with edges of length x cm, complete the table of <u>cube volumes</u>.

x cm	1	2	3	4	5	6	7
v cm³							

a) Plot a graph showing how the volume varies with the length of the edges.

b) Find the <u>edge length</u> of a cube with volume 250 cm³.

c) Find the <u>volume</u> of a cube with 3.5 cm edges.

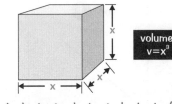

volume
v=x³

Don't forget that when you're stuck sketching a graph, you can <u>always</u> fall back on a table of values and plot the points. I'm not pretending it's quicker — but at least you know you'll <u>get it right</u>.

Q14 The cost for hiring a car is £20 plus an additional charge of 20p per mile.
Draw a graph to show the cost of hiring the car <u>for any mileage</u>, up to 100 miles.

a) Use your graph to determine the cost of a journey covering 48 miles.

b) A holidaymaker has a budget of £40. What is the <u>maximum journey length</u> the holidaymaker can afford to make?

Q15 A piece of wire gave the following values of resistance, R (Ohms), at various voltage readings, V (Volts). These experimental results are thought to follow the rule
R = mV + c, where m and c are constants.

By plotting V along the X-axis and R along the Y-axis, check whether the results lie approximately in a straight line. If so, find <u>estimates</u> for the values of m and c.

V	10	20	30	40	50
R	9.2	7.6	5.9	4.5	3.1

Q16 As a kettle boiled its temperature was recorded.

Time (mins)	0	1/2	1	1 1/2	2	2 1/2	3
Temp (°C)	19	21	24	29	40	59	100

Plot the points and join them up with a <u>smooth curve</u>.

a) Estimate how long it took to heat up the water to 50°C.

b) Estimate how long it took to heat up the water from 50°C to 100°C.

5.6   *Questions on Real Life Graphs*

Q17   In an experiment a machine lifts a load (W) and the effort (E) is recorded.
These experimental results are expected to be related by the equation E = aW + b.

Test this assumption by drawing a graph
and determine suitable values for a and b.

W	100	200	300	400	500
E	420	550	670	800	920

Q18   Three plumbers A, B and C, charge at different rates for their work.

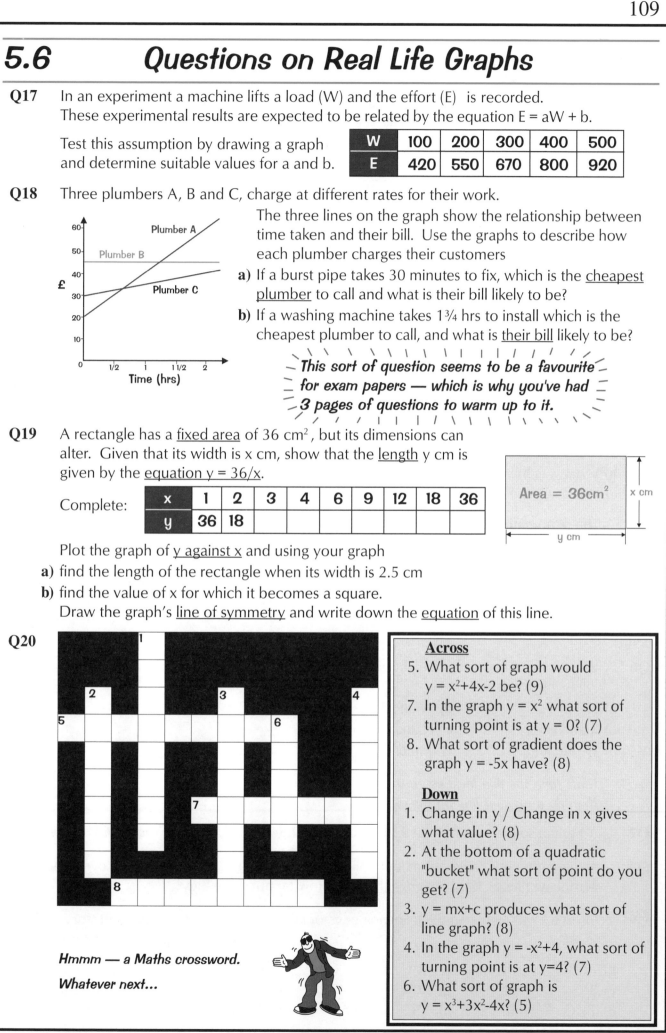

The three lines on the graph show the relationship between time taken and their bill. Use the graphs to describe how each plumber charges their customers

a) If a burst pipe takes 30 minutes to fix, which is the <u>cheapest plumber</u> to call and what is their bill likely to be?

b) If a washing machine takes 1¾ hrs to install which is the cheapest plumber to call, and what is <u>their bill</u> likely to be?

This sort of question seems to be a favourite for exam papers — which is why you've had 3 pages of questions to warm up to it.

Q19   A rectangle has a <u>fixed area</u> of 36 cm², but its dimensions can alter. Given that its width is x cm, show that the <u>length</u> y cm is given by the <u>equation y = 36/x</u>.

Complete:

x	1	2	3	4	6	9	12	18	36
y	36	18							

Area = 36cm²   x cm   y cm

Plot the graph of <u>y against x</u> and using your graph
a) find the length of the rectangle when its width is 2.5 cm
b) find the value of x for which it becomes a square.
Draw the graph's <u>line of symmetry</u> and write down the <u>equation</u> of this line.

Q20

Across
5. What sort of graph would y = x²+4x-2 be? (9)
7. In the graph y = x² what sort of turning point is at y = 0? (7)
8. What sort of gradient does the graph y = -5x have? (8)

Down
1. Change in y / Change in x gives what value? (8)
2. At the bottom of a quadratic "bucket" what sort of point do you get? (7)
3. y = mx+c produces what sort of line graph? (8)
4. In the graph y = -x²+4, what sort of turning point is at y=4? (7)
6. What sort of graph is y = x³+3x²-4x? (5)

Hmmm — a Maths crossword.

Whatever next...

6.1 Questions on Negative Numbers

Negative numbers are pretty easy when you're used to them. Start by drawing yourself a number line, then count along it. After you've done a few questions, you'll find you can work them out in your head.

-30°C -20°C -10°C 0°C 10°C 20°C 30°C 40°C 50°C 60°C

(This first one's given you a thermometer, which has got its own number line, anyway.)

Q1 Work out the temperature <u>rise</u> for each of the following:
a) 10°C to 42°C d) -4°C to 42°C g) -30°C to -25°C
b) -10°C to 0°C e) -29°C to 4°C h) -18°C to 4°C
c) -20°C to 30°C f) -19°C to -15°C i) -15°C to 49°C

Q2 Work out the <u>drop</u> in temperature for each of the following:
a) 30°C to -10°C d) 40°C to -30°C g) 50°C to -30°C
b) 24°C to -4°C e) -10°C to -25°C h) -3°C to -5°C
c) 0°C to -17°C f) -2°C to -27°C i) -4°C to -29°C

Q3 Early one morning the temperature is <u>-3°C</u>. By noon it has risen <u>by 12°C</u>, falling again to <u>-5°C</u> by midnight.
a) What was the temperature at noon?
b) What was the difference in temperature between noon and midnight?
c) What was the difference in temperature between morning and midnight?

Q4 The temperature at mid-day was 18°C. By evening it had fallen by 23°C. What was the evening temperature?

Q5 Use a <u>calculator</u> to work out the following, in each case making a <u>rough estimate</u> of the answer first:
a) -40–23+72+15–18 b) 324–78–169–89+54+178–26

Q6 What is the difference in height between the following points?

T=trees 120m
H=houses 50m
sea level
R=reef -20m
W=wreck -90m

a) H and T d) W and T
b) R and H e) H and W
c) W and R f) T and R

Hint: take the sea level as zero, then do a number line up the side.

Q7 A Roman soldier was born in 9 BC and died in the year AD 39. How long did he live?

Q8 A submarine is travelling at a depth of 500 m <u>below sea level</u> whilst directly overhead an aeroplane flies at 1300 m <u>above the sea</u>. How far apart are they?

Q9 Insert a > or < between the following pairs of numbers to make the statement true.

a) -14°C   16°C   e) 0°C   -13°C   i) 29°C   -3°C
b) -10°C   -15°C   f) -4°C   -8°C   j) -4°C   30°C
c) 8°C   -3°C   g) -20°C   -14°C   k) -4°C   -5°C
d) 14°C   -48°C   h) -3°C   0°C   l) -80°C   -78°C

6.1 Questions on Negative Numbers

Hmm, strange — when you <u>subtract</u> a negative number it's the same as adding a positive one. Eg 4 –⁻2 = 4+2 and -3–⁻1 = -3+1.

Q10 Find the value of each of the following:

a) 13–5　　**e)** -2+2　　**i)** -3+0　　**m)**-1+2-⁻4
b) 6–7　　**f)** -10+5　　**j)** -3–4　　**n)** 1-⁻2+4
c) 10–20　　**g)** -10+10　　**k)** 5–10　　**o)** -4-⁻6–10
d) 4–11　　**h)** -2+8　　**l)** -20-⁻100　　**p)** 10-⁻5-2

Q11 Which is larger and by how much:
a) -11+8–3+4–5 <u>or</u> **b)** -20+17–2–6+5 ?

Q12 Find the missing number (with <u>its sign</u>)
a) ⁺8 ? =⁺6　　**b)** ⁻4 ? =⁺2　　**c)** ⁻2 ? =⁻5　　**d)** ⁺7–⁺3 ? =⁻4

<u>Letters</u> are only there to represent <u>numbers</u>, so you treat them <u>exactly</u> the same. Eg 3a+2a=5a, 4a–6a=-2a, -4x–3x=-7x, -14y–⁻20y=6y.

Q13 Simplify the following:

a) 5x–2x　　**e)** 10y–15y　　**i)** -3w+0　　**m)**x–2x+5x
b) 10x–8x　　**f)** -2x+8x　　**j)** -8w–4w　　**n)** y+7y–4y
c) 14x–7x　　**g)** -4x+10x　　**k)** -4n–2n　　**o)** 10z–20z+8z
d) 4y–5y　　**h)** -6y+14y　　**l)** -100q–24q　　**q)** -4y–y+8y

Rules for Multiplying and Dividing		
× or ÷	＋ve	−ve
＋ ve	+	−
− ve	−	+

Multiply / divide the numbers <u>ignoring the signs</u> first, then put in the +/– signs afterwards, using that rule you've just learnt.

Q14 Work out the following:

a) -4 × ⁻3　　**d)** -8÷4　　**g)** 2 × ⁻2　　**j)** 2 × ⁻3 × ⁻2
b) 5 × ⁻2　　**e)** -20 ÷ ⁻10　　**h)** -36 ÷ ⁻12　　**k)** -4 × ⁻1 × ⁻2
c) -12 ÷ ⁻4　　**f)** -4 × 4　　**i)** -40 × 3　　**l)** 10 ÷ (1 × ⁻5)

Q15 Find the value of <u>xy</u> and <u>x/y</u> in each of the following cases:

a) x=20, y=4　　**c)** x=40, y=⁻4　　**e)** x=⁻100, y=10
b) x=36, y=⁻2　　**d)** x=18, y=⁻3　　**f)** x=24, y=⁻4

Q16 Which is <u>larger</u> and by how much:
a) (5+2) × (7–4) <u>or</u> **b)** 5+2(7–4) ?

Q17 Find the value of (a–b) ÷ c when a = -2, b = 10 and c = -4.

Q18 Simplify the following:

a) 2x × 4y　　**e)** 2p × ⁻4q　　**i)** -20x ÷ 10y　　**m)**-20x ÷ ⁻4x
b) -2x × 3y　　**f)** -8a × 2b　　**j)** -30x ÷ ⁻3y　　**n)** -100x ÷ 10x
c) 4x × ⁻10y　　**g)** -10a × ⁻2b × 3c　　**k)** -40x ÷ ⁻4y　　**o)** 10x ÷ ⁻2x
d) 2x × ⁻2y × ⁻2z　　**h)** 4x × ⁻8y　　**l)** -50x ÷ ⁻5y　　**p)** -30x ÷ ⁻10x

6.2 Questions on Standard Index Form

Writing very big (or very small) numbers gets a bit messy with all those zeros, if you don't use this standard index form. But of course, the main reason for knowing about standard form is...you guessed it — it's in the Exam.

Top Tips

Any numbers written in Standard Index Form __always__ look like:

This number must be between 1 and 10 but never equal to 10

$a \times 10^n$

This number is equal to the number of places the decimal point moves.
n is +ve for larger numbers
n is -ve for small numbers

eg.
$$580000000000000000 = 5.8 \times 10^{17}$$
$$43000000000000000000 = 4.3 \times 10^{19}$$
$$0.0000000000000017 = 1.7 \times 10^{-15}$$
$$0.00000000000000008 = 8 \times 10^{-17}$$

Q1 Complete these two tables.

Number	Standard form
4500000000	
19300000000000	
	8.2×10^{12}
82000000	
	6.34×10^8
	4.02×10^6
423400000000	
	8.431×10^7
	1.03×10^5
4700	

Number	Standard form
0.000000006	
0.00000000072	
	8.5×10^{-6}
0.000000143	
	7.12×10^{-5}
	3.68×10^{-10}
	4.003×10^{-8}
0.0000009321	
	5.2×10^{-3}
	9.999×10^{-7}
0.00000000802	
	2.3104×10^{-6}
0.000001	

Q2 Rewrite the following, either in standard form or changing standard form to normal numbers.

a) Mercury is 694000000 km from the Sun.

b) The Sahara desert covers 8600000 km².

c) The Earth is approximately 4.5×10^9 years old.

d) The average depth of the Atlantic is 3.7×10^3 miles.

e) The charge on an electron is 1.6×10^{-19} Coulombs.

f) A Uranium nucleus can release 3.20×10^{-11} Joules of energy.

g) In Chemistry, Avogadro's constant is 6.033×10^{23}.

h) The circumference of the equator is 40076 km.

i) The population of the USA is approximately 249231000 people.

j) From Washington to Tokyo is 6763 miles.

k) A tonne of coal can produce 2.8×10^{10} Joules of energy.

l) The radius of the nucleus of an atom is 0.0000000000003 cm.

m) In 2050 the population of the World will be around 1.1×10^{10} people.

You may have noticed standard form is used a lot in science, so if you're a budding nuclear physicist, get learning. Oh, you're not. Well, you've still got to learn it. Sorry.

Q3 Find the value of the following, giving your answers in __standard form__.
a) 46×4.2×5000 **c)** 0.2×0.3×0.5×0.1 **e)** 62000÷0.31
b) 20×40×50×8.2 **d)** 5000÷0.02 **f)** 40000000÷1000

6.2   Questions on Standard Index Form

Standard Index Form with a Calculator

Use the **EXP** button (or **EE** button) to enter numbers in standard index form.

Eg $1.7 \times 10^9 + 2.6 \times 10^{10}$ **1** **.** **7** **EXP** **9** **+** **2** **.** **6** **EXP** **10** **=**

The answer is   [2.77^{10}]   which is read as 2.77×10^{10}

Q4   If $x = 4 \times 10^5$ and $y = 6 \times 10^4$ work out the value of
    a) xy   **b)** 4x   **c)** 3y.

Q5   Which is <u>greater</u>, 4.62×10^{12} or 1.04×10^{13}, and <u>by how much</u>?

Q6   Which is <u>smaller</u> 3.2×10^{-8} or 1.3×10^{-9} and by how much?

Q7   The following numbers are <u>not</u> written in standard index form. Rewrite them correctly using standard index form.

    a) 42×10^6 **d)** 11.2×10^{-5} **g)** 17×10^{17}
    b) 38×10^{-5} **e)** 843×10^3 **h)** 28.3×10^{-5}
    c) 10×10^6 **f)** 42.32×10^{-4} **i)** 10×10^{-3}

> *Don't forget — when you're using a calculator, you've got to write the answer as 3.46×10^{27}, <u>not</u> as 3.46^{27}. If you do it the wrong way, it means something <u>completely</u> different.*

Q8   What is <u>7 million</u> in standard index form?

Q9   The radius of the Earth is 6.38×10^3 km. What is the radius of the Earth measured in <u>cm</u>? Leave your answer in standard form.

Q10 a) The surface area of the Earth is approximately 5.1×10^8 km². Write this <u>without</u> using standard form.
    b) The area of the Earth covered by sea is 362 000 000 km². Write this in standard form.
    c) What is the approximate area of the Earth covered by land? Write your answer <u>without</u> using standard form.

Q11   The length of a light year, the distance light can travel in one year, is 9.461×10^{15} m. How far can light travel in
    a) 2 years?
    b) 6 months?
    Write your answers in <u>standard form</u>.

Q12   One atomic mass unit is equivalent to 1.661×10^{-27} kg. What are <u>two</u> atomic mass units equivalent to (in standard index form)?

6.3 Questions on Powers (Indices)

Hang on there. Before you try this page, make sure you know the seven rules for powers — you'll find them on P.80 of The Revision Guide, or you could just ask Teach.

The small number is called the <u>power</u> or <u>index number</u>. Remember the plural of index is <u>indices</u>.

$5^4 = 5 \times 5 \times 5 \times 5 = $ _____

we say "five to the power four"

$8^3 = 8 \times 8 \times 8 = $ _____

we say "eight to the power three" or "eight cubed"

To save time try using the power button on your calculator $\boxed{x^y}$ $\boxed{y^x}$

eg. $\boxed{5}$ $\boxed{x^y}$ $\boxed{4}$ $\boxed{=}$

$\boxed{8}$ $\boxed{x^y}$ $\boxed{3}$ $\boxed{=}$

Q1 Complete the following:
a) $2^4 = 2 \times 2 \times 2 \times 2 = $
b) $10^3 = 10 \times 10 \times 10 = $
c) $3^5 = 3 \times ... \qquad = $

d) $4^6 = 4 \times \qquad = $
e) $1^9 = 1 \times \qquad = $
f) $5^6 = 5 \times \qquad = $

Q2 Simplify the following:
a) $2 \times 2 \times 2 \times 2 \times 2 \times 2 \times 2 \times 2$
b) $12 \times 12 \times 12 \times 12 \times 12$
c) $x \times x \times x \times x \times x \times x \times x$

d) $m \times m \times m$
e) $y \times y \times y \times y$
f) $z \times z \times z \times z \times z \times z$

Q3 Complete the following (the first one has been done for you):
a) $10^2 \times 10^3 = (10 \times 10) \times (10 \times 10 \times 10) \qquad = 10^5$
b) $10^3 \times 10^4 = \qquad =$
c) $10^4 \times 10^2 = \qquad =$
d) $10^5 \times 10^3 = \qquad =$
e) What is the <u>quick method</u> for writing down the final result in **b)**, **c)** and **d)**?

Easy — you'll have learnt this from your seven rules of powers.

Q4 Complete (the first one has been done for you):

a) $2^4 \div 2^2 = \dfrac{(2 \times 2 \times 2 \times 2)}{(2 \times 2)} = 2^2$

c) $4^5 \div 4^3 = \dfrac{(4 \times 4 \times 4 \times 4 \times 4)}{} =$

b) $2^5 \div 2^2 = \dfrac{(2 \times 2 \times 2 \times 2 \times 2)}{(2 \times 2)} =$

d) $8^5 \div 8^2 = \qquad =$

e) What is the quick method for writing down the final result in **b)**, **c)** and **d)**?

Q5 Which of the following are <u>true</u>?

a) $2^4 \times 2^6 = 2^{10}$
b) $2^2 \times 2^3 \times 2^4 = 2^9$
c) $2^3 \times 2^2 = 2^6$

d) $4^{10} \times 4^4 \times 4^2 = 4^{18}$
e) $2^1 \times 2^3 \times 2^4 = 2^8$
f) $10^4 \times 10^2 = 10^8$

g) $2^{20} \div 2^5 = 2^4$
h) $3^{12} \div 3^4 = 3^8$
i) $4^6 \div 6^4 = 4^2$

j) $10^{20} \div 10^3 = 10^{17}$
k) $4^6 \div (4^2 \times 4^3) = 4^1$
l) $9^2 \times (9^{30} \div 9^{25}) = 9^{10}$

Q6 Write the following as a <u>single term</u>:
a) $10^6 \div 10^4$
b) $(8^2 \times 8^5) \div 8^3$
c) $6^{10} \div (6^2 \times 6^3)$

d) $x^2 \times x^3$
e) $a^5 \times a^4$
f) $p^4 \times p^5 \times p^6$

g) $x^3 \div x^2$
h) $a^5 \div a^3$
i) $h^{12} \div (h^4 \times h^4)$

6.3   Questions on Powers (Indices)

Grab your calculator for this bit — you'd better get used to
that powers button ...

Q7   Use your <u>calculator</u> to find the exact value of
   a) 4^3 **c)** 10^4 **e)** 12^5 **g)** 13^3 **i)** 1^{28}
   b) 3^5 **d)** 4^1 **f)** 15^3 **h)** 1^{10} **j)** 5^8

Q8   Use your calculator to find the exact value of
   a) 5^{-1} **c)** 50^{-1} **e)** 10^{-5} **g)** 4^{-2}
   b) 10^{-2} **d)** 2^{-3} **f)** 100^{-1} **h)** 1^{-5}

Have another go at Q8, and don't go to Q9 until you've got
the same answers twice — go on, it won't take you long.

Q9   Which of the following are <u>true</u>?
   a) $2^{-3} = 1/6$ **c)** $4^{-2} = 1/16$ **e)** $1/9 = 3^2$
   b) $17^0 = 0$ **d)** $1^{-17} = 1$ **f)** $28^0 = 1$

Q10   Write as a <u>single power</u>:

   a) $2^4 \times 2^3$ **e)** $8^3 \div 8^1$ **i)** $x^4 \div x^1$ **m)** $3^{-2} \times (3^{-4} \div 3^0)$
   b) $2^6 \times 2^0$ **f)** $4^6 \div 4^2$ **j)** $y^3 \div y^2$ **n)** $(3^{-2})^3$
   c) $4^2 \times 4^2$ **g)** $7^{-3} \div 7^{-4}$ **k)** $y^4 \times y^4$ **o)** $(x^2)^3$
   d) $4^6 \times 4^3$ **h)** $8^{10} \div 8^{-2}$ **l)** $m^4 \times m^{-2}$ **p)** $(4^{-1})^4$

Q11   Write as a <u>single power</u>:

   a) $(x^2)^4$ **b)** $(y^6)^2$ **c)** $(z^{10})^2$ **d)** $(x^2)^{-3}$ **e)** $(y^{-1})^6$

Q12   Find the <u>value of n</u>
   where $12^5 \div 12^n = 12^7$

Remember your powers
rule for dividing — you simply
do this one backwards.

Q13   Find the <u>reciprocal</u> of 1000 and express
   as a power of 10.

Start by looking at the term <u>without</u> the x in it.
Put it in the same form as the one <u>with</u> the x
in it, and simply match them up to find x.

Q14   Find the numbers replaced by x in these statements:

   a) $3^x = 9$ **c)** $10^x = 1000$ **e)** $17^x = 1$ **g)** $(4^2)^x = 4^6$ **i)** $8^x = 1/8$
   b) $3^x = 1/9$ **d)** $4^x = 1/16$ **f)** $3^x \times 3^{-1} = 3^5$ **h)** $(5^x)^2 = 5^6$ **j)** $X^5 = 1$

Q15   Remove the brackets from the following and express as a single power:
   a) $(3^4 \times 3^2) \div (3^6 \times 3^3)$ **d)** $(3^6)^{-2}$
   b) $(4^{10} \times 4^{12}) \times 4^3$ **e)** $4^2 \times 4^{-1} \times 4^6 \times (4^2 \div 4^3)$
   c) $10^2 \div (10^3 \times 10^{12})$ **f)** $(5^2 \times 5^3) \div (5^6 \div 5^4)$

6.4 Questions on Square and Cube Roots

"Square Root" means "What Number Times by Itself gives..."

Eg. The square root of 64 is 8, the square root of 36 is 6 etc.

That's because 8 × 8 = 64 and 6 × 6 = 36... OK, I was just checking.

Q1 Write down:
- **a)** $\sqrt{4}$
- **b)** $\sqrt{16}$
- **c)** $\sqrt{9}$
- **d)** $\sqrt{49}$
- **e)** $\sqrt{25}$
- **f)** $\sqrt{100}$
- **g)** $\sqrt{144}$
- **h)** $\sqrt{64}$
- **i)** $\sqrt{81}$

Q2 Use the $\sqrt{}$ button on your calculator to find the following square roots to the nearest whole number.
- **a)** $\sqrt{60}$
- **b)** $\sqrt{19}$
- **c)** $\sqrt{34}$
- **d)** $\sqrt{200}$
- **e)** $\sqrt{520}$
- **f)** $\sqrt{75}$
- **g)** $\sqrt{750}$
- **h)** $\sqrt{0.9}$
- **i)** $\sqrt{170}$
- **j)** $\sqrt{7220}$
- **k)** $\sqrt{1000050}$
- **l)** $\sqrt{27}$

Q3 Use your calculator to find, to 1dp
- **a)** $45^{1/2}$ **b)** $18^{1/2}$ **c)** $90^{1/2}$

Remember, the power ½ means a square root.

Q4 Without using your calculator, try to predict the following to the nearest whole number. (Your answers to **Q1** will be helpful)
- **a)** $\sqrt{10}$
- **b)** $\sqrt{50}$
- **c)** $\sqrt{80}$
- **d)** $\sqrt{65}$

Check your answers using a calculator afterwards.

Q5 A square rug has an area of 235.3156 m². What is the length of an edge?

Q6 A bowling green has an area of 2025 m². What is the perimeter of the green?

"Cube Root" means "What Number Times by Itself THREE TIMES gives..."

Eg. The cube root of 64 is 4, the cube root of 27 is 3 etc.

4 × 4 × 4 = 64, 3 × 3 × 3 = 27 — you get the picture...

Q7 Use your calulator to find the following:
- **a)** $\sqrt[3]{125}$
- **b)** $\sqrt[3]{1728}$
- **c)** $\sqrt[3]{1000}$
- **d)** $\sqrt[3]{729}$
- **e)** $\sqrt[3]{1331}$
- **f)** $\sqrt[3]{8000}$
- **g)** $\sqrt[3]{1}$
- **h)** $\sqrt[3]{0.125}$
- **i)** $\sqrt[3]{216}$
- **j)** $\sqrt[3]{343}$
- **k)** $\sqrt[3]{4096}$
- **l)** $\sqrt[3]{1000000}$

Q8 Without using your calculator, try to predict the following to the nearest whole number.
- **a)** $\sqrt[3]{120}$
- **b)** $\sqrt[3]{1800}$
- **c)** $\sqrt[3]{200}$
- **d)** $\sqrt[3]{4000}$
- **e)** $\sqrt[3]{300}$
- **f)** $\sqrt[3]{0.1}$

Same again — check your answers with a calculator.

6.5   *Questions on Solving Equations*

OK, so you've noticed this page starts off all right, but, things do get a bit hairy later on — so give yourself a head start by practising your algebra skills on the easy ones.

Q1   Solve the following:

    a) $4x = 20$ **g)** $2x = -18$ **m)** $2x + 1 = 7$

    b) $7x = 28$ **h)** $x + 5 = -3$ **n)** $2x + 4 = 5$

    c) $x + 3 = 11$ **i)** $x/2 = 22$ **o)** $7x + 5 = 54$

    d) $x + 19 = 23$ **j)** $x/7 = 3$ **p)** $6x - 7 = 41$

    e) $x - 6 = 13$ **k)** $x/5 = 8$ **q)** $2x + 7 = 13$

    f) $7x = -14$ **l)** $10x = 100$ **r)** $3x - 2 = 19$

Q2   When eight is subtracted from a number the result is thirty-two.

    a) Write this information as an equation.

    b) Solve your equation to <u>find the number</u>.

Q3   When a number is multiplied by three and seven is added, the result is nineteen.

    a) Write this information <u>as an equation</u>.

    b) Solve your equation to find the number.

Q4   Andrew, Ben and Carl collect stamps. Andrew has 86 more than Ben and Carl has 156 more than Ben. If Ben has x stamps write down an expression for the number of stamps owned by:

    a) Andrew

    b) Carl

    Altogether they have 776 stamps.

    c) Using your <u>previous answers</u> write down and solve an equation in x.

    d) How many stamps do Andrew and Carl have each?

Q5   Mary is y years old. Her father is 4 times older than Mary. Her mother is 7 years younger than her father. If their three ages add up to 101 years, find the value of y.
Find the ages of Mary's parents.

Q6   A girl spent t minutes on her Chemistry homework. She spent twice as long on her Maths homework and her English homework took her 15 minutes longer than her Chemistry did. If she spent a total of 95 minutes working, find the value of t.

Q7   Mr Smith sent his car to the local garage. He spent £x on new parts, four times this amount on labour and finally £29 for an MOT test. If the total bill was for £106.50, find the value of x.

Q8   Solve the following:

    a) $3x - 4 = 2x + 4$ **h)** $5x - 2 = \frac{1}{2}x + 7$

    b) $3x - 8 = 5x - 20$ **i)** $2x - 5 = \frac{1}{2}x + 4$

    c) $23 - x = x + 11$ **j)** $3x + 7 = \frac{1}{2}x + 2$

    d) $8x + 7 = 6x - 9$ **k)** $3(x + 1) = 9$

    e) $4x + 7 = x - 2$ **l)** $2(x - 3) - (x - 2) = 5$

    f) $8x + 3 = 10x - 7$ **m)** $5(m + 2) - 3(m - 5) = 29$

    g) $3x - 2.5 = 5$ **n)** $2(x + 2) + 3(x + 4) = 31$

6.5   *Questions on Solving Equations*

*Well, the good thing about doing all of these is that soon you'll
be able to do algebra with your eyes closed. That'll be nice.*

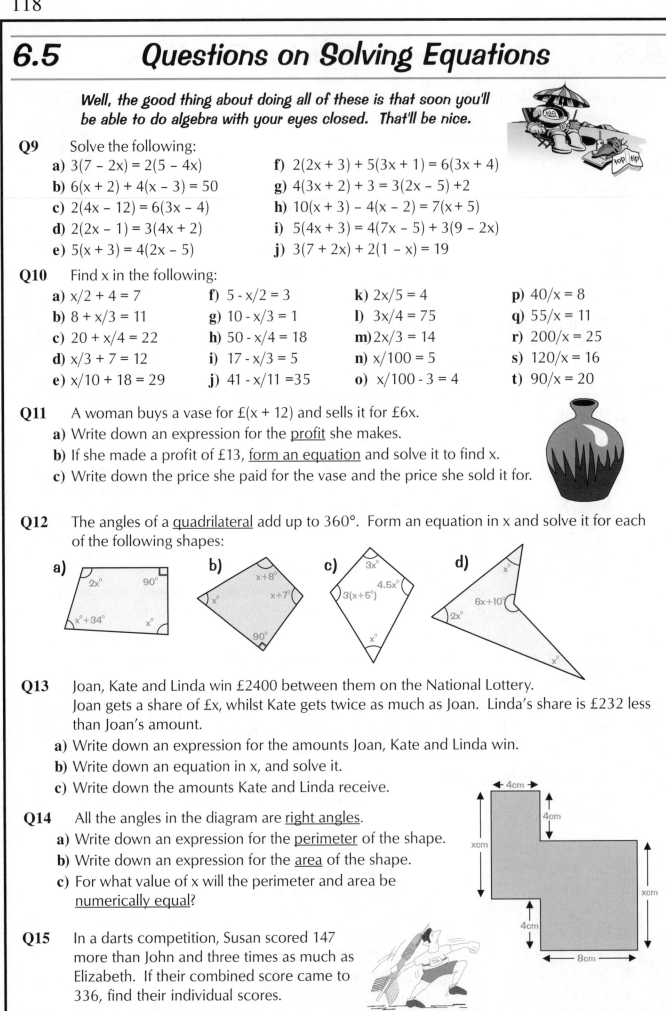

Q9   Solve the following:

a) $3(7 - 2x) = 2(5 - 4x)$ **f)** $2(2x + 3) + 5(3x + 1) = 6(3x + 4)$

b) $6(x + 2) + 4(x - 3) = 50$ **g)** $4(3x + 2) + 3 = 3(2x - 5) + 2$

c) $2(4x - 12) = 6(3x - 4)$ **h)** $10(x + 3) - 4(x - 2) = 7(x + 5)$

d) $2(2x - 1) = 3(4x + 2)$ **i)** $5(4x + 3) = 4(7x - 5) + 3(9 - 2x)$

e) $5(x + 3) = 4(2x - 5)$ **j)** $3(7 + 2x) + 2(1 - x) = 19$

Q10   Find x in the following:

a) $x/2 + 4 = 7$ **f)** $5 - x/2 = 3$ **k)** $2x/5 = 4$ **p)** $40/x = 8$

b) $8 + x/3 = 11$ **g)** $10 - x/3 = 1$ **l)** $3x/4 = 75$ **q)** $55/x = 11$

c) $20 + x/4 = 22$ **h)** $50 - x/4 = 18$ **m)** $2x/3 = 14$ **r)** $200/x = 25$

d) $x/3 + 7 = 12$ **i)** $17 - x/3 = 5$ **n)** $x/100 = 5$ **s)** $120/x = 16$

e) $x/10 + 18 = 29$ **j)** $41 - x/11 = 35$ **o)** $x/100 - 3 = 4$ **t)** $90/x = 20$

Q11   A woman buys a vase for £$(x + 12)$ and sells it for £$6x$.

a) Write down an expression for the <u>profit</u> she makes.

b) If she made a profit of £13, <u>form an equation</u> and solve it to find x.

c) Write down the price she paid for the vase and the price she sold it for.

Q12   The angles of a <u>quadrilateral</u> add up to 360°. Form an equation in x and solve it for each
of the following shapes:

a) $2x°$ $90°$ $x°+34°$ $x°$

b) $x+8°$ $x°$ $x+7°$ $90°$

c) $3x°$ $4.5x°$ $3(x+5°)$ $x°$

d) $x°$ $6x+10°$ $2x°$ $x°$

Q13   Joan, Kate and Linda win £2400 between them on the National Lottery.
Joan gets a share of £x, whilst Kate gets twice as much as Joan. Linda's share is £232 less
than Joan's amount.

a) Write down an expression for the amounts Joan, Kate and Linda win.

b) Write down an equation in x, and solve it.

c) Write down the amounts Kate and Linda receive.

Q14   All the angles in the diagram are <u>right angles</u>.

a) Write down an expression for the <u>perimeter</u> of the shape.

b) Write down an expression for the <u>area</u> of the shape.

c) For what value of x will the perimeter and area be
<u>numerically equal</u>?

4cm   4cm   xcm   xcm   4cm   8cm

Q15   In a darts competition, Susan scored 147
more than John and three times as much as
Elizabeth. If their combined score came to
336, find their individual scores.

6.5 Questions on Solving Equations

Q16 The <u>angles</u> of a triangle are $0.5x°$, $x°$ and $(4x + 4)°$
   a) Write down an equation in x and solve it.
   b) Write down the three angles and state what kind of triangle it is.

You'd better watch your step here — I think I've left some geometry lying around.

Q17 The sum of <u>two consecutive</u> numbers is 267.
   a) Write this information as an equation.
   b) Solve your equation to find the two numbers.

Q18 Solve the following:—
   a) $8m - \frac{1}{2} = 6m + 7$
   b) $\frac{1}{2}p - 13 = 3p + 7$
   c) $\frac{3}{4}t + 6 = \frac{1}{4}t + 8$
   d) $\frac{1}{2}z + 2 = \frac{1}{4}z + 6$

Get rid of any unwanted fractions by multiplying the <u>whole equation</u> by the bottom number. If you've got a couple of fractions with different numbers at the bottom, multiply by their LCM (see P.6).

Don't forget to multiply <u>each</u> term by the <u>same thing</u> or things'll go a bit pear-shaped.

Q19 Solve the following:
   a) $18 - 3(7 - 2x) + 4x = 22$
   b) $6x = 2(x - 4)$
   c) $3x + 24 + 2(x - 3) = 28$
   d) $4x - 7 - 7(6 - x) = 14$

Q20 A piece of ribbon is 26 cm long. It is cut into two pieces, which differ by 6 cm. Let the length of the shorter piece be x cm, and form an equation in x. Find the <u>two lengths</u>.

Q21 Two men are decorating a room. One has painted 20 m² and the other has painted only 6 m². They continue painting and both manage to paint another x m² each. If the first man has painted exactly three times the area painted by the second man, find x.

Q22 For what value of x is the expression $14 - 0.5x$ equal to the value $(3x - 4)/2$?

Q23 Solve the following:
   a) $4x + 2x + 20 = 62$
   b) $4(x - 2) = 16$
   c) $3(x + 2) = 21$
   d) $6(x + 3) - (x - 2) = 60$
   e) $4(x - 1) - 2(3 - x) = 50$
   f) $2(4 - x) - (x + 2) = 28$

Q24 I think of a number, multiply it by 8 and add 13. The result is <u>one less than</u> the original number. What number did I start with?

Q25 I think of a number, divide it by 5 and add 7. The result is 13 less than the original number. What number did I start with?

Q26 Carol's father was 24 yrs old when Carol was born. Now he is four times as old as Carol. How old is Carol?

Q27 Solve the following:-
   a) $5(x - 1) + 3(x - 4) = -11$
   b) $3(x + 2) + 2(x - 4) = x - 3(x + 3)$
   c) $\frac{3x}{2} + 3 = x$
   d) $3(4x + 2) = 2(2x - 1)$
   e) $5x + \frac{7}{9} = 3$
   f) $2x + \frac{7}{11} = 3$

Q28 Mr Jones is 4 years older than his wife and 31 years older than his son. Their ages add up to 82 years. If Mr Jones is x years old, find the value of x and find all their ages.

6.6 Questions on Substituting Values

BODMAS — this funny little word helps you remember in which order to work formulas out. The example below shows you how to use it. Oh and by the way "**O**ther" might not seem important, but it means things like powers, square and cube roots, etc — so it is.

Brackets, **O**ther, **D**ivision, **M**ultiplication, **A**ddition, **S**ubtraction

Example: if $z = \frac{x}{10} + (y-3)^2$ find the value of z when x = 40 and y = 13.

1) Write down the formula with the numbers substituted in,

$$z = \frac{40}{10} + (13-3)^2$$

2) **B**rackets first $\qquad z = \frac{40}{10} + (10)^2$

3) **O**ther next, so square $\qquad z = \frac{40}{10} + 100$

4) **D**ivision before **A**ddition $\qquad z = 4 + 100$

$$\underline{z = 104}$$

Q1 If x=3 and y=6 find the value of the following expressions.

a) $x + 2y$ c) $4(x+y)$ e) $2x^2$

b) $2x \div y$ d) $(y-x)^2$ f) $2y^2$

Q2 The cost of framing a picture, C pence, depends on the <u>dimensions of the picture</u>. If C = 10L + 5W, where L is the length in cm and W is the width in cm, then find the cost of framing

a) a picture 40cm by 24cm

b) a square picture of sides 30cm.

Q3 If V = lwh, find V when,

a) l = 7, w = 5, h = 2   b) l = 12, w = 8, h = 5.

Q4 Using the formula z = (x−10)², find the value of z when,

a) x = 20

b) x = 15

c) x = -1

Use the memory button on your calc, so you don't have to keep typing things in yourself.

Q5 If V = u + at find the <u>value of V</u> when u = 8, a = 9.8 and t = 2.

Q6 If V = π r²h find the value of V when r = 4 and h = 6. Take π = 3.14.

Q7 The cost, C pence, of hiring a taxi depends on the number, n, of miles you travel in it, where C = 100 + 25n. Find C when

a) n = 2   b) n = 10   c) n = 15

Q8 The time taken to cook a chicken is given as 20 minutes per lb plus 20 minutes extra. Find the time needed to cook a chicken weighing

a) 4 lb

b) 7.5 lb.

6.6 Questions on Substituting Values

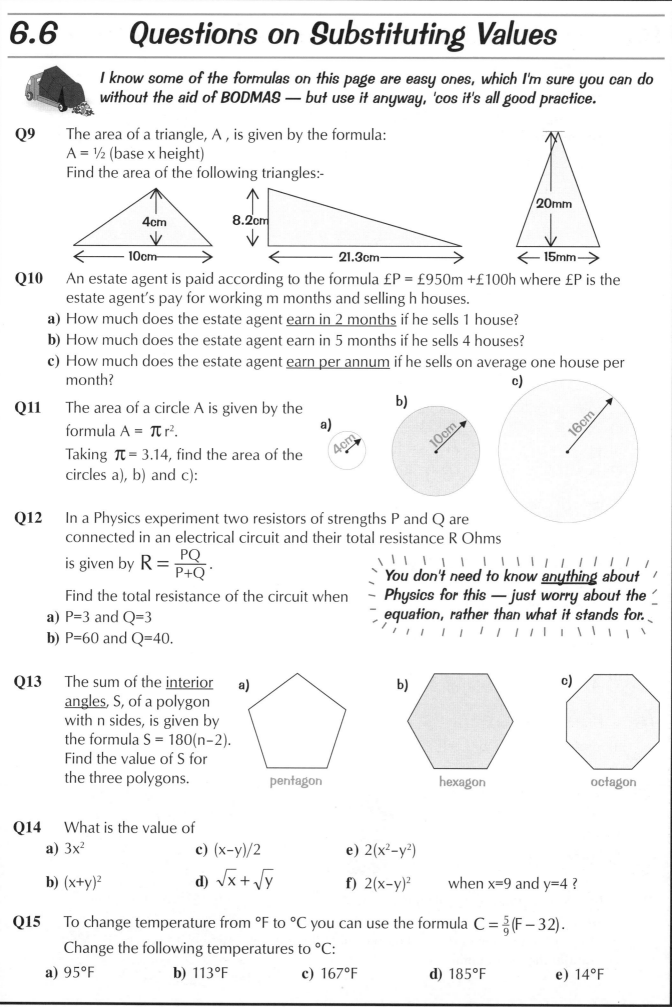

I know some of the formulas on this page are easy ones, which I'm sure you can do without the aid of BODMAS — but use it anyway, 'cos it's all good practice.

Q9 The area of a triangle, A , is given by the formula:
A = ½ (base x height)
Find the area of the following triangles:-

4cm 10cm   8.2cm 21.3cm   20mm 15mm

Q10 An estate agent is paid according to the formula £P = £950m +£100h where £P is the estate agent's pay for working m months and selling h houses.
 a) How much does the estate agent <u>earn in 2 months</u> if he sells 1 house?
 b) How much does the estate agent earn in 5 months if he sells 4 houses?
 c) How much does the estate agent <u>earn per annum</u> if he sells on average one house per month?

Q11 The area of a circle A is given by the formula A = πr^2.
Taking π = 3.14, find the area of the circles a), b) and c):

a) 4cm b) 10cm c) 16cm

Q12 In a Physics experiment two resistors of strengths P and Q are connected in an electrical circuit and their total resistance R Ohms is given by $R = \dfrac{PQ}{P+Q}$.

Find the total resistance of the circuit when
 a) P=3 and Q=3
 b) P=60 and Q=40.

You don't need to know <u>anything</u> about Physics for this — just worry about the equation, rather than what it stands for.

Q13 The sum of the <u>interior angles</u>, S, of a polygon with n sides, is given by the formula S = 180(n–2). Find the value of S for the three polygons.

a) pentagon   b) hexagon   c) octagon

Q14 What is the value of
 a) $3x^2$
 b) $(x+y)^2$
 c) $(x-y)/2$
 d) $\sqrt{x} + \sqrt{y}$
 e) $2(x^2-y^2)$
 f) $2(x-y)^2$ when x=9 and y=4 ?

Q15 To change temperature from °F to °C you can use the formula $C = \frac{5}{9}(F - 32)$.
Change the following temperatures to °C:
 a) 95°F   **b)** 113°F   **c)** 167°F   **d)** 185°F   **e)** 14°F

6.7 Questions on Solving Eq's the Easy Way

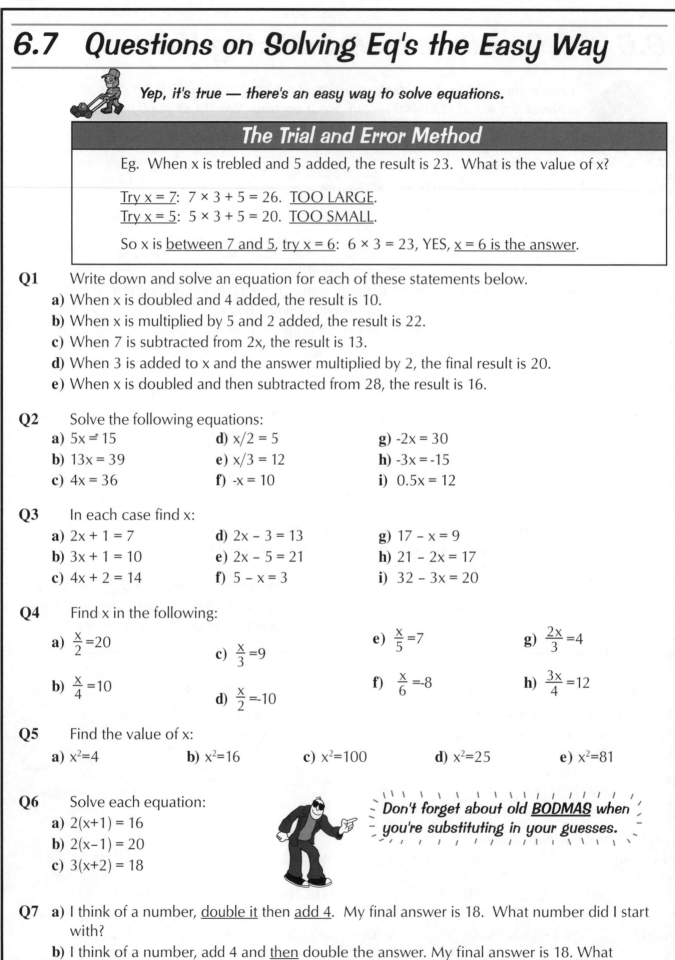

Yep, it's true — there's an easy way to solve equations.

The Trial and Error Method

Eg. When x is trebled and 5 added, the result is 23. What is the value of x?

Try x = 7: $7 \times 3 + 5 = 26$. <u>TOO LARGE</u>.
Try x = 5: $5 \times 3 + 5 = 20$. <u>TOO SMALL</u>.

So x is <u>between 7 and 5</u>, <u>try x = 6</u>: $6 \times 3 = 23$, YES, <u>x = 6 is the answer</u>.

Q1 Write down and solve an equation for each of these statements below.
a) When x is doubled and 4 added, the result is 10.
b) When x is multiplied by 5 and 2 added, the result is 22.
c) When 7 is subtracted from 2x, the result is 13.
d) When 3 is added to x and the answer multiplied by 2, the final result is 20.
e) When x is doubled and then subtracted from 28, the result is 16.

Q2 Solve the following equations:
a) $5x = 15$
b) $13x = 39$
c) $4x = 36$
d) $x/2 = 5$
e) $x/3 = 12$
f) $-x = 10$
g) $-2x = 30$
h) $-3x = -15$
i) $0.5x = 12$

Q3 In each case find x:
a) $2x + 1 = 7$
b) $3x + 1 = 10$
c) $4x + 2 = 14$
d) $2x - 3 = 13$
e) $2x - 5 = 21$
f) $5 - x = 3$
g) $17 - x = 9$
h) $21 - 2x = 17$
i) $32 - 3x = 20$

Q4 Find x in the following:
a) $\frac{x}{2} = 20$
b) $\frac{x}{4} = 10$
c) $\frac{x}{3} = 9$
d) $\frac{x}{2} = -10$
e) $\frac{x}{5} = 7$
f) $\frac{x}{6} = -8$
g) $\frac{2x}{3} = 4$
h) $\frac{3x}{4} = 12$

Q5 Find the value of x:
a) $x^2 = 4$
b) $x^2 = 16$
c) $x^2 = 100$
d) $x^2 = 25$
e) $x^2 = 81$

Q6 Solve each equation:
a) $2(x+1) = 16$
b) $2(x-1) = 20$
c) $3(x+2) = 18$

Don't forget about old **BODMAS** when you're substituting in your guesses.

Q7 a) I think of a number, <u>double it</u> then <u>add 4</u>. My final answer is 18. What number did I start with?

b) I think of a number, add 4 and <u>then</u> double the answer. My final answer is 18. What number did I start with?

6.7 Questions on Solving Eq's the Easy Way

Remember, you're still doing these the easy way —
keep those guesses flooding in.

Q8 Write down and solve an equation for each of these statements.

a) <u>Multiplying</u> a number by 4 and <u>then adding</u> 3 gives the same result as <u>trebling</u> the number and adding 9.

b) Multiplying a number by 3 then subtracting 4 gives the <u>same result</u> as adding 12 to the number.

c) When 1 is <u>added</u> to a number and the answer then <u>trebled</u>, it gives the same result as <u>doubling</u> the number and then <u>adding</u> 4.

Q9 Solve the following:

a) $2x^2=18$ b) $2x^2=72$ c) $3x^2=12$ d) $4x^2=36$ e) $5x^2=5$

Q10 Find the value of x for each rectangle.

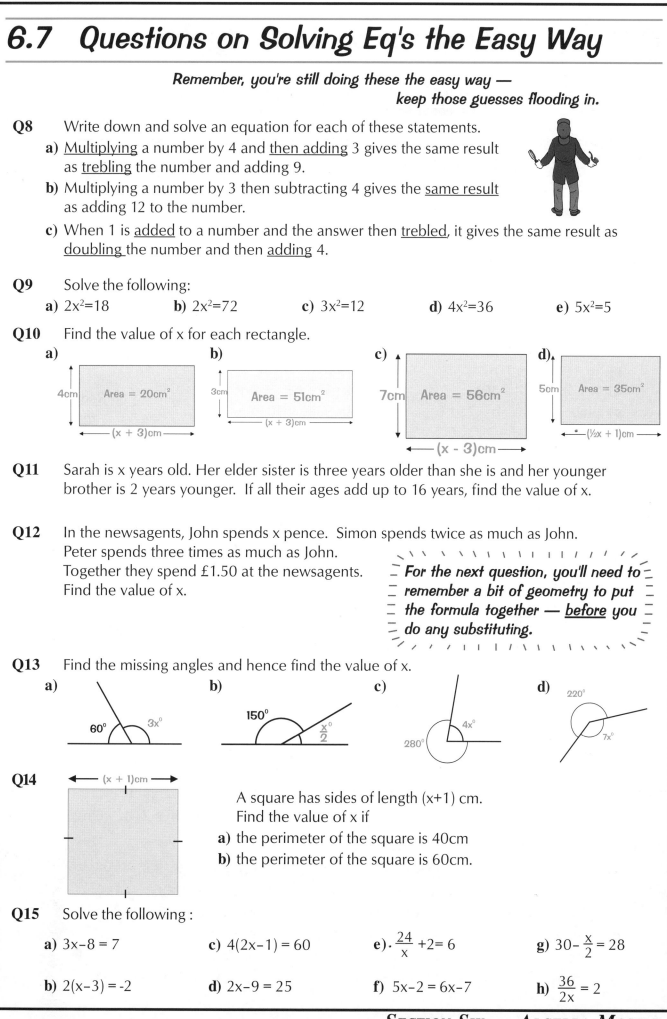

a) 4cm Area = 20cm^2 (x + 3)cm

b) 3cm Area = 51cm^2 (x + 3)cm

c) 7cm Area = 56cm^2 (x - 3)cm

d) 5cm Area = 35cm^2 (½x + 1)cm

Q11 Sarah is x years old. Her elder sister is three years older than she is and her younger brother is 2 years younger. If all their ages add up to 16 years, find the value of x.

Q12 In the newsagents, John spends x pence. Simon spends twice as much as John. Peter spends three times as much as John. Together they spend £1.50 at the newsagents. Find the value of x.

For the next question, you'll need to remember a bit of geometry to put the formula together — <u>before</u> you do any substituting.

Q13 Find the missing angles and hence find the value of x.

a) 60° 3x°

b) 150° $\frac{x}{2}$°

c) 280° 4x°

d) 220° 7x°

Q14 (x + 1)cm

A square has sides of length (x+1) cm. Find the value of x if

a) the perimeter of the square is 40cm

b) the perimeter of the square is 60cm.

Q15 Solve the following :

a) $3x-8 = 7$

b) $2(x-3) = -2$

c) $4(2x-1) = 60$

d) $2x-9 = 25$

e) $\frac{24}{x} +2= 6$

f) $5x-2 = 6x-7$

g) $30-\frac{x}{2} = 28$

h) $\frac{36}{2x} = 2$

6.8 Questions on Basic Algebra

OK, it says basic, but it isn't a doddle. Things'll easily go wrong unless you really think about what you're doing — keep going 'till your brain hurts.

Simplifying means collecting like terms together:	**Expanding means removing brackets:**
$8x^2 + 2x + 4x^2 - x + 4$ becomes $12x^2 + x + 4$	Eg $4(x + y) = 4x + 4y$
x^2 term, x term, x^2 term, x term, number term	$x(2 + x) = 2x + x^2$
	$-(a + b) = -a - b$

Q1 By collecting like terms, simplify the following:

a) $3x + 4y + 12x - 5y$

b) $11a + 6b + 24a + 18b$

c) $5p - 6q - p + 11q$

d) $9f + 16g - 15f - 30g$

e) $14ab + 12cd - ab + 2cd$

f) $4x^2 + 3x + 2x^2 - 5x$

g) $13x^2 - 9x - x^2 + 4x$

h) $8 - 3x^2 + 9x - x^2 + 4x$

i) $3y^2 + 2y - 4 + 8y^2 - y + 10$

j) $8y^2 - 4y + 16y - y^2 + 28$

k) $5xy + 6x + 2xy + 12x$

l) $9abc + 10ab + 14abc$

m) $13xy + 7yx$

n) $7pq + 8p + q + 10qp - q + p$

Remember the rule ab=ba

Q2 Simplify the following:

a) $x \times x$

b) $2x \times x$

c) $2x \times 2x$

d) $3a \times 4b$

e) $6p \times 2q$

f) $8f \times 3g$

g) $2d \times {}^-4e$

h) $2 \times a \times b$

i) $3 \times x \times y$

j) $4 \times x \times x \times 0$

k) $20x \div 4$

l) $4x \div y$

m) $x^3 \div x^2$

n) $12ab \div 3$

o) $40y^2 \div 8y$

All you really need to remember is that the thing outside the brackets multiplies everything inside the brackets — simple as that.

Q3 Remove the <u>brackets</u> and simplify if possible:

a) $2(x + y)$

b) $4(x - y)$

c) $8(x^2 + y^2)$

d) $12(x - 2)$

e) $8(y - 1)$

f) $20(2 - z)$

g) $-2(x - 5)$

h) $-(y - 2)$

i) $-4(5 - z)$

j) $x(y + 2)$

k) $x(y + x)$

l) $x(x + y + z)$

m) $8(a + b) + 2(a + b)$

n) $3(x + y) + 4(x + 3y)$

o) $9(x + y) - 2(x + y)$

p) $4(a + 2b) - (a + 2b)$

q) $4(x - 2) - 2(x - 1)$

r) $14(2m - n) + 2(3n - 6m)$

Q4 Simplify the following:

a) $x(x + 1)$

b) $y(y + 4)$

c) $z(5 + z)$

d) $-2(4 + x)$

e) $-3(y + 3)$

f) $-(z + 1)$

g) $x^2(2 + y)$

h) $x^2(x + 2y)$

i) $x^2(3x + 4 + y)$

j) $5(p^3 + p)$

k) $15(2q + 3r^2)$

l) $-4(e^2 - f + 4)$

m) $2p(p + q) - 3p(p + 2q)$

n) $2x(4 + x) + 3x(x - 1)$

o) $4x(x + 2) + 2x(3 - x)$

p) $x(2x + y) + 3y(3x + 2y)$

q) $4e(e + 2f) + 2f(e - f)$

r) $a(b + c) + b(a + c) + c(a + b)$

6.8 Questions on Basic Algebra

It's best to stick to this method — otherwise you're bound to miss one of the terms.

To multiply out double brackets use **FOIL**:	
<u>F</u>irst — Multiply the first terms in each bracket <u>O</u>utside — Multiply the outside terms <u>I</u>nside — Multiply the inside terms <u>L</u>ast — Multiply the last terms	Eg $(x+2)(3x-4)$ $= (x \times 3x)+(x \times {}^-4)+(2x \times 3)+(2 \times {}^-4)$ $=3x^2-4x+6x-8$ $=3x^2+2x-8$

Q5 For each of the large rectangles below, write down the <u>area</u> of the four smaller rectangles.

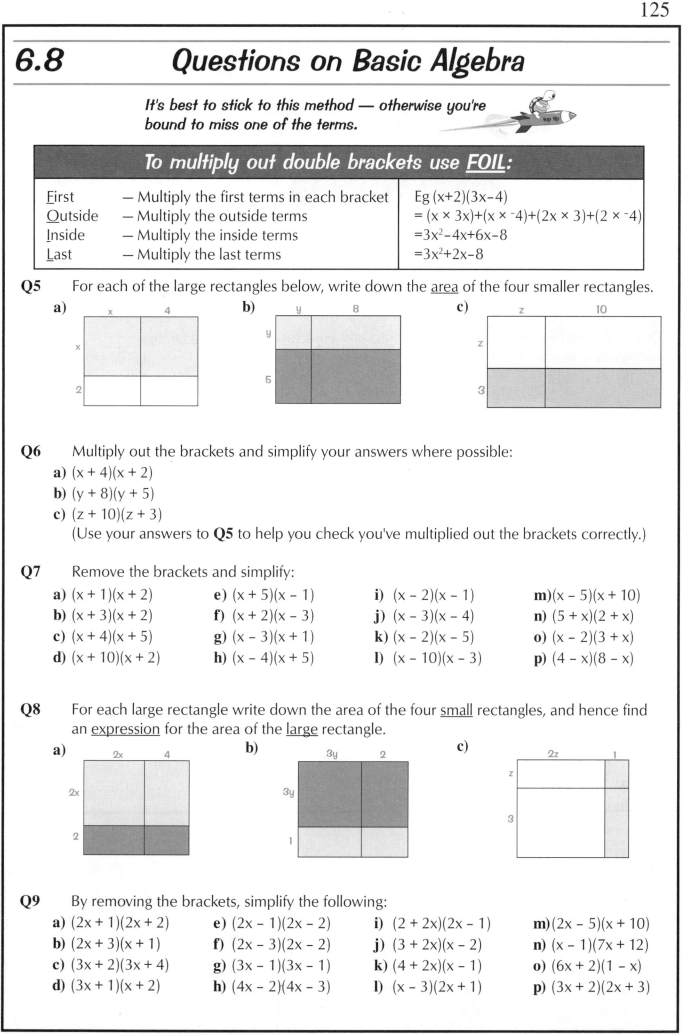

a) x   4   x   2

b) y   8   y   5

c) z   10   z   3

Q6 Multiply out the brackets and simplify your answers where possible:
a) $(x + 4)(x + 2)$
b) $(y + 8)(y + 5)$
c) $(z + 10)(z + 3)$

(Use your answers to **Q5** to help you check you've multiplied out the brackets correctly.)

Q7 Remove the brackets and simplify:
a) $(x + 1)(x + 2)$
b) $(x + 3)(x + 2)$
c) $(x + 4)(x + 5)$
d) $(x + 10)(x + 2)$
e) $(x + 5)(x - 1)$
f) $(x + 2)(x - 3)$
g) $(x - 3)(x + 1)$
h) $(x - 4)(x + 5)$
i) $(x - 2)(x - 1)$
j) $(x - 3)(x - 4)$
k) $(x - 2)(x - 5)$
l) $(x - 10)(x - 3)$
m) $(x - 5)(x + 10)$
n) $(5 + x)(2 + x)$
o) $(x - 2)(3 + x)$
p) $(4 - x)(8 - x)$

Q8 For each large rectangle write down the area of the four <u>small</u> rectangles, and hence find an <u>expression</u> for the area of the <u>large</u> rectangle.

a) 2x   4   2x   2

b) 3y   2   3y   1

c) 2z   1   z   3

Q9 By removing the brackets, simplify the following:
a) $(2x + 1)(2x + 2)$
b) $(2x + 3)(x + 1)$
c) $(3x + 2)(3x + 4)$
d) $(3x + 1)(x + 2)$
e) $(2x - 1)(2x - 2)$
f) $(2x - 3)(2x - 2)$
g) $(3x - 1)(3x - 1)$
h) $(4x - 2)(4x - 3)$
i) $(2 + 2x)(2x - 1)$
j) $(3 + 2x)(x - 2)$
k) $(4 + 2x)(x - 1)$
l) $(x - 3)(2x + 1)$
m) $(2x - 5)(x + 10)$
n) $(x - 1)(7x + 12)$
o) $(6x + 2)(1 - x)$
p) $(3x + 2)(2x + 3)$

6.8 Questions on Basic Algebra

FACTORISING is just putting the brackets back in.
And when you've just spent all that time getting rid of them...

$$7x^2 + 21xy = 7x(x + 3y)$$

largest number that will go into 7 and 21	highest power of x, that will go into each term	y is not in every term so it is not a common factor, and goes inside the brackets

Q11 Rewrite these expressions using brackets. Look for any <u>common factors</u>.

a) $2x + 4y$ e) $2x + 12$ i) $4x - 40$ m) $10x - 8y$

b) $3x + 12y$ f) $3x + 15$ j) $5x - 15$ n) $36x - 27y$

c) $9x + 3y$ g) $24 + 12x$ k) $7x - 49$ o) $24x - 32y$

d) $16x + 4y$ h) $30 + 10x$ l) $8x - 32$ p) $24x - 42$

Q12 Each expression below has <u>2x</u> as a common factor. Factorise the following:

a) $2xy + 4x^2$ c) $2xy - 16x^2z$ e) $10x^2 - 6x^2$ g) $2xy - 4xz$

b) $2xy - 8x^2$ d) $4xy - 6x^2$ f) $10x^2 - 6x$ h) $12xy + 10xz$

Q13 Factorise:

a) $2yx + yz + 3yz$ b) $4ab + 2ac - ad$ c) $9pq + 6pr + 3ps$

Q14 Each term below has <u>a^2</u> as a common factor. Factorise the following:

a) $a^2b + a^2c$ d) $2a^2b + 3a^2c$ g) $2a^2x + 3a^2y + 4a^2z$

b) $4a^2 + 7a^2$ e) $10a^2b^2 + 9a^2c^2$ h) $2a^2b + 3a^2c + a^2$

c) $5a^2 + 13a^2b$ f) $a^3 + a^2y$ i) $a^2b^2 + a^2c^2$

Q15 Each term below has x^2y as a common factor. Factorise the following:

a) $2x^2y + 3x^2y$ c) $11x^2y + x^2y^2$ e) $x^2y + x^2y^2$

b) $9x^2y + 8x^2y$ d) $5x^2y + 4x^2y^2$ f) $x^2y + x^3y + x^2y^2$

Q16 Each term below has <u>4xyz</u> as a common factor. Factorise the following:

a) $4xyz + 8xyz$ c) $8xyz + 16x^2yz$

b) $8xyz + 12xyz$ d) $20x^2y^2z + 16xyz^2$

Q17 Factorise each of the following:

a) $2x + 6$ f) $3y + xy$ k) $12x + 24xyz$

b) $4x + 16$ g) $3y + xy^2$ l) $5x^2 + 10x$

c) $5x + 30$ h) $4y - 8yz$ m) $7x^2 + 21x$

d) $3x - 18$ i) $6x + 12xy$ n) $16x^2 + 8x$

e) $2x + xy$ j) $10z + 20yz$ o) $18y^2 - 9y$

Q18 Factorise:

a) $7a^2bc^2 + 14ab^2c + 21ab^2c^2 + 28a^2b^2 c^2$

b) $100x^2yz + 90x^3yz + 80x^2y^2z + 70x^2yz + 60x^2yz^2$

6.8   Questions on Basic Algebra

It's all here — simplifying, multiplying out brackets <u>and</u> factorising.

How exciting.

Q19   Write using brackets:

a) $4x + 4y$

b) $16x + 8y$

c) $5x + 5y + 5z$

d) $14x + 7y$

e) $20x - 10y$

f) $3ax + 3ay$

Q20   What is the difference between $2a^2 + 3b^2 + 4a - b + 11$ and $a^2 + b^2 + 3a - 2b + 3$?

Q21   A flowerbed has length $(x+10)$ m and width $(x+4)$ m.

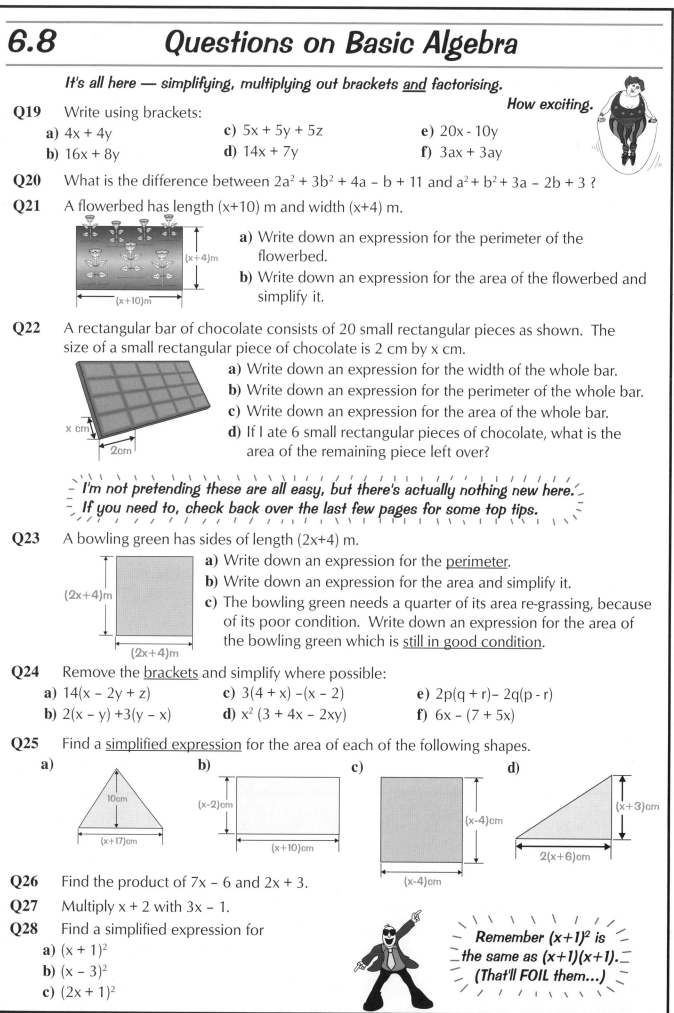

$(x+4)$m

$(x+10)$m

a) Write down an expression for the perimeter of the flowerbed.

b) Write down an expression for the area of the flowerbed and simplify it.

Q22   A rectangular bar of chocolate consists of 20 small rectangular pieces as shown. The size of a small rectangular piece of chocolate is 2 cm by x cm.

x cm

2cm

a) Write down an expression for the width of the whole bar.

b) Write down an expression for the perimeter of the whole bar.

c) Write down an expression for the area of the whole bar.

d) If I ate 6 small rectangular pieces of chocolate, what is the area of the remaining piece left over?

I'm not pretending these are all easy, but there's actually nothing new here. If you need to, check back over the last few pages for some top tips.

Q23   A bowling green has sides of length $(2x+4)$ m.

$(2x+4)$m

$(2x+4)$m

a) Write down an expression for the <u>perimeter</u>.

b) Write down an expression for the area and simplify it.

c) The bowling green needs a quarter of its area re-grassing, because of its poor condition. Write down an expression for the area of the bowling green which is <u>still in good condition</u>.

Q24   Remove the <u>brackets</u> and simplify where possible:

a) $14(x - 2y + z)$

b) $2(x - y) + 3(y - x)$

c) $3(4 + x) - (x - 2)$

d) $x^2 (3 + 4x - 2xy)$

e) $2p(q + r) - 2q(p - r)$

f) $6x - (7 + 5x)$

Q25   Find a <u>simplified expression</u> for the area of each of the following shapes.

a)

10cm

$(x+17)$cm

b)

$(x-2)$cm

$(x+10)$cm

c)

$(x-4)$cm

$(x-4)$cm

d)

$(x+3)$cm

$2(x+6)$cm

Q26   Find the product of $7x - 6$ and $2x + 3$.

Q27   Multiply $x + 2$ with $3x - 1$.

Q28   Find a simplified expression for

a) $(x + 1)^2$

b) $(x - 3)^2$

c) $(2x + 1)^2$

Remember $(x+1)^2$ is the same as $(x+1)(x+1)$. (That'll FOIL them...)

6.9 Questions on Quadratics

It's factorising Jim, but not as we know it... Better watch out with these, I reckon.

Factorising Quadratics

1) A <u>QUADRATIC</u> expression is of the form $[x^2 + bx + c]$
2) <u>FACTORISING</u> a quadratic expression means putting it into two brackets.

Eg: Factorising $x^2 - 2x - 8$
will give $(x - 4)(x + 2)$.

$-8 = -1 \times 8$
-8×1
-2×4
-4×2

To check this works,
multiply out again, using FOIL:
$(x - 4)(x + 2) = x^2 + 2x - 4x - 8$
$= x^2 - 2x - 8$

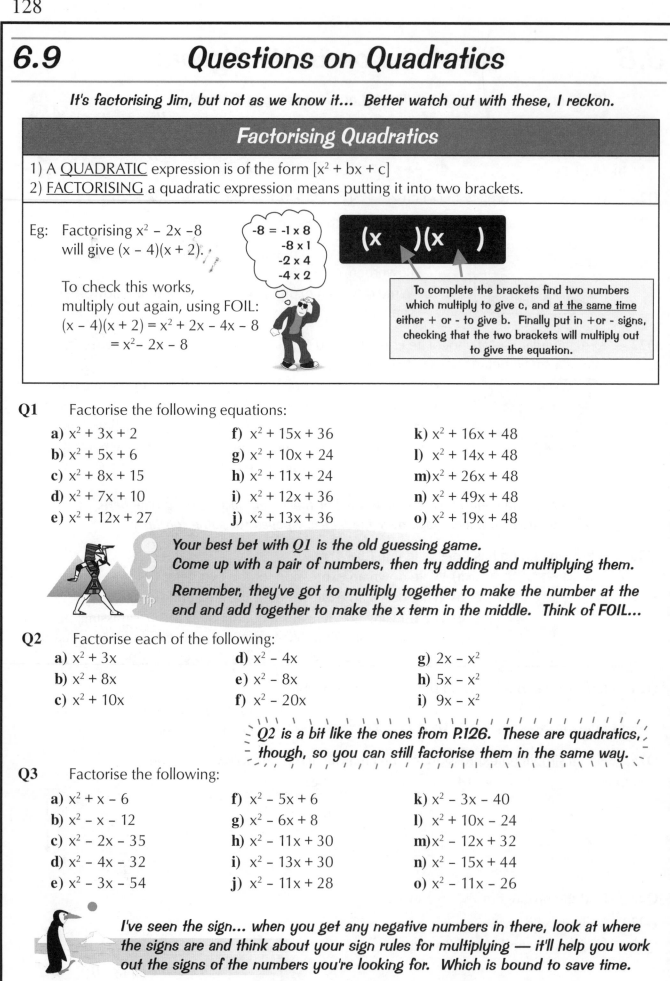

(x)(x -)

To complete the brackets find two numbers
which multiply to give c, and <u>at the same time</u>
either + or - to give b. Finally put in + or - signs,
checking that the two brackets will multiply out
to give the equation.

Q1 Factorise the following equations:

a) $x^2 + 3x + 2$
b) $x^2 + 5x + 6$
c) $x^2 + 8x + 15$
d) $x^2 + 7x + 10$
e) $x^2 + 12x + 27$

f) $x^2 + 15x + 36$
g) $x^2 + 10x + 24$
h) $x^2 + 11x + 24$
i) $x^2 + 12x + 36$
j) $x^2 + 13x + 36$

k) $x^2 + 16x + 48$
l) $x^2 + 14x + 48$
m) $x^2 + 26x + 48$
n) $x^2 + 49x + 48$
o) $x^2 + 19x + 48$

Your best bet with Q1 is the old guessing game.
Come up with a pair of numbers, then try adding and multiplying them.

Remember, they've got to multiply together to make the number at the
end and add together to make the x term in the middle. Think of FOIL...

Q2 Factorise each of the following:

a) $x^2 + 3x$
b) $x^2 + 8x$
c) $x^2 + 10x$

d) $x^2 - 4x$
e) $x^2 - 8x$
f) $x^2 - 20x$

g) $2x - x^2$
h) $5x - x^2$
i) $9x - x^2$

Q2 is a bit like the ones from P.126. These are quadratics,
though, so you can still factorise them in the same way.

Q3 Factorise the following:

a) $x^2 + x - 6$
b) $x^2 - x - 12$
c) $x^2 - 2x - 35$
d) $x^2 - 4x - 32$
e) $x^2 - 3x - 54$

f) $x^2 - 5x + 6$
g) $x^2 - 6x + 8$
h) $x^2 - 11x + 30$
i) $x^2 - 13x + 30$
j) $x^2 - 11x + 28$

k) $x^2 - 3x - 40$
l) $x^2 + 10x - 24$
m) $x^2 - 12x + 32$
n) $x^2 - 15x + 44$
o) $x^2 - 11x - 26$

I've seen the sign... when you get any negative numbers in there, look at where
the signs are and think about your sign rules for multiplying — it'll help you work
out the signs of the numbers you're looking for. Which is bound to save time.

Q4 Factorise the <u>quadratic expression</u> $x^2 + 90x - 1000$.

6.9 Questions on Quadratics

We're solving them now — but it's OK, it's only an (easy) step on from factorising.

Solving Quadratic Equations

1) A <u>QUADRATIC EQUATION</u> is usually of the form $[x^2 + bx + c = 0]$
2) It can be factorised to give $(x \pm ?)(x \pm ?) = 0$
3) To find the <u>two</u> answers <u>either</u> the <u>first</u> bracket must equal zero, <u>or</u> the <u>second</u> bracket must <u>equal zero</u>.

Eg: Solve
$x^2 - 4x = 21$
$x^2 - 4x - 21 = 0$
$(x - 7)(x + 3) = 0$
<u>x=7</u> or <u>x=-3</u>

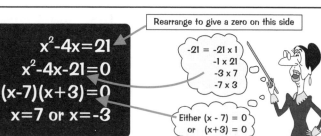

Rearrange to give a zero on this side

$x^2 - 4x = 21$
$x^2 - 4x - 21 = 0$
$(x-7)(x+3) = 0$
x=7 or x=-3

$-21 = -21 \times 1$
-1×21
-3×7
-7×3

Either $(x - 7) = 0$
or $(x+3) = 0$

Q5 Solve the following quadratic equations:

a) $(x + 4)(x - 3) = 0$
b) $(x + 2)(x + 8) = 0$
c) $(x - 1)(x - 7) = 0$
d) $(x + 4)(x + 18) = 0$
e) $(x - 3)(x - 11) = 0$
f) $(x - 2)^2 = 0$
g) $(x + 3)^2 = 0$
h) $(x - 9)^2 = 0$

i) $(x + 4)^2 = 0$
j) $(x - 25)^2 = 0$
k) $x(x + 4) = 0$
l) $x(x - 7) = 0$
m) $x(x + 30) = 0$
n) $x(x + 2) = 0$
o) $(3 - x)(4 - x) = 0$

For the ones where you get one bracket squared, eg $(x+1)^2 = 0$, there's only the one answer (Which is x=-1, in this case).

Q6 Find x by solving the following quadratic equations:

a) $x^2 + 6x + 8 = 0$
b) $x^2 + 3x - 10 = 0$
c) $x^2 + 10x + 25 = 0$
d) $x^2 - 5x + 6 = 0$
e) $x^2 - 6x + 9 = 0$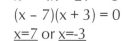

f) $x^2 - 2x + 1 = 0$
g) $x^2 - 3x - 18 = 0$
h) $x^2 - 4x + 3 = 0$
i) $x^2 - 7x + 10 = 0$
j) $x^2 - x - 20 = 0$

k) $x^2 - 4x - 5 = 0$
l) $x^2 + 9x + 8 = 0$
m) $x^2 + 6x - 7 = 0$
n) $x^2 + x - 12 = 0$
o) $x^2 + 14x + 49 = 0$

(Don't forget you've got to factorise before you start solving.)

Q7 Rearrange into the form $x^2 + bx + c = 0$, then solve by factorising:

a) $x^2 - 2x = 15$
b) $x^2 + 5x = 14$
c) $x^2 + 6x = 16$
d) $x^2 + 4x = 21$
e) $x^2 + 5x = 36$

f) $x^2 + 4x = 45$
g) $x^2 - 3x = 10$
h) $x^2 = 5x$
i) $x^2 = 7x$
j) $x^2 = 11x$

k) $x^2 - 21 = 4x$
l) $x^2 - 63 = 2x$
m) $x^2 - 300 = 20x$
n) $x^2 + 48 = 26x$
o) $x^2 + 36 = 13x$

Q8 David is 3 years younger than his sister Jane.

a) If David is x years old, write down Jane's age as an expression containing x.

b) If the product of David and Jane's age is 130, use **a)** to form an equation involving x and then solve it.

c) How old is David?

Just in case you wondered... yes you do need to form a quadratic equation for Q8. Multiply out the expression from a), then treat it like Q7 — rearrange, factorise, solve. You'll have to pick the sensible answer though — there'll be one that doesn't make sense.

6.9 *Questions on Quadratics*

Most quadratics have 2 answers, but sometimes one isn't a sensible one so ignore it. You can't have negative lengths, for example — that would just be silly.

*(You've had a sneak preview of this type of question...
if you did Q8 OK, these won't be much trouble either.)*

Q9 When a number x is added to its <u>square</u>, the total is 30. Find the value of x.

Q10

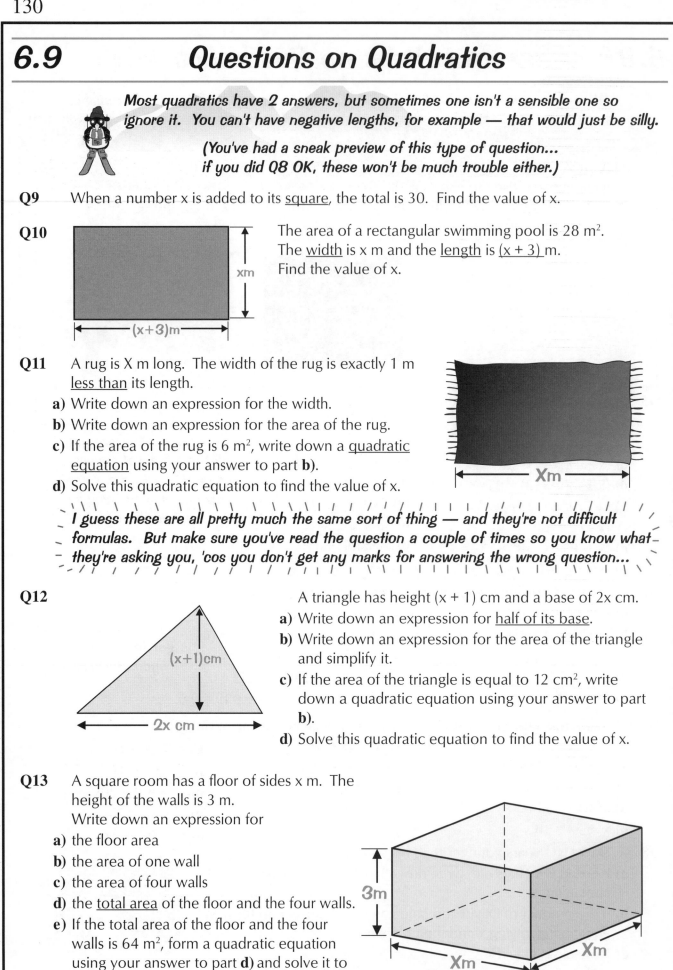

The area of a rectangular swimming pool is 28 m². The <u>width</u> is x m and the <u>length</u> is <u>(x + 3)</u> m. Find the value of x.

Q11 A rug is X m long. The width of the rug is exactly 1 m <u>less than</u> its length.

  a) Write down an expression for the width.
  b) Write down an expression for the area of the rug.
  c) If the area of the rug is 6 m², write down a <u>quadratic equation</u> using your answer to part **b)**.
  d) Solve this quadratic equation to find the value of x.

I guess these are all pretty much the same sort of thing — and they're not difficult formulas. But make sure you've read the question a couple of times so you know what they're asking you, 'cos you don't get any marks for answering the wrong question...

Q12

A triangle has height (x + 1) cm and a base of 2x cm.

  a) Write down an expression for <u>half of its base</u>.
  b) Write down an expression for the area of the triangle and simplify it.
  c) If the area of the triangle is equal to 12 cm², write down a quadratic equation using your answer to part **b)**.
  d) Solve this quadratic equation to find the value of x.

Q13 A square room has a floor of sides x m. The height of the walls is 3 m. Write down an expression for

  a) the floor area
  b) the area of one wall
  c) the area of four walls
  d) the <u>total area</u> of the floor and the four walls.
  e) If the total area of the floor and the four walls is 64 m², form a quadratic equation using your answer to part **d)** and solve it to find the value of x.

6.10   Questions on Solving Eq's with Graphs

Seems there's no end to the number of ways you can solve these equations — this next one's really easy, too.

Finding solutions to equations

a) $x^2 - 2x = 0$, so x=0 or x=2

Solve $x^2-2x=0$
by looking at the y=0 line
ie. where the graph cuts the x axis

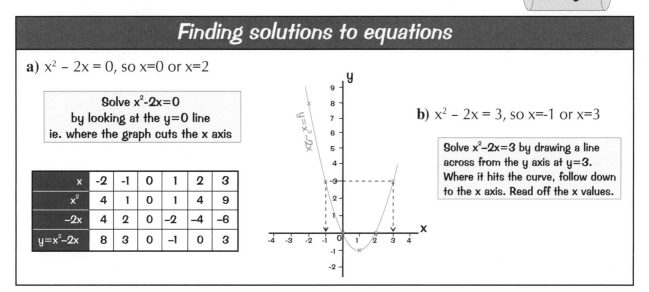

b) $x^2 - 2x = 3$, so x=-1 or x=3

Solve $x^2-2x=3$ by drawing a line across from the y axis at y=3. Where it hits the curve, follow down to the x axis. Read off the x values.

x	-2	-1	0	1	2	3
x^2	4	1	0	1	4	9
$-2x$	4	2	0	-2	-4	-6
$y=x^2-2x$	8	3	0	-1	0	3

Write down the <u>solutions</u> of the <u>quadratic equations</u> by reading them from the graphs below. Check your answers by <u>substituting</u> them into the equations.

Q1   Solve:
   a) $3x - x^2 = 0$ and **b)** $3x - x^2 = 2$

   e) $x^2 - 2x + 1 = 0$ and **f)** $x^2 - 2x + 1 = 4$

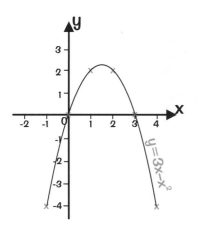

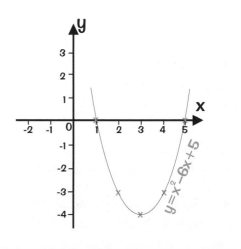

   c) $3 - x^2 = 2$ and **d)** $3 - x^2 = -1$

   g) $x^2 - 6x + 5 = 0$ and **h)** $x^2 - 6x + 5 = -3$

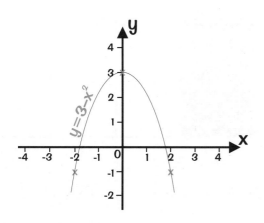

6.10   Questions on Solving Eq's with Graphs

Q2   Use the graph opposite to solve the following:
a) $x^2 - 7x + 6 = 0$
b) $x^2 - 7x + 6 = -4$
c) $x^2 - 7x + 6 = -6$

(graph labelled $y = x^2 - 7x + 6$)

Q3   Solve:
a) $x^2 - 3x + 1 = 0$
b) $x^2 - 3x = 0$

(graph labelled $y = x^2 - 3x + 1$)

 top tip

You'll need quite a good graph with a nice smooth curve to solve these equations, so be as neat as you can with your plotting. If you don't draw it carefully, then the line won't cross the axis in the right place and your answer won't be right either.

Q4 a) Complete the table of values for the <u>quadratic graph</u> $y = x^2 - 2x - 3$.

x	−2	-1	0	1	2	3	4
x^2	4					9	
−2x	4					−6	
−3	−3					−3	
$y=x^2-2x-3$	5					0	

b) Draw a pair of axes with the axis from −2 to 4 and the Y-axis from −5 to 5.
Plot the graph $y = x^2 - 2x - 3$, joining the coordinates from the table of values, with a <u>smooth</u> curve. Label the curve.

c) Using your graph, solve the following quadratics:
i) $x^2 - 2x - 3 = 0$
ii) $x^2 - 2x - 3 = -3$

Q5 a) Complete the table of values for the quadratic graph $y = x^2 + x - 4$.

x	−3	−2	-1	0	1	2
x^2						
x						
−4						
$y=x^2+x-4$						

b) Draw pair axes with the X-axis from −3 to 2 and the Y-axis from −5 to 2.
Plot the graph $y = x^2 + x - 4$ and label it.

c) Using your graph solve the quadratic equation $x^2 + x - 4 = 2$

d) Using your graph <u>estimate</u> the solutions to the quadratic equation $x^2 + x - 4 = 0$, giving your estimates to 1 dp.

6.10 Questions on Solving Eq's with Graphs

As if that wasn't exciting enough, you can do the
same thing with Cubic graphs...

Solving Cubic Equations

1) Construct a <u>table of values</u> and <u>plot the graph</u>.
2) The graph will always be a smooth curve so you must plot <u>several points</u> to enable you to draw the curve <u>accurately</u>.
3) Use your graph to find the solution.

Q6 Solve (to 1 DP):

a) $x^3 - 3x + 4 = 4$
b) $x^3 - 3x + 4 = 2$
c) $x^3 - 3x + 4 = 6$

Q7 Solve:

a) $2x - x^3 + 2 = 2$
b) $2x - x^3 + 2 = 6$
c) $2x - x^3 + 2 = 3$

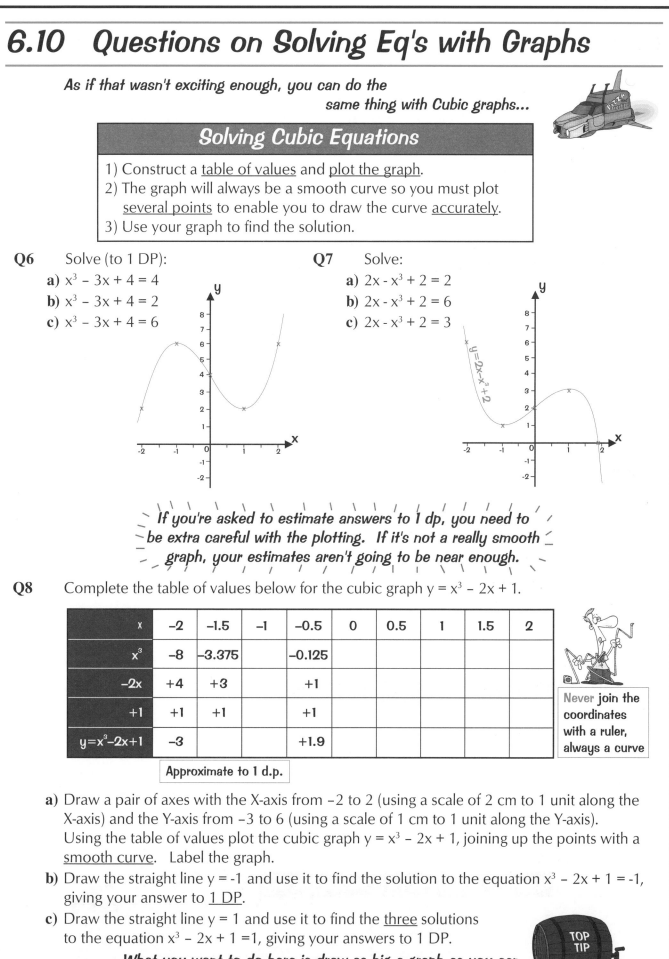

If you're asked to estimate answers to 1 dp, you need to be extra careful with the plotting. If it's not a really smooth graph, your estimates aren't going to be near enough.

Q8 Complete the table of values below for the cubic graph $y = x^3 - 2x + 1$.

x	–2	–1.5	–1	–0.5	0	0.5	1	1.5	2
x^3	–8	–3.375		–0.125					
–2x	+4	+3		+1					
+1	+1	+1		+1					
$y = x^3 - 2x + 1$	–3			+1.9					

Approximate to 1 d.p.

Never join the coordinates with a ruler, always a curve

a) Draw a pair of axes with the X-axis from –2 to 2 (using a scale of 2 cm to 1 unit along the X-axis) and the Y-axis from –3 to 6 (using a scale of 1 cm to 1 unit along the Y-axis). Using the table of values plot the cubic graph $y = x^3 - 2x + 1$, joining up the points with a <u>smooth curve</u>. Label the graph.

b) Draw the straight line y = -1 and use it to find the solution to the equation $x^3 - 2x + 1 = -1$, giving your answer to <u>1 DP</u>.

c) Draw the straight line y = 1 and use it to find the <u>three</u> solutions to the equation $x^3 - 2x + 1 = 1$, giving your answers to 1 DP.

What you want to do here is draw as big a graph as you can — it'll be easier to read off the answers, especially when you have to make them accurate to one decimal place.

TOP TIP

6.11   *Questions on Trial and Improvement*

Solving a Cubic Equation

Eg The cubic equation $x^3 + 2x = 15$ has a solution between 2 and 3. Find this to 1 d.p.

Guess (x)	value of x^3+2x	Too large or too small
2	$2^3+2(2)=12$	Too small
3	$3^3+2(3)=33$	Too large
2.3	$(2.3)^3+2(2.3)=16.767$	Too large
2.2	$(2.2)^3+2(2.2)=15.048$	Too large …Just!
2.1	$(2.1)^3+2(2.1)=13.461$	Too small
2.15	$(2.15)^3+2(2.15)=14.238$	Too small

> 2 gave an answer closer to 15 so the next guess should be nearer to 2 than 3.

> In this example it looks like x=2.2, but to be totally sure, always try exactly halfway when you reach this stage.

∴ To 1 d.p the solution is **x=2.2**

Q1   The cubic equation $x^3 + x = 24$ has a solution between 2 and 3.
Copy and complete the table below and use it to find this solution to <u>1 DP</u>.

Guess (x)	value of x^3+x	Too large or too small
2	$2^3+2=$	
3	$3^3+3=$	

> Extend the table as necessary

Q2   The cubic equation $x^3 - x = 34$ has a solution between 3 and 4.
Copy and complete the table below and use it to find this solution to <u>1 DP</u>.

Guess (x)	value of $x^3- x$	Too large or too small
3	$3^3- 3=$	
4	$4^3- 4=$	

Q3   The cubic equation $3x - x^3 = 20$ has a solution between −4 and −3.
Copy and complete the table below and use it to find this solution to <u>1 DP</u>.

Guess (x)	value of $3x-x^3$	Too large or too small
-4	$3(-4)-(-4)^3=52$	
-3	$3(-3)-(-3)^3=$	

> Remember
> $(-4)^3 = -4\times-4\times-4$
> $= -64$

> Remember
> $-(-4)^3 = -(-64)$
> $=+64$

6.11   *Questions on Trial and Improvement*

Q4 The cubic equation $2x^3 - x = 40$ has a solution <u>between 2 and 3</u>. Use the table to find this solution to 1 DP.

Guess (x)	value of 2x³ - x	Too large or too small
2	2(2)³ - (2) =	
3	2(3)³ - (3) =	

Q5 The cubic equation $x^3 - x^2 = 0.7$ has a solution <u>between 1 and 2</u>. Use the table to find this solution to 1 DP.

Guess (x)	Value of x³ - x²	Too large or too small
1	(1)³ - (1)² =	
2	(2)³ - (2)² =	

Q6 The cubic equation $x^3 - x^2 + x = 7$ has a solution between 2 and 3. Use the table to find this solution to <u>1 DP</u>.

Guess (x)	Value of x³ - x² + x	Too large or too small
2	(2)³ - (2)² + (2) =	
3	(3)³ - (3)² + (3) =	

Q7 The cubic equation $2x^3 - x^2 = 50$ has a solution between 3 and 4. Use the table to find this solution to <u>1 DP</u>.

Guess (x)	value of 2x³ – x²	Too large or too small
3	2(3)³ - (3)² =	
4	2(4)³ - (4)² =	

*Just to go one better than the quadratics, cubics have **3** solutions. How about that. I hope you're really impressed...*

Q8 The cubic equation $x^3 + x^2 - 4x = 3$ has <u>three solutions</u>.
The first solution lies between –3 and –2. The second solution lies between –1 and 0.
The third solution lies between 1 and 2.

Guess (x)	value of x³ + x² - 4x	Too large or too small
-3	(-3)³ + (-3)² -4(-3) =	
-2	(-2)³ + (-2)² -4(-2) =	
-1	(-1)³ + (-1)² -4(-1) =	
0	(0)³ + (0)² -4(0) =	
1	(1)³ + (1)² -4(1) =	
2	(2)³ + (2)² -4(2) =	

The first solution is _____ to 1 d.p.

Extend the table where needed

The second solution is _____ to 1 d.p.

The third solution is _____ to 1 d.p.

6.12   Questions on Rearranging Formulas

Rearranging is getting the letter you want out of the
formula and making it the subject.

Example:- Rearrange the formula $p = 3q + r$ to make q the subject.

$p = 3q + r$

$p - r = 3q$ Subtract r from each side

$\dfrac{p - r}{3} = q$ Divide by 3

$q = \dfrac{p - r}{3}$ Rewrite starting with new subject

Remember
The same method applies to rearranging formulas as solving equations

Q1   Rearrange the following formulas to make the <u>letter in brackets</u> the new subject:

a) $y = x + 4$ ....(x)   **f)** $s = 4t - 3$ ....(t)   **k)** $y = 4 - 2x$ ....(x)   **p)** $a = 3(b - 2)$ ....(b)

b) $y = 2x + 3$ ....(x)   **g)** $y = 3x + \frac{1}{2}$ .....(x)   **l)** $x = 8 - 3z$ ....(z)   **q)** $d = \frac{1}{2}(c + 4)$ ......(c)

c) $y = 4x - 5$ ....(x)   **h)** $y = 3 - x$ ....(x)   **m)** $g = 10 - 4h$ ......(h)   **r)** $e = 5(f - 3)$ ....(f)

d) $a = 7b + 10$ ....(b)   **i)** $p = 4 - q$ ....(q)   **n)** $y = 5(x + 2)$ ......(x)   **s)** $g = -(h + 2)$ ....(h)

e) $w = 14 + 2z$ ...(z)   **j)** $f = 12 - g$ ....(g)   **o)** $s = 3(t + 4)$ ....(t)   **t)** $j = -2(3 - k)$ ....(k)

Q2   Rearrange the following, to make the <u>letter in brackets</u> the subject of the formulas:

a) $y = \dfrac{x}{10}$ ....(x)   **d)** $d = \dfrac{3e}{4}$ ....(e)   **g)** $y = \dfrac{x}{2} - 3$ ......(x)

b) $s = \dfrac{t}{14}$ ....(t)   **e)** $f = \dfrac{3g}{8}$ ....(g)   **h)** $a = \dfrac{b}{3} - 5$ .....(b)

c) $a = \dfrac{2b}{3}$ ....(b)   **f)** $y = \dfrac{x}{5} + 1$ ...(x)   **i)** $c = \dfrac{d}{4} + 3$ ....(d)

Q3   A car sales person is paid £w for working m months and selling c cars, where
$W = 500m + 50c$.

a) Rearrange the formula to make <u>c the subject</u>.

b) Find the number of cars the sales person sells in 11 months if he earns £12,100 during that time.

Q4   The cost of hiring a spacetaxi is £28 per light year plus 25p per mile.

a) Find the cost of hiring the spacetaxi and travelling

   i) 40 miles   **ii)** 80 miles

b) Write down a formula to give £c the cost of hiring a spacetaxi, in pounds, for one light year and travelling n miles.

c) Rearrange the formula to make <u>n the subject</u>.

d) Find out how many miles you can travel during one light year if you have a budget of

   i) £34   **ii)** £50   **iii)** £56.50

Q5   The rectangle has length l cm and width w cm. Its perimeter is p cm.

a) Write down a <u>formula</u> with p as the subject.

b) Rearrange this to make l the subject.

c) Find the length of a rectangle of width 7.5 cm and perimeter 44 cm.

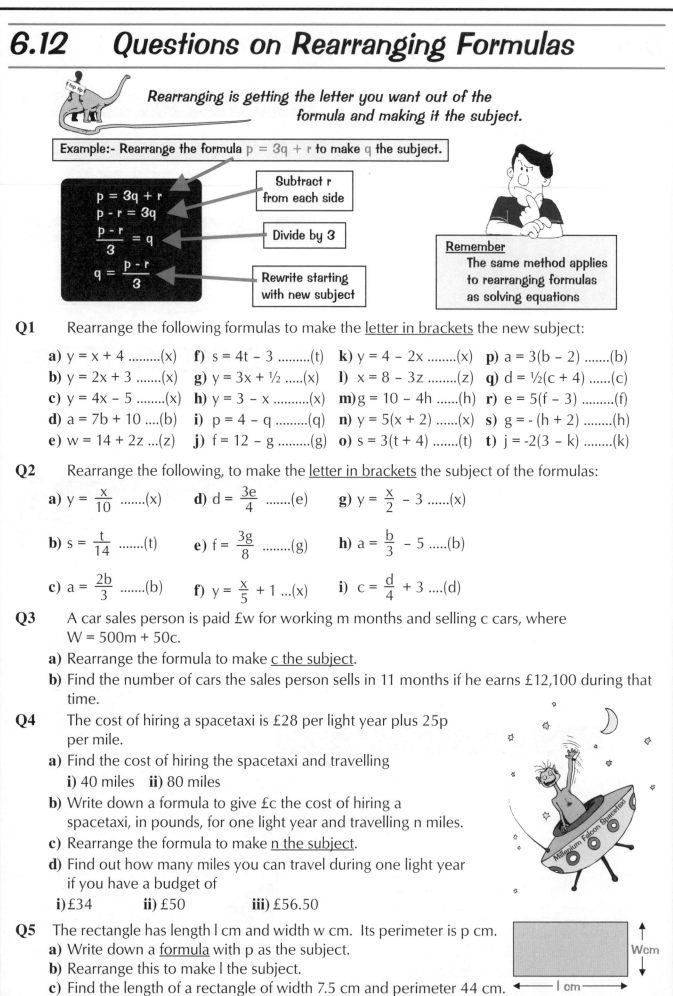

6.12   Questions on Rearranging Formulas

Q6   Rearrange the following formulas to make the letter in brackets the new subject.

a) $y = x^2$ ....(x)

b) $a = 2b^2$ ....(b)

c) $p = 4q^2$ ....(q)

d) $d = e^2 + 1$..........(e)

e) $y = x^2 - 2$ ....(x)

f) $y = \sqrt{x}$ ....(x)

g) $y = \sqrt{x} + 1$ ....(x)

h) $a = \sqrt{b} - 2$ ....(b)

i) $y = \sqrt{x+3}$ ....(x)

j) $y = (x + 2)^2$ ....(x)

k) $s = (t - 3)^2$ ....(t)

l) $y = (2x)^2$ ....(x)

m) $p = (3q)^2$ ....(q)

n) $r = \left(\dfrac{s}{2}\right)^2$ ....(s)

o) $a = \dfrac{b-2}{3}$ ....(b)

p) $y = \dfrac{x+5}{2}$ ....(x)

q) $f = \dfrac{g+5}{2}$ ....(g)

r) $w = \dfrac{5-z}{2}$ ....(z)

Q7   Rearrange each of these scientific formulas to make the letter in brackets the new subject.

a) $C = 2pr$ ....(r)

b) $A = pr^2$ ....(r)

c) $V = u + at$ ....(u)

d) $V = u + at$ ....(t)

e) $V = \frac{1}{3}x^2h$ ....(h)

f) $V = \frac{1}{3}x^2h$ ....(x)

g) $E = \frac{1}{2}mv^2$ ....(v)

h) $V^2 = u^2 + 2as$ .....(a)

i) $V = \sqrt{2gh}$ ....(g)

j) $F = \dfrac{9}{5}C + 32$ ..(C)

k) $I = \dfrac{PRT}{100}$ ....(R)

l) $t = 2p\sqrt{\dfrac{l}{g}}$ ....(l)

Q8   Mrs Smith buys x jumpers for £J each and sells them in her shop for a total price of £T.

a) Write down an expression for the amount of money she <u>paid</u> for all the jumpers.

b) Using your answer to **a)**, write down a formula for the <u>profit</u> £P, Mrs Smith makes selling all the jumpers.

c) Rearrange this formula to make <u>J the subject</u>.

d) Given that Mrs Smith makes a profit of £156 by selling 13 jumpers for a total of £364 find the price she paid for each jumper originally.

Q9   The cost of developing a film is 12p per print plus 60p postage.

a) Find the cost of developing a film with **i)** 12 prints **ii)** 24 prints.

b) Write down a formula for the cost C, in pence, of developing x prints.

c) Rearrange the formula to make <u>x the subject</u>.

d) Find the number of prints developed when a customer is charged
  i) £4.92 **ii)** £6.36 **iii)**£12.12.

Don't forget to change £ into pence. (That's the sort of crafty trick they'll pull on you in the Exam, so watch out for it...)

Q10   The number of chrysanthemums n, Mr Green plants in the Spring depends on the area of his flower bed, F m², and the area of his vegetable plot, V m². If n = 3(F + 2V),

a) Find the value of n when F = 12 m² and V = 8 m².

b) Rearrange the formula to make F the subject.

c) Find the value of F when n = 30 and V = 3 m².

d) Rearrange the formula to make <u>V the subject</u>.

e) Find the value of V when n = 42 and F = 6 m².

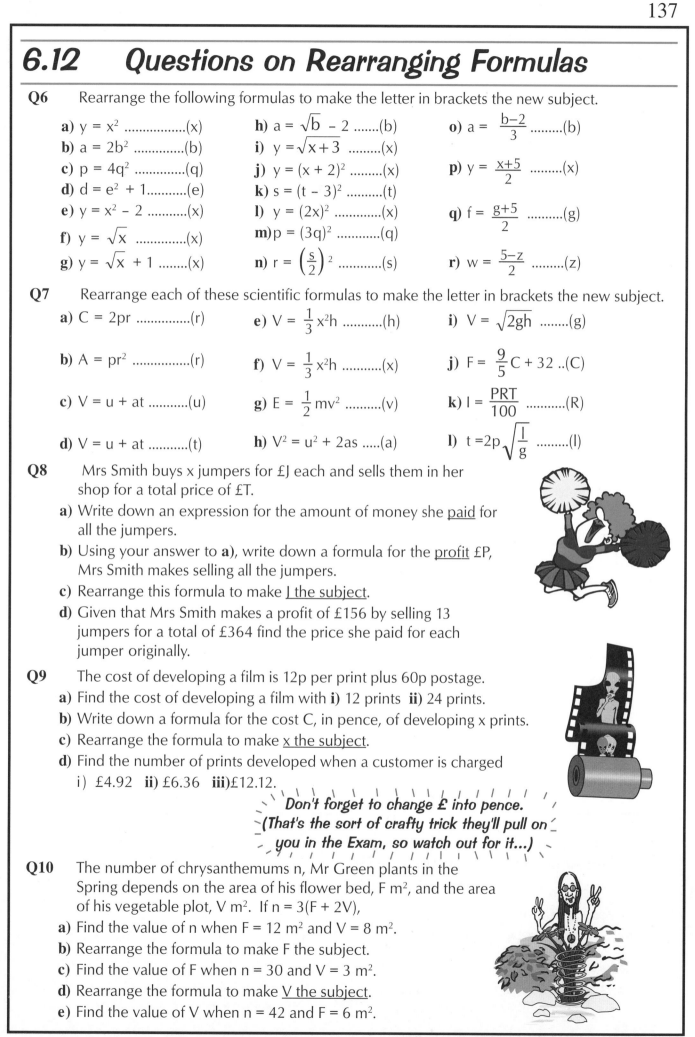

6.13 Questions on Simultaneous Equations

The name makes it sound scary, but these are just 2 equations with the same solutions.

Q1 By substituting x = 3 and y = 4 into the following equations, show that these values are solutions to the equations: $4x + y = 16$ $2x - y = 2$.

Q2 Show by substitution that x = 4 and y = -2, are the solutions to both these equations:
$3x - 4y = 20$ $5x + 2y = 16$.

Q3 Show by substitution that x = -5 and y = 0, are the solutions to both these equations:
$3y - 2x = 10$ $3x + 2y = -15$

Q4 Given that x and y satisfy the following equations, find the value of y when x = 4:
$2x - y = 8$ $3x - 4y = 12$

Q5 Given that x and y satisfy the following equations, find the value of x when y = 3:
$3x + 4y = 24$ $5x - 5y = 5$

Q6 Given that x and y satisfy the following equations, find the value of y when x = -2:
$5y - 3x = 16$ $4y + x = 6$

To solve simultaneous equations from scratch, you've got to get rid of either x or y first — to leave you with an equation with just one unknown in it. You do this by adding or subtracting equations — have a look at this example:

Eg: solve the simultaneous equations $2x + 3y = 13$ and $2x - y = 1$.

1) There is a <u>2x</u> in both equations, so <u>eliminate x</u> by <u>subtracting</u> one equation from the other: $(2x - 2x) + (3y - ^-y) = (13 - 1)$,
so $4y = 12$ hence $y = 3$

2) Then <u>substitute</u> y = 3 back into either equation, to find x: $2x + 9 = 13$
$2x = 13 - 9 = 4$ hence $x = 2$

Q7 Use the above example as a guide to solve the following:

a) $3x + y = 7$
     $2x - y = 3$

b) $x + y = 12$
     $x - y = 2$

c) $x + 3y = 10$
     $x - y = -2$

d) $5x + 2y = 3$
     $2x - 2y = 4$

e) $4x - y = 13$
     $2x - y = 5$

f) $8x + 3y = 8$
     $5x - 3y = 5$

g) $x + 3y = 10$
     $2x - 3y = 2$

h) $8x + 6y = 2$
     $2x - 6y = 3$

i) $x - 12y = 16$
     $5x + 12y = 8$

j) $10x - 2y = -8$
     $10x + y = 19$

k) $11x + 3y = 5$
     $7x - 3y = 13$

l) $2x + 7y = 11$
     $2x + 3y = 7$

m) $x + 8y = 7$
     $4x + 8y = 4$

n) $5x - 3y = -2$
     $-5x + y = 4$

Q8 Rearrange <u>one</u> of the equations <u>before</u> eliminating either the x term or y term by adding or subtracting the pair of equations, then solve:

a) $3y - 4x = 10$
     $4x - 2y = -8$

b) $3x + y = 13$
     $2y - 3x = 8$

c) $3y + 4x = 10$
     $4x - 2y = -8$

d) $y + 1 = 3x$
     $y - x = 3$

e) $y + x = 2$
     $y - \frac{1}{2}x + 1 = 0$

f) $y - 3 = 2x$
     $y = x - 1$

g) $4y - 3x = 22$
     $3x - 2y = -14$

h) $y = 5 - 2x$
     $y = x - 4$

i) $2y + x = 2$
     $y + x + 1 = 0$

j) $3y + 2x = 19$
     $2x + y = 1$

k) $9x - y = 12$
     $4y - 9x = 6$

l) $6x + 2y = 5$
     $3y - 6x = 15$

6.13 Questions on Simultaneous Equations

The first thing you've got to do is label the equations A and B.

Multiply one equation by a number before adding or subtracting. Solve the equations.

eg. Solve $3x + y = 17$ ...... (A)
$4x - 2y = 36$ .... (B)

Multiplying (A) by 2, then adding
$6x + 2y = 34$
$+ 4x - 2y = 36$
$10x = 70$
$x = 7$

SUB INTO (A)

$3(7) + y = 17$
$21 + y = 17$
$y = -4$

Remember
When you multiply an equation by 2 *every* term in that equation doubles.
When you multiply an equation by 3 *every* term in that equation trebles.

Remember
Always substitute your first answer back into an *original* equation to find the second answer.
There is less chance of making a mistake this way.

Each time you do a step, write it down — "Multiply A by 2" — that sort of thing. I know it sounds a waste of time, but if you hash things up, it'll be easier to check what went wrong.

Q9 Find x and y in the following:

a) $3x + 2y = 12$
$2x + y = 7$

b) $5x - y = 17$
$2x + 3y = 0$

c) $x + 3y = 11$
$2x + 5y = 19$

d) $5x + 3y = 24$
$x + 5y = -4$

e) $3x + 2y = 3$
$2x + y = 23$

f) $4x + 2y = 8$
$x + 3y = 2$

g) $x + 14y = -2$
$2x + 3y = 21$

h) $3x + 2y = 21$
$2x - y = 7$

i) $6x - y = -4$
$3x - 2y = 1$

j) $5x - 4y = 7$
$7x - 2y = 17$

k) $8x - y = 6$
$7x + 5y = 17$

l) $8x + 3y = 27$
$2x - 5y = 1$

You've got to multiply both equations now — remember to keep writing down all your steps or you'll get in a bit of a pickle with these.

Q10 Multiply **both** equations by a number before adding or subtracting. Solve the equations:

a) $3x + 2y = 13$
$2x + 3y = 7$

b) $4x + 2y = 10$
$7x + 3y = 16$

c) $2x + 3y = 16$
$3x + 2y = 9$

d) $6x - 3y = 3$
$5x - 2y = 4$

e) $7x - 3y = 18$
$5x + 2y = 17$

f) $11x - 3y = 8$
$9x + 4y = 13$

g) $7y - 3x = 2$
$5y - 2x = 2$

h) $5x - 8y = 12$
$4x - 7y = 9$

i) $4x - 2y = -6$
$5x + 3y = 20$

j) $7x + 5y = 66$
$3x - 4y = 16$

k) $10x + 4y = 2$
$8x + 3y = 1$

l) $3x + 4y = 19$
$4x - 3y = -8$

The next few questions are a bit of a mixed bag — there's some rearranging, some multiplying and some plain and simple adding or subtracting. Enjoy.

Q11 Solve the following <u>simultaneous</u> equations:

a) $4x - y = 5$
$2x + y = -2$

b) $5x - 4 = 4y$
$2y + 2 = x$

c) $4x - 3y = 15$
$2x + 3y = 3$

d) $3x + 8y = 24$
$x + y = 3$

e) $3y - 8x = 24$
$3y + 2x = 9$

f) $y = 13 - 4x$
$3x + 2y = 16$

g) $2x - 3y = 1$
$11y - 7x = 5$

h) $y + 1 = 2x$
$y = x + 2$

6.13 Questions on Simultaneous Equations

It's DIY time — you've got to write your own equations, and then solve them. Not asking for much...

Q12 Two numbers x and y have a <u>sum</u> of 15 and a <u>difference</u> of 3.

a) Write a pair of simultaneous equations in x and y.

b) Solve for x and y.

Q13 Two numbers x and y have a sum of 4 and a difference of 12. Find the values of x and y.

(Hint — one is negative.)

Q14 A farmer has a choice of buying 6 sheep and 5 pigs for £430 <u>or</u> 4 sheep and 10 pigs for £500 at auction.

a) If sheep cost £x and pigs cost £y, write down his <u>two choices</u> as a pair of simultaneous equations.

b) Solve for x and y.

Q15 Six apples and four oranges cost £1.90, whereas eight apples and two oranges cost £1.80. Find the cost of an apple and the cost of an orange.

Q16 Find the value of x and y for each of the following rectangles, by first writing down a pair of simultaneous equations and then solving them.

Rectangle 1: top side $3y + 2x$, left side $y + 3x$, right side 6, bottom side 18.

Rectangle 2: top side 12, left side $4y + 5x$, right side 7, bottom side $2x - 3y$.

Rectangle 3: top side $4x - 6y$, left side $x + y$, right side 2, bottom side 13.

Q17 Two groups of people place two orders in a cafe. The first group orders 4 cups of coffee and 2 cups of tea and their bill is for £4.80. The second group orders 3 cups of coffee and 5 cups of tea and their bill is for £6.05.

a) Write down two simultaneous equations involving a cup of coffee (c) and a cup of tea (t).

b) Find the value of c and t, <u>in pence</u>.

Q18 A box has length (x + y) cm, height (y + 4) cm and width 2x cm, where the length is 12 cm and the height is 11 cm.

a) Write down a pair of simultaneous equations involving x and y.

b) Solve the simultaneous equations to find the value of x and y.

c) By substituting in either your value of x or y, find the <u>volume</u> of the cube in cm².

Q19 Two customers enter a shop to buy milk and corn flakes. Mrs Smith buys 5 pints of milk and 2 boxes of corn flakes and spends £3.44. Mr Brown buys 4 pints of milk and 3 boxes of corn flakes and receives £6.03 <u>change</u> after paying with a £10 note.

Write down a pair of simultaneous equations and solve them to find the price in pence of a pint of milk (m) and a box of cornflakes (c).

6.14 Questions on Simultaneous Eq' Graphs

The solution of two simultaneous equations is simply the X and Y values where their graphs cross

1) Simultaneous equations can be plotted as two <u>straight-line graphs</u> on the <u>same axes</u>.
2) The point where the lines cross will have <u>coordinates</u> equal to the <u>values of x and y</u> which satisfy both equations.

Eg: Solve:
$y = x + 1$
$2y + x = 14$

The two lines <u>intersect</u> where <u>x = 4</u> and <u>y = 5</u>, so this is the solution.

Q1 Solve these simultaneous equations by looking at the graphs. Then check your answers by substituting the values back into the equations.

a) $y + 2x = 9$
$3y = x + 6$

b) $y = 2x + 14$
$2y = 8 - x$

c) $x + y = 6$
$3y = x + 6$

d) $y = x + 6$
$3y + x = 18$

e) $y + x = 1$
$3y = x + 11$

f) $y = 2x - 13$
$2y + x + 6 = 0$

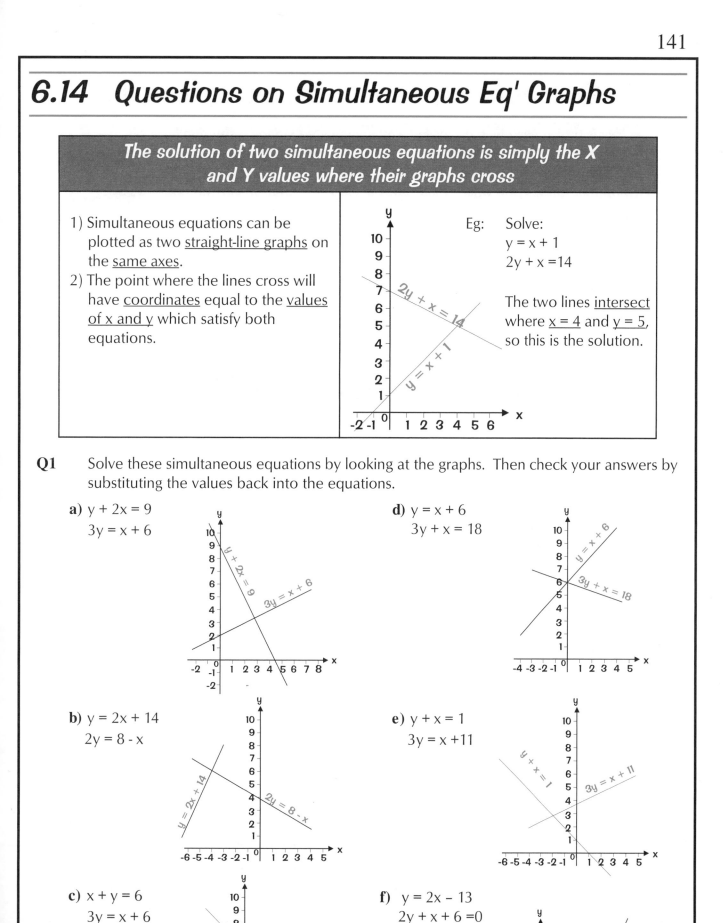

6.14 Questions on Simultaneous Eq' Graphs

This is a nice easy way of solving simultaneous equations. You don't need to do all those steps that can make the other method a little bit tricky. All you have to be able to do is draw two straight line graphs and read off a value where they cross each other. That means you've got to be up to speed with your straight line graphs, though...

For each pair of simultaneous equations below:

a) draw and label a pair of axes with x from –3 to 7, and y from –6 to 6

b) complete the <u>two tables of values</u>

c) plot <u>two straight-line graphs</u> onto your axes, remembering to label each graph

d) use your graphs to find the value of <u>x</u> and <u>y</u>

e) check your answers by <u>substituting</u> them into both of the equations.

Q2 $y = x + 2$
   $y = 3x - 2$

x	–2	0	4
y = x+2	0	2	

x	0	1	2
y = 3x–2	–2		

Q3 $y = 2x - 2$
   $2y = x + 8$

x			
y = 2x-2			

x			
y = ½x+4			

Q4 $y = x + 1$
   $y = 2x - 2$

x			
y = x+1			

x			
y = 2x–2			

Q5 $y = x + 3$
   $y = 3x - 1$

x			
y = x+3			

x			
y = 3x–1			

Q6 $y = 2x + 3$
   $y = x - 1$

x			
y = 2x+3			

x			
y = x–1			

Q7 $y = 2 - x$
   $y = ½x - 1$

x			
y = 2-x			

x			
y = ½x–1			

Q8 $y = x - 1$
   $2y = x + 1$

x			
y = x-1			

x			
y = ½x+½			

Q9 $y = 1 - x$
   $y = 3 - 2x$

x			
y = 1-x			

x			
y = 3-2x			

Q10 $y + 6 = 4x$
   $y - x = 3$

x			
y = 4x-6			

x			
y = 3+x			

Q11 $y = x - 2$
   $y = ½x + 1$

x			
y = x-2			

x			
y =½x+1			

6.15   *Questions on Travel Graphs*

Travel graphs are also called <u>distance-time graphs</u>, because they always show the distance (along the Y-axis) against time (along the X-axis).

Q1 The travel graph shows the <u>journey</u> of a girl cycling from home to her grandparents' house and returning.

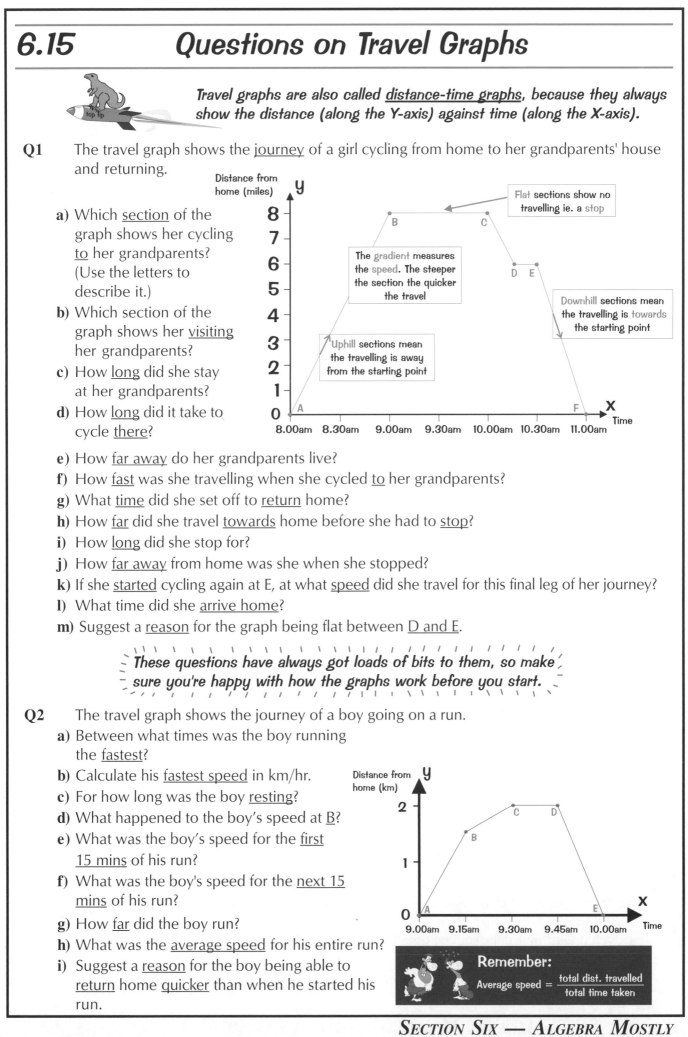

Flat sections show no travelling ie. a stop

The gradient measures the speed. The steeper the section the quicker the travel

Downhill sections mean the travelling is towards the starting point

Uphill sections mean the travelling is away from the starting point

a) Which <u>section</u> of the graph shows her cycling <u>to</u> her grandparents? (Use the letters to describe it.)

b) Which section of the graph shows her <u>visiting</u> her grandparents?

c) How <u>long</u> did she stay at her grandparents?

d) How <u>long</u> did it take to cycle <u>there</u>?

e) How <u>far away</u> do her grandparents live?

f) How <u>fast</u> was she travelling when she cycled <u>to</u> her grandparents?

g) What <u>time</u> did she set off to <u>return</u> home?

h) How <u>far</u> did she travel <u>towards</u> home before she had to <u>stop</u>?

i) How <u>long</u> did she stop for?

j) How <u>far away</u> from home was she when she stopped?

k) If she <u>started</u> cycling again at E, at what <u>speed</u> did she travel for this final leg of her journey?

l) What time did she <u>arrive home</u>?

m) Suggest a <u>reason</u> for the graph being flat between <u>D and E</u>.

These questions have always got loads of bits to them, so make sure you're happy with how the graphs work before you start.

Q2 The travel graph shows the journey of a boy going on a run.

a) Between what times was the boy running the <u>fastest</u>?

b) Calculate his <u>fastest speed</u> in km/hr.

c) For how long was the boy <u>resting</u>?

d) What happened to the boy's speed at <u>B</u>?

e) What was the boy's speed for the <u>first 15 mins</u> of his run?

f) What was the boy's speed for the <u>next 15 mins</u> of his run?

g) How <u>far</u> did the boy run?

h) What was the <u>average speed</u> for his entire run?

i) Suggest a <u>reason</u> for the boy being able to <u>return</u> home <u>quicker</u> than when he started his run.

Remember:
Average speed = $\dfrac{\text{total dist. travelled}}{\text{total time taken}}$

SECTION SIX — ALGEBRA MOSTLY

6.15 *Questions on Travel Graphs*

***Don't worry — there's never anything too tricky in here and they're
all pretty much the same — if you can do one, you can do them all.***

Q3 Two towns A and B are 100 miles apart.
<u>Mr Brown</u> lives in A and decides to drive to <u>town B</u> one afternoon.
<u>Mr Smith</u> lives in B and decides to drive to <u>town A</u> on that same afternoon, along the same route.
Use the travel graph showing their journeys to answer the following:

a) What time did Mr Brown set off?

b) What time did Mr Smith set off?

c) <u>Which motorist</u> completed the 100 mile journey in the <u>shortest time</u>?

d) What was the maximum speed reached by <u>either</u> motorist?

e) Which motorist had to stop and for how long?

f) Suggest a reason for him stopping.

g) Which motorist arrived at their destination <u>first</u>?

h) What occurred at the point X on the travel graph?

***If you're not sure what all the different bits
mean, have a look back on the previous page.***

Q4 A train departs from London at 9 am and travels a total distance of 250 miles, stopping at three stations, Oxford, Derby and then York along the way. His journey is shown on the travel graph below.

a) How many miles is it <u>to Oxford</u> from London?

b) What time did the train <u>arrive</u> in Oxford and how long did it stay?

c) What <u>speed</u> was the train travelling to Oxford?

d) At what speed did the train leave Oxford?

e) For how long did it <u>stop</u> at Derby?

f) How many miles is it from Oxford <u>to Derby</u>?

g) At what speed did it leave Derby?

h) What time did it arrive in York?

i) How long did it stop at York?

j) At what speed did it <u>leave York</u>?

k) What was the <u>average speed</u> for the train's 250 mile journey?

l) What was the total stopping time for the train?

m) If the train had <u>not</u> had to stop at the three stations, what would its average speed have been?

SECTION SIX — ALGEBRA MOSTLY

6.15 Questions on Travel Graphs

Q5 Three boys decide to have a <u>race</u> over a distance of 200 m.
The travel graph below shows the outcome of the race.

a) Who <u>won</u> the race?

b) Who came <u>second</u>?

c) Who did <u>not complete</u> the race and by what distance?

d) How many seconds split 1st and 2nd place?

e) Did Mehmet <u>slow down</u> or <u>speed up</u> as the race progressed?

f) From the graph how would you describe <u>David's</u> speed throughout the race?

g) How many seconds elapsed before Mehmet was able to overtake David?

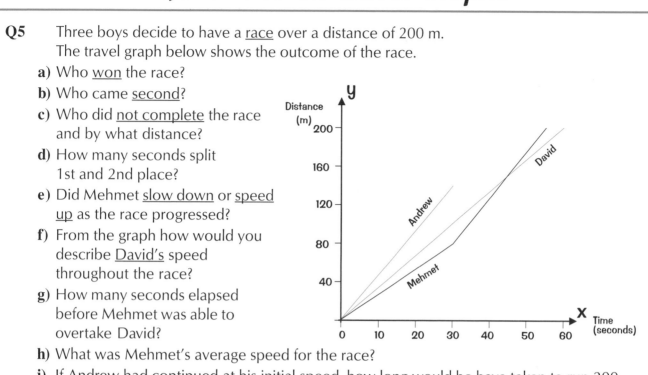

h) What was Mehmet's average speed for the race?

i) If Andrew had <u>continued</u> at his initial speed, how long would he have taken to run 200 metres?

Q6 A cyclist starts from <u>Town A</u> at <u>8 am</u> and cycles at an average speed of <u>10 miles per hour</u>. At <u>9 am</u> a motorist starts the same journey from <u>Town A</u>, but travels at an average speed of <u>30 miles per hour</u>. <u>Draw</u> a <u>travel graph</u> to show these two journeys, then state:

a) at what time the motorist <u>overtakes</u> the cyclist

b) how many <u>miles</u> from Town A this occurs.

Remember that the gradient of the graph is the speed. When you're drawing these graphs, make sure you choose sensible units for your axes, and when you read off the answer, remember to use those units. Don't measure it in cm!!

Q7 A car travels a distance of 80 km in 2 hours. It then <u>alters</u> its speed and travels a further 40 km in 1 hour 45 mins. Assuming that the two speeds are <u>constant</u>, draw a travel graph and use it to determine the <u>average speed</u> for the entire journey.

Q8 A woman sets off on a 4 mile <u>walk</u> from her home. At 12 noon she stops for lunch at a friend's house, where she borrows a bicycle to return home.

a) Describe what the travel graph shows us about her 4 mile walk.

b) How long does she stop for lunch?

c) What is her cycling speed?

d) How far was her friend's house away from her home?

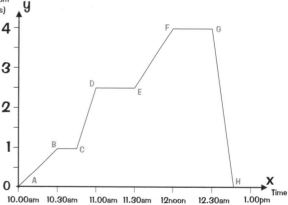

You need to remember what the different bits of a travel graph mean — what it looks like when it's stopped, what it looks like when it's changing speed and what it looks like when it's coming back to its starting point. Have a look back at all these questions and if there are any bits you aren't sure on give them another go until you feel happy with it.

6.16 Questions on Inequalities

Yet another one of those bits of Maths that looks worse than it is
— these are just like equations, really, except for the symbols.

The 4 Inequality Symbols:

> means greater than   < means less than
⩾ means greater than or equal to   ⩽ means less than or equal to

Inequalities can be represented on number lines. You need to know this notation, too:

Eg

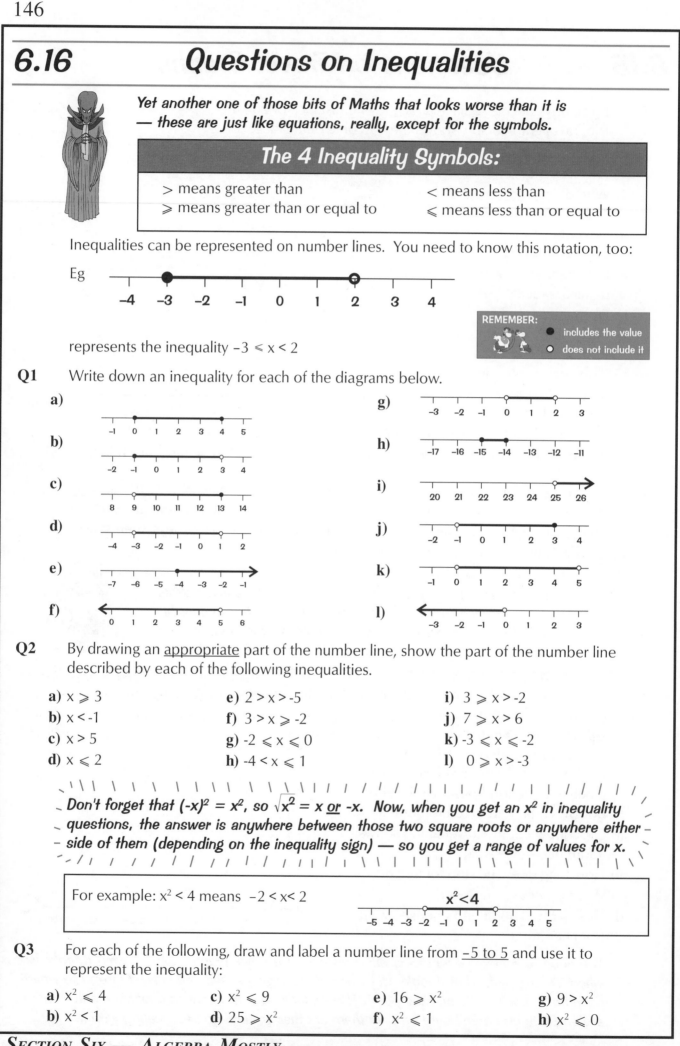

REMEMBER:
● includes the value
○ does not include it

represents the inequality $-3 \leqslant x < 2$

Q1 Write down an inequality for each of the diagrams below.

a)

b)

c)

d)

e)

f)

g)

h)

i)

j)

k)

l)

Q2 By drawing an <u>appropriate</u> part of the number line, show the part of the number line described by each of the following inequalities.

a) $x \geqslant 3$ e) $2 > x > -5$ i) $3 \geqslant x > -2$

b) $x < -1$ f) $3 > x \geqslant -2$ j) $7 \geqslant x > 6$

c) $x > 5$ g) $-2 \leqslant x \leqslant 0$ k) $-3 \leqslant x \leqslant -2$

d) $x \leqslant 2$ h) $-4 < x \leqslant 1$ l) $0 \geqslant x > -3$

Don't forget that $(-x)^2 = x^2$, so $\sqrt{x^2} = x$ <u>or</u> $-x$. Now, when you get an x^2 in inequality questions, the answer is anywhere between those two square roots or anywhere either side of them (depending on the inequality sign) — so you get a range of values for x.

For example: $x^2 < 4$ means $-2 < x < 2$

$x^2 < 4$

Q3 For each of the following, draw and label a number line from <u>−5 to 5</u> and use it to represent the inequality:

a) $x^2 \leqslant 4$ c) $x^2 \leqslant 9$ e) $16 \geqslant x^2$ g) $9 > x^2$

b) $x^2 < 1$ d) $25 \geqslant x^2$ f) $x^2 \leqslant 1$ h) $x^2 \leqslant 0$

6.16   *Questions on Inequalities*

Remember to solve inequalities the same as you would solve equations __EXCEPT__:

> ### Whenever you MULTIPLY OR DIVIDE BY A __NEGATIVE__ __NUMBER__, you must __FLIP THE INEQUALITY SIGN__.

Eg $6 - 3x > 15$	1st subtract 6 from each side
$-3x > 9$	Next $\div$ by -3
$\underline{x < -3}$	Change the direction of the inequality sign

Top Tips

Q4   Solve the following inequalities:

a) $2x \geqslant 16$	**f)** $10x > -2$	**k)** $5x + 4 < 24$
b) $4x > -20$	**g)** $5 + x \geqslant 12$	**l)** $5x + 7 \leqslant 32$
c) $x + 2 > 5$	**h)** $x/4 > 10$	**m)** $3x + 12 \leqslant 30$
d) $x - 3 \leqslant 10$	**i)** $x/3 \leqslant 1$	**n)** $2x - 7 \geqslant 8$
e) $x + 4 \geqslant 14$	**j)** $x/2 \leqslant 4$	**o)** $17 + 4x < 33$

Q5   Solve:

a) $x - 10 \leqslant 0$	**f)** $-x > 2$	**k)** $2(5x - 4) < 32$
b) $3x \geqslant 27$	**g)** $2x/3 > 9$	**l)** $5(x + 2) \geqslant 25$
c) $-2x > 12$	**h)** $3x/4 > -9$	**m)** $4(x - 1) > 40$
d) $-4x < 16$	**i)** $3x + 2 > 11$	**n)** $4(x + 3) \leqslant 32$
e) $-5x < -25$	**j)** $2(x + 3) < 20$	**o)** $9(4 - x) \leqslant 18$

Q6   When a number is __doubled__ and 5 is added, the result is always less than 15. Write this information as an __inequality__ and solve it to show the __possible values__ of the numbers.

When you do wordy questions like these you need to write your own inequality — just the same as you wrote your own equations for questions on p117-119. You'll have to remember to put the right sort of inequality sign in, though. Think about it — can it be the same as the number you're given or will it always be more or less than that number?

Q7   There are __1,130__ pupils in a school and no classes have more than __32__ pupils. How many __classrooms__ could be used? Show this information as an inequality.

Q8   A person is prepared to spend __£300__ taking friends out to celebrate. If the restaurant charges __£12 per head__, how many guests could be invited? Show this information as an inequality.

Q9   Solve the following:

a) $5x - x \geqslant 3x - 10$	**e)** $-2x - 7 \geqslant 9$	**i)** $-4 - x > 8$
b) $4 - 3x < 2x - 1$	**f)** $-x - 8 \geqslant 2$	**j)** $2 - x \leqslant 6$
c) $7 - 2x > 4x - 8$	**g)** $8 - 3x \geqslant 14$	**k)** $16 - x > 1$
d) $7 - 2x \leqslant 4x + 10$	**h)** $16 - x < 11$	**l)** $12 - 3x \leqslant 18$

6.17 Questions on Graphical Inequalities

Inequalities can be represented quite neatly by shading areas on graphs — but it can get quite confusing when you're trying to work out which side of the line to shade. Instead of rushing in with a guess, always check with a coordinate first.

Example:

Show on a graph the region satisfying the inequality $y \leqslant 2x + 1$

Table of values for $y = 2x + 1$

x	0	1	2
y	1	3	5

To decide which side of the line to shade try (0,0)

$y \leqslant 2x + 1$

$(0) \leqslant 2x(0) + 1$

$0 \leqslant 1$ which is <u>true</u>

∴ the region with (0,0) is the region showing $y < 2x + 1$

REMEMBER:

For $y \leqslant$ or $\geqslant$, the line is a solid line. For $<$ or $>$, the line is a dotted line.

$y \leqslant 2x + 1$

The easiest coordinate to try is (0,0), but you can't use it if the line goes through (0,0), so try something like (1,0), (0,1) or (1,1) — it's always best to keep it simple.

Q1 Choose the correct inequality represented by the <u>shaded regions</u> on the following graphs.

a) Is the shaded region

$x + y > 4$

$x + y \geqslant 4$

$x + y < 4$ or

$x + y \leqslant 4$?

$x + y = 4$

c) Is the shaded region

$y \geqslant x - 1$

$y \leqslant x - 1$

$y > x - 1$ or

$y < x - 1$?

$y = x - 1$

b) Is the shaded region

$x + y \geqslant 2$

$x + y \leqslant 2$

$x + y > 2$ or

$x + y < 2$?

$x + y = 2$

d) Is the shaded region

$3y \geqslant 3 - 2x$

$3y \leqslant 3 - 2x$

$3y > 3 - 2x$ or

$3y < 3 - 2x$?

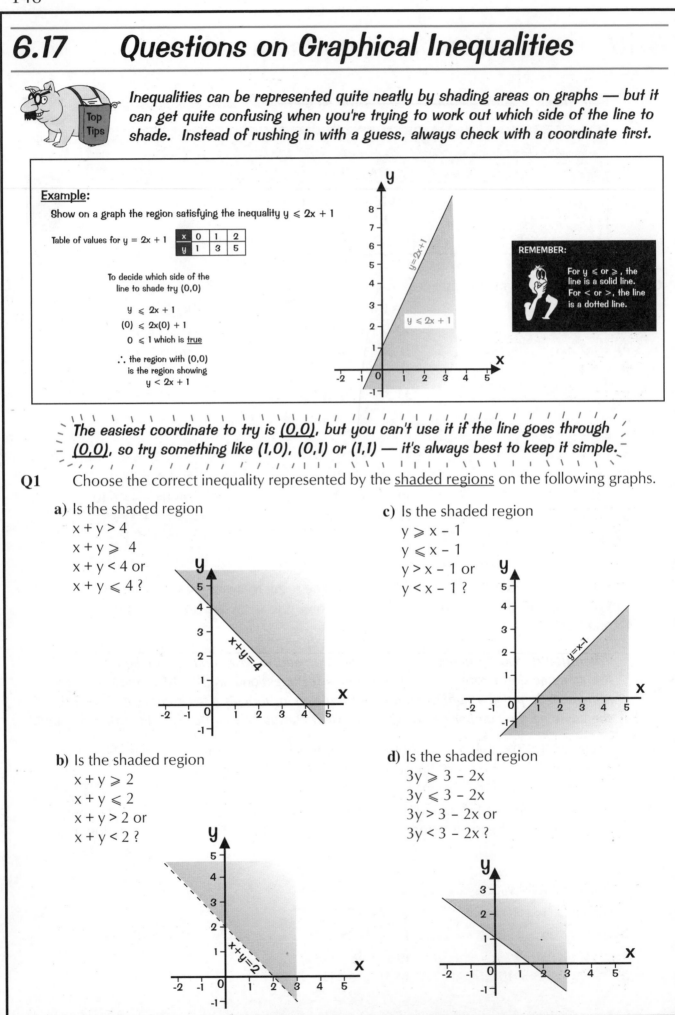

MIW4U